The New York Times

BIG BOOK

of Science Questions
and Answers, Vols. 1 and 2

D0324510

The New York Times

BIG BOOK

of Science Questions and Answers, Vols. 1 and 2

C. Claiborne Ray
Drawings by Victoria Roberts

QUALITY PAPERBACK BOOK CLUB
NEW YORK

*The New York Times Big Book of Science
Questions and Answers, Vols. 1 and 2*

This edition was especially created in 2003 for Quality Paperback
Book Club by arrangement with Anchor Books, a division of
Random House, Inc., New York.

Printed in the United States of America

The New York Times
Book of Science Questions and Answers

200 of the Most Unusual, Intriguing, and Just Plain Bizarre Inquiries into Everyday Scientific Mysteries

Contents

Introduction   1

Section I: Hard Science Made Easy

The Earth Below: The Material World   7

The Sky Above: Weather Report   20

By the Sea   29

Heavens! The View from Spaceship Earth   36

Outward Bound: Space Travel for Beginners   44

Man Is the Measure of All Things   51

Industrial Secrets   66

Section II: The Softer Side of Science

A Modern Bestiary   81

Domestic Animals, Pets—and Cats   105

Insects, Bugs and Creepy-Crawlies   120

It's a Jungle Out There: Plants   133

Watch What You Put in Your Mouth   143

Sound Bodies and Unsound Bodies   163

True Lies: Old Wives' (and Husbands') Tales
and Urban Legends   195

Notes   214

The New York Times

BOOK OF

Science
Questions &
Answers

Introduction

For every thousand people who have wondered why ice floats and why glass is clear, whether your hair can turn gray overnight and why your nose runs, or why dogs bark and why cats purr, at least one seems to have taken pen or keyboard in hand to write to the science Q&A column of *The New York Times*. That means a huge backlog of unanswered mail, spilling out of boxes in a surprisingly small and cluttered office that houses "Science Times," the weekly section that first appeared in 1978. Since 1988, those boxes have been on, under and around my desk.

Many of these inquirers are asking questions that have already been answered in the column; some are asking questions that may never have been asked of anyone or that would require a lifetime of research to answer. To these wonderful and persistent people, this book is dedicated, and also to every school class practicing the business letter by writing to *The Times*, and to every parent who has helped a five-year-old scrawl a question in crayon.

The unquenchable human curiosity about why things are as they are is, after all, the driving force behind all science.

The Times has one great advantage over most of the curious: the experts, both those who know a lot about a little and those who seem to know a lot about almost everything, will actually answer phone calls from *Times* reporters and columnists. (My late father always said a journalist doesn't have to know anything, he, or in this case she, just has to know whom to ask.) My thanks for the generosity of all those experts who have taken the time to respond with fascinating explanations of why and how and whether, and sometimes with equally fascinating explanations of why nobody knows.

The search for definitive answers to all questions will continue to elude both the general public and its most specialized scientists. For example, *The Times* has printed at least three different answers to the question why spiders don't stick to their webs, and the answer is still uncertain, at last attempt.

But here is a compendium of some of the latest best guesses by some of America's true experts, interspersed with the graceful and witty illustrations of Victoria Roberts, which have added so much to the popularity of the Q & A column over the past few years. The experts are identified at the back of the book, most of them with their title and affiliation at the time the question arose.

What *do* people want to know about? Though they come from many places, many of these questions reflect a sidewalk-bound New Yorker's suspicion of the natural world, perhaps masking an ignorance and awe that come from seeing it mainly in Central Park and on the Discovery Channel.

One subject of universal interest is animals, of all sorts, which are discussed in chapters called "A Modern Bestiary," "Domestic Animals, Pets—and Cats" and "Insects, Bugs and Creepy-Crawlies." Bird queries are voluminous. A reader's complaint that the column too often discussed birds was met with a reasonable response from the then Science and Health editor, Nicholas Wade: Maybe it is just that birds are the only wild animals many urban dwellers encounter.

After animals, there must follow vegetables: vegetation both edible and inedible. The comedian Dick Gregory's abstemious philosophy to the contrary, eating is not just a bad habit for most people, it is a continuing fascination, even obsession. Questions about the foods and nutrients and potential poisons one might ingest, and especially those one's children might eat, are ubiquitous. People are afraid of not getting enough, of getting too much, even of being poisoned (sometimes with some justification) by the foods and vitamins they consume. And where did these allegedly edible things come from in the first place? Some answers are in the chapter "Watch What You Put in Your Mouth."

Urbanites do still see a few growing things outside supermarkets, thanks to the street trees that grow in Brooklyn and our generous botanical gardens in Brooklyn and the Bronx. And there is a remarkable stand of hot-pink potted oleanders outside a long-established eating place in Manhattan; I have often wondered if the proprietors know how poisonous they are. Check out some other suspect greenery in "It's a Jungle Out There: Plants."

After the animal and vegetable categories, we inevitably come to minerals, the material world: elements, chemicals, the very soil we walk on, in short, "The Earth Below." Then, looking up from the mud to the sky, we must do something about "The Sky Above: Weather Report," then regard "Heavens! The View from Spaceship Earth," then consider our own tentative missions off that ship, in a chapter called "Outward Bound: Space Travel for Beginners."

Then there are the "Industrial Secrets" that industry is surprisingly eager to share with the public: Du Pont's Better Things for Better Living Through Chemistry is just the tip of the iceberg. Speaking of icebergs, don't forget "By the Sea."

But let's face it, what really holds people's attention is their own earthbound bodies, in sickness and in health, from fingernails to hiccups. For details, see "Sound Bodies and Unsound Bodies."

It was the ancient Greek philosopher Protagoras who first said that "Man Is the Measure of All Things." The foot may no longer be Henry VIII's shoe size, but humankind is still trying to lay a yardstick, or a meter bar, on everything from mountains to the ingredients in a recipe.

And finally, "True Lies" are things your grandmother told you, "facts" your neighbors know for certain, folk wisdom from the old country and brand-new urban legends. Believe it or not, some of them turn out to contain at least a grain of truth when held up to scientific scrutiny. Centuries of weather observations by outdoor people living in hunting and agricultural societies were bound to offer some empirical knowledge. On the other hand, your cactus from Ikea is probably not full of tarantulas, and your house plants will not completely suffocate you in the night.

So after surviving another night with your aspidistra, why not take your own pen in hand and send in your own question?

—C. CLAIBORNE RAY

Readers are invited to submit questions about science to Questions, Science Times, The New York Times, 229 West 43d Street, New York, NY 10036. Questions of general interest will be answered in this column, but requests for medical advice cannot be honored and unpublished letters cannot be answered individually.

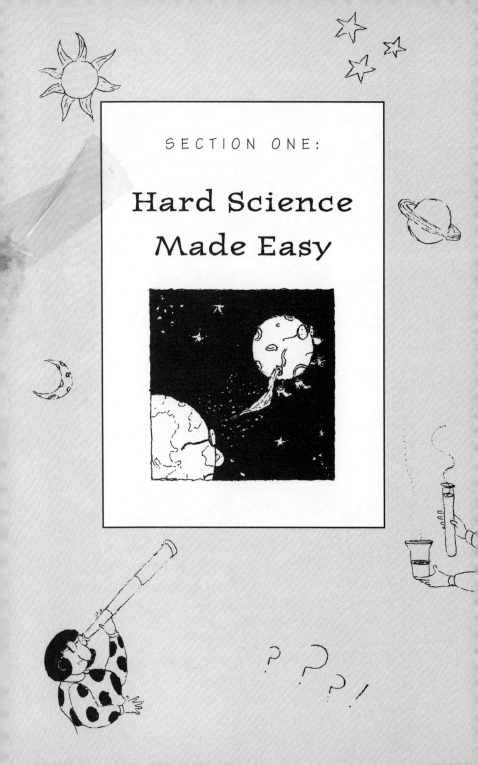

SECTION ONE:

Hard Science Made Easy

The Earth Below:
The Material World

TRANSPARENCY

Q. *Why is glass transparent? Or anything, for that matter?*

A. The short answer is that light behaves like a wave of electromagnetic energy, and any material that can transmit the wave is transparent.

So why do some materials transmit the wave, while others absorb or reflect the light energy? The answer is more complex. It involves the state of the electrons in the material and the ways they are bound to the nuclei of the atoms, with resulting differences in the way they behave when an electromagnetic wave impinges on the material.

If the electrons cannot absorb any energy, then the wave is passed through unmolested, and the material is transparent. If they can rob the wave of any energy, then it is dimmed, obscured or absorbed, and the material is more or less opaque. Some materials, like polished metal, can absorb and reemit energy, so they are reflective.

Clear glass and most pure crystals can neither reflect nor absorb much light energy, so most of it passes through, though the waves are slowed down dramatically, and if the light enters at an angle, it emerges bent.

Until this century, it was not known why a diamond is transparent while a piece of coal is not. They are formed of the same carbon atoms with the same electrons. Now scientists know that the optical wavelengths of light do not have quite enough energy to reach the threshold of excitation for the more tightly bound electrons in a diamond, so light passes through.

Silver Tarnish

Q. *What makes silver tarnish? Is tarnish the same thing as rust?*
A. Silver does not oxidize, or rust, on exposure to air. In fact, compared with most other elements, it is not particularly reactive. It does, however, react with sulfur or sulfur compounds, like hydrogen sulfide in the air, forming tarnish, a compound that is chiefly silver sulfide.

Silver sulfide, Ag_2S, also called argentous sulfide, is 87.06 percent silver and 12.94 percent sulfur. It is a grayish-black heavy

powder that is completely insoluble in water. It occurs in nature as argentite, an important ore of silver.

Silver is also tarnished by many sulfur-containing organic compounds, including proteins like albumin, or egg white, which is why eggs tarnish silver spoons so readily. Another threat to the family silverware is posed by common rubber bands, which are vulcanized with sulfur compounds. Low-grade cardboard may also emit tarnishing fumes.

Common silver polishes remove tarnish with elbow grease and a mild abrasive, along with a thin layer of the silver.

Tarnish may be removed chemically by heating the article in a dilute solution of sodium chloride (table salt) and sodium hydrogen carbonate (baking soda), or by placing the item in contact with a more active metal, like aluminum, which reacts with the sulfur and eventually leaves the silver clean; this may be done with a wad of aluminum foil in a dishpan of soapy water.

LIBERTY'S COMPLEXION
Q. Is the green stuff that covers the Statue of Liberty harmful?
A. On the contrary, it is a thin waterproof protective layer, called a patina, that forms when copper is exposed to air. One of the challenges in the 1986 restoration of the Statue of Liberty was maintaining it.

Copper and copper-rich alloys used for roofs or statues oxidize slowly to yield an insoluble mixture of hydroxo-carbonate and hydroxo-sulfate $Cu(II)$ salts, that is, salts containing either hydrogen, oxygen and carbon or hydrogen, oxygen and sulfur. The (II) refers to one of the valence states, or arrangements of electrons, possible for copper.

Thanks to the patina, the Statue of Liberty's skin, a tenth of an inch thick, had eroded only 5 percent in its first one hundred years. Restorers replaced about 1 percent of the exterior copper, aging it chemically to match the existing patina and speed up oxidization.

Scientists from AT&T's Bell Laboratories in Murray Hill, New Jersey, called in as skin-care consultants, sprayed on corroded copper particles from a dismantled Bell building's roof that matched and adhered to the statue's surface. They were expected to breed enough new patina to cover the streaks. The streaks are still a problem. The current thinking is that they may be a water-loving fungus or mold, but the statue's guardians are not sure why more water would collect where the streaks form than at other places.

VOLCANO DATING

Q. *How do we know when ancient volcanic eruptions occurred?*

A. There are several ways to approximate an eruption date. Historical excavations can reveal when a known settlement was covered by lava. For prehistorical eruptions, some large ones near polar regions left a layer of ash trapped in the polar ice, and oxygen isotopes can be used to tell when the ice solidified around it.

However, dating charred wood or any kind of vegetation from close to the eruption site is the most common method. Carbon dating relies on the rate of radioactive decay of one carbon isotope, carbon 14. It is used for eruptions that took place in the last forty thousand years, but more than two hundred years ago.

Living things take on carbon from the carbon dioxide in the atmosphere, and when they die, they cannot take on any more. It is assumed that the percentage of carbon in the atmosphere has remained constant and that the radioactivity of carbon 14 has decayed at a constant rate, approximately by half in 5,700 years.

Charcoal from trees burned in an eruption is nearly pure carbon and so is ideal for tracing the minuscule amounts of carbon 14 present. Tree rings are not useful because it is hard to find a tree close to the site that did not burn, while ash and trees from farther out tend to wash away.

The dates are given in a range of plus or minus one hundred years, but it is sometimes possible to determine a more exact date. For example, the eruption at Sunset Crater, Arizona, has been placed at 1066 A.D.

Carbon dating put the year around 1065, and Indians' oral historical records helped place the event in 1066. Pottery that showed an eclipse of the sun in conjunction with an eruption helped confirm that date.

RED CLAY

Q. *What makes red clay red?*

A. The famous soil found in Georgia, South Carolina and elsewhere in the southern Piedmont region is mainly a grayish-white clay called kaolin colored by a small amount of iron oxides.

It doesn't take a lot of red paint to paint a barn red, and it doesn't take a lot of these iron oxides to color the soil red. The oxides can be magnetically separated or chemically reduced in the laboratory, leaving a light-colored residue.

The Piedmont clays were mostly formed in place, not washed there from somewhere else by ancient seas or rivers. The oxides, which are very finely divided particles, come from iron-bearing minerals in deposits of solid crystalline igneous or metamorphic rocks. These minerals spend thousands and thousands of years under rainfall in well-drained conditions that promote oxidation.

The color is tenacious in clothes, possibly because the particles are so fine and dusty. Soaps emulsify oils, and this is not an oily dirt at all.

In many parts of the South, many of the nutrients have been leached out of the clay by millennia of rain, but the warm, well-watered red-clay regions are actually fairly green, and the clays will support grass, trees and shrubs. Some of the soils are extensively eroded, so that the red clay subsoil is much closer to the surface and the topsoil is thin or missing.

NEW OIL

Q. *Is crude oil still being created in the earth?*
A. Yes, new oil is being naturally cracked, or distilled, inside the basins of earth this very minute, petroleum geologists believe.

It is believed that petroleum is created when deposits of incompletely oxidized plant and animal sediment are subjected to great heat and pressure from overlying sediments, causing partial distillation. Such deposits and sediments collect in ocean basins today, replicating the conditions under which oil was formed in the past. Once oil is formed, it migrates, sometimes long distances, and may form pools that are accessible to drillers.

One great example is the Gulf of California, where new diesel oil is being made today. Geologists also list places like the Gulf of Mexico, the Persian Gulf, the Orinoco Delta and the Caspian Sea as oil incubators.

The processes of oil formation are no different from what happened a million or a hundred million years ago, and the clock is still moving with geological slowness. In order to make all the supply we have found it would take about twenty-seven million years. A lot has been made in the last million years, a short time for a geologist, but a long time for would-be users.

OZONE, GOOD AND BAD

Q. *Why do I hear about ozone pollution in the cities when dwindling ozone is considered a threat?*

A. These are two very different and basically unrelated problems. Down here, it is dangerous to health, but in the upper atmosphere it is protective of health.

Ozone, or O_3, is a gaseous molecular form of oxygen with a distinctive odor. It is a powerful oxidizer and is used commercially as a bleaching agent.

In the upper atmosphere, ozone plays a vital role in absorbing dangerous radiation from the sun, primarily ultraviolet radiation.

If that ozone layer is thinned too much, it allows more of the dangerous rays to reach the ground, where they can cause not just sunburn but skin cancer. In the upper atmosphere, some of the chemicals that have been used in refrigeration are destroying ozone by reacting with it, and there may be other causes for the variable depletion that has appeared in the polar ozone layer.

Unrelated to that problem, ozone is also produced at ground level by various chemical and electrical processes. Even computer laser printers have ozone filters to protect people from the ozone they produce, and it is ozone that causes the funny smell after a short circuit makes sparks.

Breathing ozone is dangerous to health because it is a strongly reactive chemical and can damage sensitive tissues, like the lungs.

GLACIER ICE

Q. *Is glacier ice purer than regular ice?*

A. Yes, and it is not surprising that some entrepreneurs have marketed it commercially for drinks.

There are several scientific and esthetic reasons for the superiority of glacier ice.

First, the ice in glaciers is relatively pure water because after thousands of years of compression of the tiny snow grains laid down in ancient times, all the impurities have moved to the boundaries of the grains and been flushed out. The final ice, especially if it comes from a single crystal, is much purer than the original precipitation, almost like triple-distilled water.

From an esthetic point of view, a glacier has crystals in it as large as or larger than refrigerator ice cubes. In a single crystal, all the molecules are lined up, while a regular ice cube is many long thin crystals. As a result, light refracted through a cube of glacier ice is much more beautiful than the cloudy light play of refrigerator ice.

There may also be sound effects with glacier ice. When the snow was deposited in the pack, a lot of air was buried with it, and over time, the air is compressed into little bubbles surrounded by ice. A thousand meters deep, the air is under fairly high pressure, but when the bubbles are freed by melting, the air pops out with a pleasing crackle, creating a sparkling drink without adding carbon dioxide.

EARTH AS BILLIARD BALL

Q. *Is the earth really proportionately as smooth as a billiard ball?*

A. On average, certainly yes. The earth is more than 12,000 kilometers in diameter. Mount Everest is less than 10 kilometers high, and the profoundest depths of the ocean are around 11 kilometers. Thus, the most extreme variations in the earth's surface are roughly on a scale of one part in a thousand, and an Everest is very rare. The equivalent bump on a 2¼-inch billiard ball would be about two-thousandths of an inch, so most parts of the earth are a lot smoother.

But smoothness is one thing and roundness is another. The earth is flattened from top to bottom, so it is an ellipsoid, not a sphere. The deviation between an equatorial radius and a polar radius is about 20 kilometers, and so no one would want to play billiards with a ball shaped like the earth.

DROPPING A PENNY

Q. *What would happen if you dropped a penny from the top of the Empire State Building? Would it make a difference if the penny fell flat or on edge?*

A. If the coin fell straight down on edge and did not catch on the many overhangs and projections of a building of that era, it could build up its velocity to 150 miles an hour. If the penny fell flat, the drag of the air through which it fell would be much higher and the speed would be about 30 miles an hour by the time it reached the ground. The velocity is more likely to be in that range because of the likelihood of tumbling.

By way of comparison, a bullet fired from a pistol might reach a speed of 600 miles an hour, but the penny would still be a dangerous projectile.

According to the laws of physics, an object accelerates when it is dropped, starting at zero velocity. As the speed through the air increases, the resistance also increases, until the resistance is equal to the force of gravity pulling the object down, as measured by weight. That is what is meant by an object's terminal velocity.

Whether the penny fell flat or on edge, it would certainly have reached terminal velocity by the time it reached the ground. The big uncertainty is how it would fall. It would not make much difference how you held it when you dropped it, because an object falling that far tends to be unstable. Any little disturbance will get it out of position so it wobbles back and forth, which increases the resistance.

DUSTBUSTERS

Q. *Where does dust come from and why does it reappear so soon after we dust?*

A. Terrestrial dust is mostly tiny fragments abraded from larger things; some of it may be even smaller things aggregating together to form motes of dust.

The larger things that turn to dust can be almost anything in the world, from shoes (one study found fragments of shoe leather to be a significant part of the dust in Grand Central Station) to ships to sealing wax, not to mention cabbages (fragments of dried vegetable matter) and kings (especially if cremated).

Ordinary flying dirt in industry is tiny bits of any substance being worked on. In drilling, for example, you would get the dust of whatever was being drilled. The motes in the light beam of a movie projector might be bits of soil carried into the theater on shoes.

Wind-driven dust composed of fragments of stone and clay is so powerful that over the millennia it has cut fantastically shaped canyons and pillars in the badlands of the American West.

Drought created the Dust Bowl with its penetrating clouds of dry plowed soil; the fires of ancient Plains Indians probably added to the dust in teepees; soot from unburned automobile fuel plagues city apartments.

Dust knows no borders, and dust from volcanic ash lingers in the upper atmosphere to produce brilliant sunsets thousands of miles away from the eruption.

On earth, dust is mostly big stuff being broken down. That is also true of moon dust, where the outer layer of the moon was apparently pulverized by chunks of rock hitting it from space.

There is also a lot of dust in space, and one of the big questions of astronomy is "What is space dust made of?" It only absorbs light, so it is very hard to study, but it is believed to be mostly small stuff, individual atoms and molecules, getting together.

As for why dusting seems worse than futile, one reason is

that a dust cloth may simply stir up dust temporarily while the friction simultaneously creates a static electric charge. Charged particles of dust are attracted to surfaces with the opposite charge.

An antistatic spray may help control dust by providing a very thin layer of insulation between the opposite charges.

SLIPPERY ICE

Q. Why is ice slippery?

A. One simple reason is that pressure and friction from shoes or skates can melt a very thin layer at the top of snow or ice, forming a watery lubricant between ice and skate (good) or ice and shoe (bad). Skis also glide on a layer of water.

The process by which ice melts under pressure and almost immediately freezes again when the pressure is off is called regelation.

CAVERNOUS CAVES

Q. What is the deepest below the surface people have gone in a cave? What is the longest passageway system known?

A. The deepest cave found up to 1992 is in France, the Reseau Jean Bernard. Its total depth, not just the length of its shaft, is 5,256 feet, almost a mile straight down.

The longest system of passageways in the world is the Mammoth Cave system in Kentucky. The numbers change with new exploration, but as of June 1991, the sum of all known passages was 340 miles.

The deepest cave known in the United States is a new discovery, Lechuguilla Cave, in Carlsbad Caverns National Park, New Mexico. Its depth is 1,565 feet.

A large part of the United States is underlain by cavernous limestone aquifers. The Mammoth Cave National Park system was basically formed by the solution of limestone. As water falls on the surface of the earth, it mixes with organic matter and forms a weak solution of carbonic acid, like weak Coca-Cola.

Given sufficient time, perhaps millions of years, the solution feeds into the cavities of the limestone and gradually creates a cave, a little like tooth decay.

Amateur exploration of caves is an important source of knowledge about them and can be safe if undertaken by properly trained and supervised people. For example, from the standpoint of structural stability, caves are relatively much safer than mines.

A PLANE ABOVE EARTH
Q. Why doesn't a plane flying east to west, against the rotation of the earth, move faster relative to the ground below than a plane flying in the other direction?
A. The earth spins under a plane as it travels, at 15 degrees per hour. The air mass that supports the plane as it travels is rotating along with the earth, under its gravitational pull and at the same speed, and therefore the earth's rotation does not have any effect on when the plane arrives.

REAL PEARLS
Q. I have been told that you can tell real pearls from imitation ones by rubbing them on your teeth. Does it work?
A. Yes. Natural pearls and cultured pearls feel slightly rough or gritty when brushed lightly on the front teeth, while imitation pearls are glassy-smooth (or plastic-smooth) to the bite. The tooth test does not work as well if the teeth are capped, however, as their sensation is somewhat deadened.

Natural pearls and cultured pearls are both made by irritated mollusks, which coat grains of sand or beads inside their shells with layers of nacre secreted by folds of special tissue. Nacre is mostly aragonite, a form of calcium carbonate that forms hard lustrous crystals, and these fine crystals are responsible for the grit.

All mollusks can secrete nacre, but oysters do the best job of making pearls. The best imitation pearls are made by dipping beads in a soup of finely ground fish scales and glue and drying and polishing them. The surface resembles the luster of pearls but is not gritty.

SKYSCRAPERS

Q. *How long will skyscrapers last?*

A. If they are properly maintained, they will last forever, structural engineers believe.

After proper design, the key is the integrity of the materials. Steel or concrete can be damaged by things like acid rain, but if damaged material is replaced, the building will survive.

If a structure like the World Trade Center were abandoned and not maintained at all, the first thing to go would probably be the curtain wall, the skin of the building. As it was weathered by rain, pieces would probably start to fall off. However, it would probably take twenty-five to fifty years for the core to be affected.

Massive buildings of masonry may have a longer lease on life than those with a glass skin, but advances in sealants and other materials and techniques mean modern buildings may have more staying power.

Except for disaster damage from things like earthquakes, bombs and fires, the reason buildings come down is often economic, because there is no money for maintenance or because the real estate is too valuable for the structure that is on it. In a throw-away economy, we throw away buildings, too.

DUST OF AGES

Q. *Why do the structures of ancient civilizations sink so far below the surface?*

A. Although archeologists tend to uncover things, that is not necessarily because ruins have sunk beneath the surface. Instead they are usually covered over with newer buildings or natural deposits of sand and debris. There are exceptions; for example, in Mexico City, the Aztecs built temples on a lake bed, where they did sink. Modern buildings sink there for the same reason. But in the Maya area, the buildings on bedrock are right there where they always were.

The remains of ancient settlements like Ur in southern Iraq may have mounds that cover many hundreds of acres, 70 feet or more above the original ground level. Successive human civilizations were built on top, and then the cities were abandoned long enough to be covered over with dirt, debris and sand.

Another factor is the use of mud bricks in the construction of ancient settlements in the Middle East. Such construction is fairly durable as long as it receives occasional maintenance and is protected from rain, but when it is abandoned, often with the removal of its valuable timbers, it eventually settles into a mound of earth, forming permanent hills called tells.

A tell may eventually become a town site once again, and thus successive layers of history may build up like a layer cake.

The successive rebuildings of ancient cities is like what might happen if the South Bronx were leveled by bulldozers and new buildings were built on top of a 10-foot layer of rubble. The basements and foundations might still be there for future archeologists to study.

The Sky Above:

Weather Report

TORNADOES AND TRAILER PARKS

Q. *Do tornadoes ever strike big cities, or are they really attracted to trailer parks? And what causes dust devils?*

A. Meteorologists joke about building trailer parks to attract tornadoes, and there is more than a grain of truth in the jest, because trailer parks tend to occupy the kind of terrain that allows tornadoes to develop.

About 80 to 90 percent of the time, tornadoes are the offspring of a thunderstorm that is rotating, spinning about a vertical axis. For that to occur, generally speaking, the storm must move over a wide, open area to get the wind circulation that would permit a tornado to form.

Tornadoes rarely strike large metropolitan areas, though in this century large ones hit Wichita Falls, Texas, in 1979, Topeka, Kansas, in 1966 and Worcester, Massachusetts, in 1953. They have not struck cities on the scale of Chicago, New York, St. Louis or Dallas.

Tornadoes formed outside the area have a better chance of making it to an urban environment. In fact, the Wichita Falls, Topeka and Worcester tornadoes formed outside the city and reached maximum intensity as they came to the city.

In the more urbanized areas, winds are altered by urban topography. When you look at the city environment, it is not surprising that winds would become so contorted by buildings and large structures that the obstacles would interfere with the structure of the tornado and weaken or dissipate it.

The probability of any particular area of ground's being struck by a tornado is phenomenally small, so the chances of any specific urban area's being hit are just minuscule.

A mini-tornado or dust devil in the canyons of a city is the second cousin once removed of the tornado. It may be caused by air flowing around a building, especially when it is breezy. The downwind side of a building is an area of low pressure, the same thing that causes an airplane to be lifted, but in this case the system is vertical, not horizontal, and picks up dust, leaves or other debris.

The building acts as an airfoil, an impedance to wind, splitting the stream of air. On the leeward, downwind side, the pressure is lower because the streams of air have to go a longer path around the building before meeting. On the windward side, the pressure is higher, as air is forced against that side of the building.

These very small whirls depend on the shape of the building, wind strength and the configuration of doors, because the pressure may be slightly different inside a building. That is also why doors may be hard to open in a high wind.

MOON RINGS

Q. *What does it mean when there is a ring around the moon?*
A. Rain or snow is coming soon. The old folk rhyme is accurate, because high clouds typically streak out ahead of a fall or winter storm.

This veil of wispy cirrus clouds, about 20,000 feet up, is

mostly ice crystals that act like tiny prisms in the sky. They refract or bend the light coming from the moon or sun, forming a halo.

THUNDER SNOW

Q. *Why doesn't there ever seem to be lightning in a snowstorm?*
A. There is sometimes lightning in a snowstorm, although it is somewhat rare. In fact, the biggest snowstorms are those marked by thunder and lightning, a phenomenon meteorologists call "thunder snow."

Most "regular" thunderstorms are summer events in which warm, moist air in the lower atmosphere has very cold air over it. In this unstable system, upward drafts of air create thunderstorms.

The turbulence created by such a storm somehow establishes a separation of areas of positive and negative electrical charges, and when a lightning bolt tries to even out the difference, there is a clap of thunder. Thunder is the sound generated when the lightning bolt heats the atmosphere near it very rapidly to a temperature higher than the sun's surface. The fast expansion of the air creates a sonic boom.

But the vertical division of temperatures and the high moisture at lower levels that typically lead to storms with thunder and lightning are rare in winter. Only in the most powerful winter storms is there such an immense pool of very cold air above warmer, moister air at ground level.

Thunderstorms with snow are more likely to occur near the coast, because the storm can form over the comparatively warm water of the ocean and move inland, meeting much colder conditions. Then the rain thunderstorm becomes a snow thunderstorm, or thunder snow.

FREEZE-DRIED AIR

Q. *Can it really get too cold to snow?*
A. It can certainly get so cold that precipitation is highly unlikely, because the colder the air is, the less water vapor it can hold. At

temperatures around 40 degrees below zero Fahrenheit, it is very difficult to produce precipitation, and if it does snow, there is very little of it.

At very low temperatures there is essentially no moisture in the air, because most of the water that vaporized into the air at higher temperatures has already condensed or sublimated in the form of rain or snow. When the temperatures rise closer to the freezing point, the water content of the air, and hence of any snow that precipitates, can be much higher.

If you look at precipitation records in Antarctica and the Arctic, when temperatures are very cold, there is little snowfall.

POLAR CHILL

Q. *Which is colder, the North Pole or the South Pole?*

A. The South Pole is considerably colder.

At about 56 degrees Fahrenheit below zero, the average temperature at the South Pole is about 35 degrees lower than the average at the North Pole, and the coldest weather on record was minus 129 degrees, recorded at Vostok, Antarctica, on July 21, 1983.

There are at least two reasons for the colder temperatures at the South Pole. The observing station is on a plateau at an elevation of about 12,000 feet; at that height, there is less air to hold in the heat from solar radiation, and most of it is reradiated as soon as the sun goes down.

Also, the South Pole is surrounded by the large snowy continent of Antarctica, not just the smaller ice pack around the North Pole, so very little radiation from the sun is retained at the earth's surface there. Most, about 80 percent, is reflected away by the perpetual snow cover.

HURRICANE SEASON

Q. *When is it too late for a hurricane?*

A. It is never too late for hurricanes, but there is a difference in when they usually occur. The official hurricane season in the

Atlantic begins June 1 and ends November 30. To become a hurricane, a storm must first be a tropical storm, and tropical storms in the Atlantic have formed in every month except April. Some of the worst occur in late September and early October.

Factors in the timing of hurricanes include weather patterns in Africa and the water temperature in the ocean in regions where hurricanes form. From late September into October, the water is probably the warmest it ever gets, not just on the surface but down to a certain depth.

Thus, when a storm hits, it doesn't just churn up cold water, but warm water, which feeds the storm, keeping its updrafts and downdrafts going.

Water temperatures cool off in November, and air currents change. The westerly jet stream is strong in mid-autumn. If high-level winds are strong and from the west, tropical storms don't do so well. They do better when high winds are light and from the east.

BALL LIGHTNING

Q. My family saw what looked like a ball of lightning enter the glass front door, go right past us (or possibly even through us) in the living room and leave by the back window, where it hit a tree, causing some damage. What was it and why weren't we hurt?

A. It was a poorly understood and comparatively rare phenomenon called ball lightning, so next time, try to take a picture. Perhaps 1 percent of the population will see ball lightning in a lifetime.

Though there have been thousands of reports of ball lightning, it is still very hard to study, because scientists do not know how to reproduce it in the laboratory.

As for why it is not usually destructive, it seems to be some sort of derivative of a lightning flash without the intensity of the flash itself, a phenomenon that splits off from the main channel, not the 50,000 degrees and huge current of lightning. A lot of trees hit by ball lightning survive.

Ball lightning is also commonly reported to travel through enclosed spaces, rather than in the open field. It is possible that the building contains part of the charge or flash, but that is speculative. It may be just that the observers are there.

DOUBLE RAINBOWS

Q. *Why are rainbows round, and often double?*
A. The most common rainbows form when sunlight enters raindrops. The drops act like prisms and disperse the sun's light into the familiar spectrum of colors: red, orange, yellow, green, blue, indigo and violet.

Rainbows are round by necessity because of the geometry involved in seeing them. You see a rainbow when you have the sun to your back and the raindrops are in clouds in front of you. Rays of light come over your head from behind you, enter raindrops, get dispersed into colors, bounce off the backside of raindrops and come down into your eyes.

The eye must intercept the beam of light coming from the drops at a particular angle in order to see the colors. A visible rainbow will form only if the drops are in the right place, so that there is a certain angle between the sun, the drops and your eyes. The angle must be a constant angle, and the only geometry that keeps that angle constant involves a circle.

You only see the part of the circle that is above the horizon. If you imagine where the rest of the circle is, you will see that you can draw a straight line from the sun through your head to the middle of the circle that the rainbow is part of.

It sounds poetic, but it is scientifically true that no two people see the same rainbow. If three people are looking at a rainbow, each is at the right angle for that particular rainbow. Occasionally people will see a second rainbow outside the first rainbow, a bigger circle. The colors in that second rainbow are reversed. The second rainbow is also typically fainter.

What happens is that the light follows a similar path, but the light beam bounces twice inside the raindrops. The two reflections have two effects: the order of the colors is flipped, and on each reflection, light is lost, scattered out of the drop, making the second rainbow fainter and less often observable.

To test all this yourself, in warm weather, you can make a rainbow with a garden hose set to a fine spray and the sun at the right point behind you.

HAILSTONES

Q. *What determines how big hailstones are?*
A. The strength of what meteorologists call the updraft in a thunderstorm is what determines the size.

A storm forms at a place in the atmosphere where the air is moving up very rapidly. When the air cools in the cold upper atmosphere, its water vapor condenses into a storm cloud.

Eventually precipitation forms in the cloud, first as a snowflake, then as a raindrop as it falls.

If this raindrop is caught in the updraft once more, it moves up past the freezing level again and becomes a little ball of ice. It then takes on added ice from droplets in its environment. Then, when it is heavy enough, it falls again, perhaps to be caught up once again in the turbulent motion of the air.

With each trip up and down, the hailstone adds material. A fresh hailstone can actually be sliced to reveal layers like a tree ring, showing how many trips it has made.

An updraft of around 100 miles an hour is needed to support hailstones of 5 inches in diameter or more. Areas of great air turbulence thus give birth to the largest hailstones.

The hail capital of the United States is Wyoming, especially the southeastern part, where a convergence of dry air currents from the mountains to the south and cold air currents from southeastern Wyoming conspires to produce remarkable hail.

It is possible for hail to reach the size of a grapefruit. This grapefruit is not necessarily perfectly round, but may have strange protuberances.

One notable hailstone that fell at Coffeyville, Kansas, in 1979 weighed 1.67 pounds and was about 7½ inches in diameter.

Hail forms only in thunderstorms, which arise in part from air currents generated by the heat of the summer sun.

WEATHER VANES

Q. Does a weather vane point to the direction the wind is coming from or the direction it is going to?

A. The arrow points into the wind. If the arrow is to the north, the wind is from the north. The tail of the weather vane is heavier than the nose, and in some but not all weather vanes, there is some type of flap that moves as the wind blows so that the vane is always aligned with the wind.

Weather vanes have been used for centuries, perhaps even millennia. Many are in the form of roosters, an old symbol related to their use on Christian church steeples, high up so that everyone could see where the wind was blowing. The rooster is symbolic of the apostle Peter's denials of Christ, which Jesus had predicted would occur three times before the cock crowed. It signifies how easily faith could be swayed, like a weather vane in the wind.

NORTHEASTERS

Q. Why was the big East Coast storm of December 1992 called a northeaster when it came up from the south?

A. Because the surface winds and the high-level winds of such a storm often go contrary to one another; the high-altitude winds moved the storm from south to north, but the surface winds spiraled from the northeast.

For another example, in the blizzard of March 12 and 13, 1993, the winds at an altitude of 15,000 feet were blowing 120 miles an hour from the south, while the surface winds were blowing from the northeast.

The realization that a storm might be moving in a different direction from that of its surface winds goes back to the days of Ben Franklin.

In the late eighteenth century, Franklin, an avid weather watcher in his adopted city of Philadelphia, corresponded with his brother, who lived to the north, in Boston. When they were both trying to observe an eclipse of the moon, Franklin noticed that as the winds picked up from the northeast, he felt them before his brother did. He was the first to notice this phenomenon in a documented way.

The high-level winds direct the storms, but they have their own low-level circulations. If a cork floating in a stream is spinning, and you are a bubble on the surface of the stream, you may be spun around the cork in one direction, while the cork itself is moving with the stream. It is the 3-D aspect of the atmosphere that adds intrigue to why storms move as they do.

By the Sea

Salt in the Sea

Q. *Why is the ocean salty?*

A. Rocks that erode on the continents contain salt, which is brought by the rivers to the ocean. In fact, fresh water rivers carry a certain amount of dissolved minerals. Most of it is common table salt, NaCl, or sodium chloride.

Once the salt gets to the sea, it tends to stay there and accumulate.

Sodium chloride is very soluble in water, and the interconnected oceans of the world are very large, so the solution does not get saturated and the salt does not precipitate out.

Earlier in the century, it was thought that the age of the earth could be calculated by comparing the saltiness of all the rivers of the world to the saltiness of the ocean. The figure the theorists came up with was 300 million years. In fact, the earth is about 4.5 billion years old.

The reason for the discrepancy is relatively simple. The salty spray of the ocean goes into the air, evaporates, dries, is blown onto the continents, and is recycled back to the rivers, so their salt content is too high for the calculation. If you subtracted the approximate amount of salt that is recycled, you would come closer to the real age of the earth. The concentration of salt in the sea does vary somewhat from place to place. For example, it is lower in the tropics, where rainfall is heavy, and near the mouths of big rivers. The average concentration is usually taken to be 3.5 percent, with about three-quarters of the total in the form of sodium chloride.

WAVE DAMAGE

Q. Does a violent storm at sea cause damage on the ocean floor?
A. Big waves can damage a coastal reef when they break, but 100 miles at sea, waves do not affect the sea floor.

As a rough formula, if the wavelength, the distance between successive crests, is less than four times the depth of the ocean at that point, the waves do not affect the bottom.

In other words, with a 1,000-foot wavelength (a fairly big wind-generated wave), 250 feet is where the wave begins to feel the bottom and the bottom begins to feel it. If a submarine is in water deeper than 250 feet, it would avoid the effects of the turmoil on the surface.

SEA LEVEL

Q. If water seeks its own level, shouldn't all the major connected bodies of water find a single sea level? Why are locks necessary in the Panama Canal, linking the Atlantic and Pacific, for example?
A. While scientists have calculated a mean sea level for the earth as a whole, it is only a mathematical average value taken from a series of observations around the world. In fact, there is no single

"sea level," and the large bodies of water in the world have different and constantly varying levels because of several factors.

In the case of Panama, the oceans aren't at the same level.
They are connected at the bottom of South America, but as the
world spins around, you get rises and falls in the sea level at different points. (It would have been theoretically possible to dig a
"sea level" canal, and water within such a canal would theoretically
find its own average level, but the idea was rejected because of the
expense of digging that deep. Locks over the highlands of Central
America were chosen instead.) Furthermore, the influence of the
moon's gravity, which causes tides, varies depending on position
relative to the moon.

It takes time for water to flow, and all these factors change
faster than water can accommodate to. Sea levels can even vary
from one side of a large island to another, as they do around Vancouver Island in Canada.

Scientists also cite differences in the amount of water returned to the oceans from the continents. For example, several giant rivers feed the Atlantic Ocean, but only a few empty into the
Pacific Ocean.

DOUBLE TIDES

Q. Why are there two high tides and two low tides each day?
A. We have all been taught that the tides are chiefly the result of
the gravitational attraction of the moon on the waters of the
earth's oceans, but there are actually two rotational systems involved, and two bulges of water.

First, the moon goes around the earth, or so it appears. Actually, both the earth and moon are rotating around the common
center of mass, the center of gravity of the earth-moon system,
which is a point inside the earth. About once a month, a circle
around this common center is completed.

There is a slight excess of gravity force on the side of the
earth toward the moon, producing a giant bulge in the water on
that side.

On the other side, the side away from the moon, the centrifugal force of the earth going around the center of gravity is slightly larger than the gravitational force, so it pushes the water out, away from the moon, making another bulge.

Meanwhile, every day the earth rotates on its axis, so the earth is moving under those two bulges twice a day. This accounts for the pair of high tides. The pair of low tides occurs because the water has to come from somewhere.

The centrifugal force involved can be visualized by thinking of a pan of water on a phonograph turntable. There would be a low tide in the middle and a high tide on the outside, because the force tends to push water out from the center of rotation.

The tidal forces are tremendously more complicated than this simplified explanation, because the earth is not entirely covered by water. There are continents in the way and the bulges in the ocean vary immensely because of these different land masses.

MELTING THE ICE

Q. If the polar ice caps were to melt completely, what would happen to the ocean level? How much dry land would be lost?

A. Scientists have estimated how much the sea level would rise, but the exact amount of land lost would require a very complicated worldwide coastal survey. Perhaps only the military knows.

Melting the East Antarctic Ice Sheet would raise sea levels about 60 meters worldwide, or about 200 feet, while melting the West Antarctic Ice Sheet would raise the level about 6 meters, or just under 20 feet.

Greenland would also make a contribution, though its ice is viewed as being more stable than either of the halves of Antarctica. The official estimates for the effect of a Greenland meltoff are between 7.1 meters and 7.4 meters, something less than 24 feet.

The potential total would thus be approximately 244 feet.

If the ice at the North Pole melted, it would not affect sea levels much at all, because it is frozen sea water itself, a giant ice cube of ocean that occupies just a few meters on the top. The concern is fresh water ice, which comes from precipitation on the continents; if it melted, it could create a pulse of fresh water into the ocean.

A wild guess of acreage lost would be based on figuring out how much of the ever-changing coastline, with an estimated slope of one foot in a thousand, would be below the new sea level.

Scientists would also have to account for continental rebound after the load from the Antarctic ice mass went away. The weight has kept the continent below sea level, and if the load were removed, the mantle of the earth would move up to compensate. Scandinavia is actually still rising from the ice load that left it about ten thousand years ago.

FLOATING ICE
Q. *Why does ice float?*
A. Ice floats because water molecules occupy more space in the solid state than in the liquid state, so that a given volume of ice is lighter than the same volume of water.

The way molecules fit together in ice crystals is not as compact as in water. They don't change size, it is just the way they are arranged. Most substances have more tightly packed molecules in the solid state. If this were true of ice, it would sink to the cold bottom of the ocean and never melt, so that the seas would be frozen nearly to the surface.

UNDERSEA VOLCANOES
Q. *If the ocean was allowed to pour into a volcano, would the cold sea water put it out?*
A. No, and in fact there are submarine volcanoes, called guyots or seamounts. Their molten rock spreads on the ocean floor and is eventually cooled by sea water, creating what is called pillow lava.

At depths below 6,600 feet high pressure prevents the explosive formation of steam that results when water meets molten rock at higher levels.

For example, during the volcanic eruption at Surtsey, an island off Iceland, there were explosions every three minutes equivalent to roughly 20 to 40 kilotons.

Something like an effort to drown a volcano was considered in 1973, when a volcanic eruption threatened the harbor of the island of Heimaey, off Iceland. Sea water was piped in to try to freeze the advancing lava front in place. For a time, a plan was also considered to use explosives to rupture the relatively cool crust on the part of the flow that had invaded the island's harbor, permitting the sea water to quench the red-hot lava inside and thus check its advance.

However, experts calculated that if sea water came into contact with the hot lava under such circumstances, a steam explosion would rip open more of the lava, admitting more water, in what could become a chain reaction.

The experts feared that the reaction could propagate through the entire underwater body of lava, producing an explosion equal to a hydrogen bomb of several megatons, creating a disaster for the island and huge ocean waves that would threaten seaports around the rim of the North Atlantic.

The plan was called off, and the outpouring of lava eventually subsided, leaving the harbor usable.

SPIRALING DRAINS

Q. If water draining from a bathtub swirls counterclockwise above the equator and clockwise below the equator, how does it behave at the equator?

A. It would probably go as straight down as possible.

Theoretically, water draining from a bathtub is affected by the Coriolis force, the inertial force caused by the earth's rotation. It would have a tendency to go straight down.

North or south of the equator, the water would tend to go back to its preferred direction unless deranged by mechanical intervention, such as stirring with a finger, or even plumbing idiosyncrasies. In a small tub, intervention would win out.

Exactly at the equator, however, there would be no preferred sense of rotation. Water would tend to try to avoid crossing the equator. It would be more likely to go straight down and would in fact be inhibited from going around.

EARTH'S WATER

Q. *Where does the earth's water come from?*

A. There are two chief schools of thought on the origins of the earth's water. Some believe the water was here from the start; some think it came later, from comets.

Years ago, people tended to assume that the water concentrated at the earth's surface was locked up inside and slowly emerged over the 4.5 billion years of the earth's existence. This water would have been present ever since the earth's materials coalesced because of the force of gravity. That is still a popular theory, and water from the earth's interior does emerge as steam in volcanic eruptions.

But in the last few decades, thought has been given to the possibility that water may have come from comets, or cometlike things, striking the surface of the earth. These objects, the theory goes, are mostly water, so they left little sign in the geological record, and all that remains is water.

On the moon, the biggest and most important craters are about four billion years old, or about 90 percent as old as the solar system. Many interpret this as a sign of a heavy influx of materials in the early history of the solar system. It is thought that part of this meteoric bombardment may have been cometlike materials, and these extraterrestrial objects are believed to be a likely source for the earth's water. Under this theory, the steam from volcanoes could be water that has sunk to the interior by plate tectonics and come back to the surface.

? ? ? !

Heavens!
The View from
Spaceship Earth

SOUTHERN STARS

Q. *If you take a winter vacation in the southern hemisphere, it's summer, so do you see the summer constellations?*

A. Yes, but you won't see our summer stars, but their summer stars. You see another set of constellations, including many we never see, summer or winter.

As you travel south, the constellations near Polaris, our north star, get lower and lower in the sky. The Big Dipper has disappeared by the time you get to Argentina. Among the striking features never seen in the northern hemisphere are the Southern Cross and Centaurus, the man/horse. Alpha Centauri, the brightest star of Centaurus, is the closest star to the earth save for the sun.

We have these different views of the universe because the earth is a ball and is in orbit around an axis that is pretty much fixed with respect to the stars. From the southern half of the ball, we see the stars in the "southern" part of the universe as if they were going around in a circle above us.

SOUTHERN ZODIAC
Q. *Since the zodiac was invented in the northern hemisphere, can a person born in the southern hemisphere have a sign of the zodiac?*
A. The real sky that the zodiac corresponds to is simply those constellations through which the sun appears to move during the course of the year as seen from the earth. People living anywhere on the surface of the earth would pretty much see the sun take the same path in the sky relative to these stars.

The constellations that make up the zodiac are on a plane that can be seen in both hemispheres. The orientation is different, but the stars are in the same positions relative to each other.

Ancient thinkers observing the changing positions of the stars that accompanied the changes in seasons developed the idea of the zodiac more than two thousand years ago. They divided the sky into twelve equal sections, or signs. Later astrologers came to believe that the position of the stars at the time of birth influences people's lives.

Dividing the sky according to the zodiac is of little scientific use to astronomers. The position of the earth in space has changed since ancient times, so the dates for each sign of the zodiac no longer represent the time when the sun is in the related constellation.

FRICTION ON EARTH
Q. *As the earth rotates on its axis, does it lose speed because of friction with the atmosphere?*
A. Yes, sometimes, but it is not a simple slowing because of friction with a stationary air mass. The effect of the atmosphere on the rotation came about because of the way the sun's heat and the absence of it alternate to stir up the atmosphere. The result-

ing wind patterns sometimes speed up the earth and sometimes retard it.

However, many other factors influence the earth's speed of rotation far more than the negligible effects of air friction. For example, there is some wobble related to the shifting of internal masses.

A very big influence, geologically speaking, comes from the fact that the pull of the moon in its orbit and that of the sloshing tides on earth affect each other, in turn. The net outcome of the alternate braking and acceleration is that the moon is gradually retreating from the earth, climbing to a higher and higher orbit and moving faster. As a result, you lose a bit of the angular momentum from the earth, which is transferred to the moon, so the earth goes slower.

It would take a long time to notice even this big effect, as it amounts to days in a hundred million years. However, it has left its mark. Corals from the Devonian period show daily and monthly growth rings. They precipitated calcium carbonate as they formed their skeletons. And we can see that at that period, a month had fewer days.

TWINKLING STARS

Q. *Why do stars and planets twinkle?*

A. Stars and to a lesser extent planets twinkle simply because we are seeing them through the many layers of the atmosphere of the earth. These layers of different densities move around, bending or scattering some of the light.

The upshot is that all the rays of light that could reach your eyes from a star don't necessarily come in together, but sometimes more, sometimes less, depending on the danciness of the atmosphere.

There are several types of variable stars, stars that truly vary in their light output or are periodically eclipsed by other bodies, but the variations usually take place over a longer period than a mere twinkle. Planets are closer and brighter in terms of the amount of light that reaches us, so they vary less.

EARTH'S TILT

Q. *Why does the earth tilt approximately 23 degrees on its axis?*

A. Scientists believe the earth's tilt results from the impact of another celestial body during the later stages of the formation of the solar system.

The planets are believed to have formed when smaller bodies were drawn together by gravity, hitting each other at high speeds. One of the later, larger impacts may not have been square on, but at a glancing angle.

This could have tilted the angle of the planet's axis of rotation over to varying degrees. This is the best theory we have as to why this happened to the earth and why it may have happened to the other planets.

The earth's tilt as it moves around the sun has remained fairly constant over a long period of time, deviating from its current value by at most 2 degrees.

Other planets are not so stable, researchers believe. For example, the tilt of Mars is believed to have varied from the current 25 degrees to as low as 15 and as high as 35.

The variations can be determined by calculating how one planet's gravity affects another's rotation and spin axis. In the earth's case, the moon acts as a stabilizing influence, somewhat like a balance wheel, preventing wild variations.

ROUND BODIES

Q. *Why are heavenly bodies round?*

A. They are not perfectly round, of course. They only seem spherical, or almost spherical.

Earth, for example, is flattened at the poles, and Jupiter and Saturn, because their extremely dense atmospheres are all we can see, appear even flatter at the poles.

The reason that stars, planets and so forth are even almost spherical, as opposed to a square or some strange shape, has to do with the law of gravitation.

Any bit of matter will attract other units of mass, and as

Newton said, the force of this attraction is proportional to the inverse square of the distance between these masses. It doesn't matter in which direction these masses are located. A finite number of uniformly distributed uniform particles would thus tend to coalesce into a spherical clump. Meanwhile, many other forces are at work in the formation of planets and stars.

We assume that at some time well after the big bang, we have a collection of particles that are not uniform and not uniformly distributed, an inhomogeneous cloud of matter, in which all the particles are attracting each other, but the forces of gravity do not totally balance out. But there is also along the way some kind of perturbing force that sets the thing rotating. In particular, you are likely to have a neighboring body, so there is gravitational interaction between the two bodies. There are also tangled questions of electromagnetism, friction, heat, etc.

So you have gradual coalescence, under the force of gravity, and things beginning to spin, because of inhomogeneities and outside forces. The result is a roughly but not perfectly spherical rotating body. The shape is going to be determined by how fast the thing is spinning. The faster it spins, the more oblate it's going to be, and it depends on the density of matter in the body, too.

Assuming a perfectly spherical billiard ball, for example, it will retain its spherical shape closely, but a rotating water balloon would become quite oblate, bulging around the equator. In fact, with a heavenly body, you are liable to have so much matter and so high a rate of rotation that matter around the equator will spin off, leaving the body without its "spare tire." The spare tire can be dispersed, or under some circumstances can form a roundish satellite, by a similar process.

MOON IN DAYLIGHT
Q. Why can you see the moon in the daytime?
A. What makes that question interesting is that it presumes

there is some reason you couldn't. The moon is just as much out in daytime as it is at night.

In the daytime, the sun is so much brighter than everything else that the moon may not be noticeable even when it is visible. At night, however, it is the brightest thing in the sky.

As the moon orbits around the earth over the month, it is in all parts of the sky over a twenty-four-hour period. How much of it is visible depends on the phase, or how much of it is illuminated by the sun at a particular time. The daytime sky is bright because the atmosphere scatters sunlight, but the moon is close enough and large enough to reflect enough sunlight so that it is brighter than the surrounding sky.

That is not true of the stars. However, an astronaut on the moon can see stars even when the sun is out, because the moon has no atmosphere to scatter the sunlight and make the daytime sky bright.

ONE FACE FORWARD

Q. *How does it happen that the moon always shows the same face to the earth? And why is it true for so many moons of other planets, including Neptune's Triton?*

A. Many researchers think the phenomenon, gravitational phase locking, occurs because of the uneven distribution of matter in the bodies involved.

Normally, when two bodies join in holy matrimony and decide to go around together forever, their spins would stay what they were beforehand. But because they may be a little heavier on one side than another, over long periods the gravitational pull of one body on the other tends to slow down or speed up each one in response to the other.

If a moon has a bulge, for example, the bulge would be attracted to the planet it orbits. The smaller body would eventually settle down with its bulge facing the larger one; its rotational period and revolutionary period would be the same.

THE HEAT OF STARS

Q. How can scientists determine the temperature of planets or stars when I can't even tell when a rack of lamb is done in my own oven?

A. Astronomical temperatures are usually estimated from spectroscopic measurements. The spectroscope was invented in 1859 by two German scientists, Robert Wilhelm Bunsen of Bunsen burner fame and Gustav Robert Kirchoff. It was first used to analyze the elements in a substance heated to incandescence; each element gave off characteristic wavelengths of visible light. Bunsen used the device to identify two new elements, cesium and rubidium.

It was later discovered that the presence of certain elements in distant heavenly bodies, and their corresponding temperatures, could be analyzed by the same color yardstick, and by spectral lines, the patterns created by the emission and absorption spectra of the elements in stars and other heavenly bodies.

Over the years, scientists refined their classification of stars. One early scheme was alphabetical, based on the strength of hydrogen absorption lines in the stellar spectrum, with the classification running from A to P. A later rearrangement was designed to correspond to a sequence of decreasing surface temperatures; most stars could be divided into seven spectral types. It dropped some letters, and this famous sequence could be remembered by the initials for the words "Oh Be A Fine Girl, Kiss Me." It runs from the hottest blue O stars to the coolest red M stars.

Astronomers now take the entire electromagnetic spectrum

into account, not just visible light. In general, cool objects give off radiation of long wavelengths while hotter objects give off short wavelengths. Infrared telescopes sent into space far beyond the obscuring atmosphere of the earth measure the short wavelengths below those of red visible light, and X-ray and

gamma ray telescopes are trained on longer and longer wavelengths and hotter and hotter astronomical objects and events.

STARS AND SAND

Q. Now that all those new galaxies have been reported, what is the
latest on the relative numbers of grains of sand on the earth and
stars in the heavens?

A. Grains of sand are in the lead. The recently published data from
Hubble Space Telescope images help confirm scientists' long-held
suspicion that the universe has
many galaxies invisible to ground-
based telescopes, so an increase
from ten billion galaxies to fifty billion was not unexpected. Some estimates have gone even higher, up to
one hundred billion galaxies.

When you multiply by the average number of stars per galaxy, you
get anywhere from 10 to the 20th power to 10 to the 22d power
for the estimated number of stars in all the galaxies of all the
known universe; 10 to the 20th is a 1 followed by twenty zeroes.

A beach with a coastline of a few kilometers, with sand grains
fitting a few to the millimeter, has a mere 10 to the 18th power, or
one quintillion, grains, far fewer than the number of stars.

However, if you add up all the grains of sand on all earth's
beaches, in all earth's mighty deserts and below earth's oceans,
you have handily outnumbered all the stars in the known universe.

? ? ? !

Outward Bound:
Space Travel
for Beginners

Q. *On earth we use latitude and longitude for orientation. What is used for the moon?*

A. Latitude and longitude are also used on the moon by the astro-geology department of the United States Geological Survey in Flagstaff, Arizona, which maps extraterrestrial bodies.

Like the earth, the moon has an axis of rotation and an equator, so latitude is indicated in degrees of latitude north or south of that equator, just as it is on earth. Because the sphere of the moon is smaller, each degree represents a smaller distance.

Another difference in moon maps is the starting point for lunar meridians of longitude. A spot in one crater has been specified as the equivalent of Greenwich, England. It is the point through which the line marking zero degrees of longitude runs. The crater, called Mosting A, lies near the center of the disk of the full moon as we see it.

COMPASS IN SPACE

Q. *How does a compass behave in orbit and in outer space?*

A. Astronauts do not use compasses in space, National Aeronautics and Space Administration spokesmen said, but near-earth orbit would not change the behavior of the magnetic needle significantly.

If the compass were in the cockpit of an orbiter, they said, it would probably behave much as it does on earth, with the needle following the lines of the planet's doughnut-shaped magnetic field and pointing toward the north.

There might be some areas of magnetic flux in which the lines might not be exactly aligned, NASA said, but that would be an occasional exception.

In outer space, the situation is not so clear. Theoretically, a compass is affected by the most prevalent and biggest magnetic source available, NASA spokesmen said, and would follow whatever lines of force there were. Depending on how far out the vessel carrying the compass is, that source might be the earth or even something in the vessel, but NASA scientists said that it was impossible to predict such behavior exactly from what is now known.

AIR SUPPLY

Q. *Where will the air supply come from for extended space missions?*

A. On space flights up to now, the components of breathable air, oxygen and nitrogen, have been brought up in canisters.

However, when the space station is built, plans have been announced to have it carry equipment to recover oxygen indirectly from the carbon dioxide crew members exhale.

Meanwhile, NASA's Johnson Space Center is testing means

to recycle air and water used by volunteers sealed in an airtight chamber with a limited amount to breathe and to drink. Mechanical and chemical means are being used to recycle all the air and water, including urine. Past tests involved using wheat plants to recycle breathing air, and by 1997, sixty- and ninety-day tests using plants and/or physiochemical recycling are planned.

In a life-support system for the space station designed earlier at NASA's Marshall Space Flight Center in Huntsville, Alabama, carbon dioxide will be reclaimed from the exhaled air by a concentrator. The 95-percent-pure carbon dioxide will then be burned with hydrogen in a carbon dioxide reduction device, yielding water and some waste products, either carbon or methane. This water will then be used as drinking water on the space station.

Then some water from the hygiene system, dirtier water, will be put in an oxygen generator, an electrolyzer that breaks it down into its two components, hydrogen and oxygen, by electrolysis. The oxygen is to be fed back into the cabin, closing the cycle. The hydrogen is used in the propulsion system to keep the space station at the proper attitude and to reboost it into the proper orbit as the orbit decays.

Oxygen requirements are about 1.8 pounds per day per person. On past flights, carbon dioxide was recaptured but not reused.

Initially, the Soviet Union used a multistep chemical recovery system to obtain oxygen for its extended space flights, but is now understood to have switched to an electrolyzer-type process, with the supply vehicle, Progress, bringing up water that is then electrolyzed. U.S. missions have also supplied breathable air.

SPACE SUITS

Q. *Why doesn't a space suit explode in the vacuum of space?*
A. The space suits worn by United States astronauts are made of several layers of superstrong fibers and other materials that are tough enough not to rupture in the vacuum of space.

The materials in the nine or ten protective layers include Orthofabric, which is Teflon with Kevlar ripstop protection; a layer of aluminized Mylar film reinforced with Dacron scrim; neoprene-coated nylon cloth; Dacron cloth; polyurethane-coated nylon cloth; dipped polyurethane film; multifilament stretch nylon; ethylene vinyl acetate tubing for the water coolant; and a nylon chiffon lining for body comfort.

But the pull of the vacuum is not the main threat they are guarding against. More immediate dangers are loss of internal pressurization because of a tiny hole from a micrometeorite and exposure to extremely high or extremely low temperatures, depending on whether the astronauts are on the side of the earth that is toward or away from the sun.

The astronauts' backpacks provide the pressurization for their life support system, maintaining a breathable atmosphere and temperature control.

"Weight" in Space

Q. *How do you weigh a person (or anything else) in space?*
A. Since we can't actually weigh astronauts in weightlessness, body mass measurements are used to determine any change in weight, that is, what the astronaut would weigh under the influence of earth gravity.

Such measurements are made with a spring-like device and a highly accurate timer. By measuring the time, or periodicity, between the oscillations, the back-and-forth or up-and-down movement, of the spring, a correlation can be drawn between body mass and actual weight. The periodicity of the motion varies based on the mass of the object or person on the springs. On the shuttle, a chair-like device is used. The astronaut climbs in the chair, which then moves back and forth. The speed of the motion is determined by the mass in the chair. On *Mir,* cosmonauts crouch over a device that moves up and down, but the result is the same.

THE SLINGSHOT EFFECT

Q. When the Galileo spacecraft swung by earth to get a "gravity assist" on its way to Jupiter, where did the energy come from?

A. Galileo did not get this lift for free, but took some kinetic energy from the earth, just a trace.

First of all, the gravity-assist phenomenon does not occur as something between the spacecraft and earth alone. Galileo did not come from infinity and fall away from the earth to infinity; both are just parts of the solar system, in orbit around the sun.

The earth can influence the speed and direction of Galileo in a certain way because it is large and in motion around the sun. If the earth were standing still relative to the sun, then the interaction would be symmetrical, and there would be no gravity assist.

The interaction between the spacecraft and the earth involves a perturbation of both their orbits, with a change of direction and energy.

When Galileo flew by earth on December 8, 1992, it increased its speed in orbit by 8,280 miles per hour. Simultaneously, earth changed its speed in its orbit, slowing down by a speed of 2.3 billionths of an inch per year, a truly small but calculable amount.

As a consequence of this interaction, Galileo's orbit changed from a two-year elliptical orbit taking it out to the asteroid belt to approximately a six-year orbit reaching out to Jupiter. Earth's orbit of the sun stayed roughly circular but shrank by something less than a billionth of an inch.

BEAM ME UP?

Q. Are scientists working on the kind of transporter that the Star Trek television show depicts beaming people up from planet surfaces?

A. Not now, and probably never, scientists suspect.

In a sense, the human genome project would be the first step in such a project, because you would need the whole genetic blueprint of a person, present in each cell, to copy the cells. But even if you had all that information, you would basically be making a Xerox of the person. In principle it would involve disassembling the body into atoms of the constituent elements and reassembling the body elsewhere with the atoms present there.

But as anyone who uses an electronic copier knows, a copy is never better than the original, always worse, though it may still be perfectly readable. And with each subsequent copy, more little mistakes creep in.

The same thing would happen with a copy of a human being. It would deteriorate. An imperfect copy is okay in a document, but a disaster in a human being.

LIFE AND DEATH

Q. *What would happen to a person who died in space? And how would fertilization, gestation and birth in space differ from what would happen on earth?*

A. In effect, a person who died in the icy vacuum of space would be freeze-dried, space experts theorize. The water in the body would freeze and eventually dissipate into space.

Ice can evaporate without going through the liquid phase; because there is no oxygen, there would be no decomposition, and there is little evidence that there could be microbial degradation. It would be like storing dead tissue in the deep freeze. How long it would take to freeze-dry nobody really knows. The process would be similar but much slower if a person died in a space suit.

As for birth in space, copulation, embryology and delivery are three separate questions, and subsequent development is still another. The entire process has certainly not been tested from beginning to end in one species of mammals in space. For example, it is not known if gravity is essential for human conception, scientists said.

Radiation levels in space, especially deep space, would be higher than on earth, so there would be a higher risk of birth defects associated with it, unless there were proper shielding, which NASA is, in fact, trying to develop.

The big question involves the early stages of fetal development. In most species, gravity is involved in bilateral symmetry (the fact that the two halves of the body develop symmetrically) and head-foot differentiation, etc.

In a Soviet study of rat gestation in space, the rats were reported to be normal at birth. But they had been conceived on earth before the space trip and then were born on earth, so the study was not conclusive.

Other medical problems known to occur in space could theoretically interfere with a healthy pregnancy: calcium loss in the bones; disruption of hormones and body fluids; and loss of muscle tone in the absence of gravity.

All of these questions of developmental biology are things the long-term residents of the space station might possibly look into.

Labor might be slightly longer if the space babies do not drop down toward the birth canal as earth babies do in the last weeks of pregnancy. But delivery itself would probably take place much as deliveries do on earth, because the muscular contractions of labor are not dependent on gravity.

Man Is the Measure
of All Things

WHAT TIME IS IT?

Q. *I am told that radio stations' time can differ considerably from "real" time. Is there any way a member of the general public can synchronize a watch accurately?*

A. There are two federal agencies that offer very accurate time signals by telephone, and one of them offers shortwave radio broadcasts of the same information.

Dialing the United States Naval Observatory Master Clock at (202) 762-1401 puts you in touch with a time signal in hours, minutes and seconds, on a twenty-four-hour clock in Eastern daylight or standard time, followed five seconds later by the Coordinated Universal Time, calculated for the Greenwich meridian, at zero degrees longitude. The call is billed at regular long-distance rates.

Another source of time, the Division of Time and Frequency of the National Institute of Standards and Technology at Boulder, Colorado, is one of the sources of Coordinated Universal Time. Time scales calculated by timekeeping agencies all over the world were fed into the International Bureau of Weights and Measures in Paris and averaged; the result is Coordinated Universal Time.

The National Institute of Standards and Technology, an agency of the United States Department of Commerce, is the source of official time in the United States. It maintains its own atomic clock, which determines the time based on vibrations of the cesium atom. A second takes exactly 9,192,631,770 vibrations.

Calling (303) 499-7111 reaches the institute's Coordinated Universal Time signal. The identical signal is heard on the agency's radio station, broadcasting at shortwave frequencies of 2.5, 5, 10, 15 and 20 megahertz. The time delay involved in the telephone transmission would vary according to how the call was switched, but would not exceed 70 milliseconds. In setting a wristwatch, the time delay would be so small you probably couldn't calculate for it.

Irregularities in the earth's spin require adding an occasional leap second, so for those interested in an even more precise time, the station also broadcasts coded information, heard in the double tick of the first fifteen seconds of each minute, that tells the caller how far from Universal time the earth time is for any particular moment. Earth time changes, atomic time doesn't.

DEGREE DAYS

Q. What are degree days?

A. Degree days are used as an approximate measure of energy demand to let utilities and householders keep track of what energy use for heating or cooling ought to be from day to day or year to year.

To calculate degree days for a given day, add the high and low temperatures, divide by two and compare that value with 65 degrees Fahrenheit.

If the value is 60, there were five heating degree days. If the value is 70, there were five cooling degree days. The only time there are zero degree days is when the daily average temperature is 65 degrees, because the same theory that says you turn on the furnace when the temperature is below 65 degrees says you turn on the air conditioner when it is above 65 degrees.

110 IN THE SHADE

Q. *If the wind-chill index measures the misery of cold, what index is used for the misery of heat?*

A. The term humiture was coined in 1937 by O. F. Hevener, a meteorologist, to refer to the discomfort felt in the upper temperature ranges when the humidity rises. The higher the humidity, the warmer it feels to the human body, because it cannot evaporate sweat as easily.

Many indexes have been devised to quantify the discomfort. All are faulty, because discomfort varies from person to person and from day to day for the same person.

All the indexes are based on similar concepts. For example, the humiture is equal to the temperature in degrees Fahrenheit plus a reading equal to the actual vapor pressure of the air, in millibars, minus twenty-one. (A millibar is a unit of pressure, the amount of force over a given area that the air is exerting; 1,000 millibars equals 29.53 inches of mercury. Total air pressure, measured with barometers, is the weight of the air above you; part of that weight is the vapor in the air.) The humiture is close to another index, the apparent temperature, which is calculated by a much more complex formula, but approximates it under most circumstances.

Another familiar measure, relative humidity, is based on the percentage of moisture present in the air compared with how much it could hold at that temperature. But the hotter air gets, the more water vapor it can hold, so as the temperature goes up, the relative humidity actually goes down.

The dew point, the temperature at which dew forms, might be a much better and simpler number for defining discomfort. Virtually everyone is comfortable when the dew point is less than 60 degrees Fahrenheit. When it is more than 60, some will be comfortable. Most will be uncomfortable over 65. When it is 70 or more, virtually everyone agrees that the air is oppressively humid.

MEASURING CUPS

Q. *Why is the measurement visible on the outside of a clear measuring cup about an ounce more than it is for the same contents if you look inside?*

A. The curved surface of a clear measuring cup, either glass or plastic, acts as a simple convex lens, very much like the ones in eyeglasses. The light rays passing through the cup are bent in such a way as to magnify the image from inside the cup. The result is that looking down into the cup shows a lower content reading than the one obtained from looking at the level sideways from outside.

Over the years, most manufacturers have chosen to print clear cups so the accurate reading is readable from outside when the cup is held at eye level. This may not be the most convenient for the cook, but it is the most consistent.

There is often a significant variation in the contents that will fit into cheap measuring cups and spoons. A little home experimentation with an expensive set may be in order to make sure of exact measurements.

RAINFALL, SNOWFALL

Q. *How do meteorologists measure rainfall and snowfall?*

A. The measurement of rainfall is fairly straightforward, but snowfall presents problems that make measurements somewhat arbitrary. For rain, the meteorology department at Pennsylvania State uses a simple cylindrical tube to catch it. The amount that falls in a given period is poured into a smaller cylindrical tube that is carefully gradated and measured with something like a dipstick.

Many things can affect the depth of snow, especially wind and how frequently it is measured, both during and after a storm. Because the weight of the falling snow packs down what is underneath, it might compact from 10 inches to 8 inches as air holes fill in. The National Weather Service guidelines call for using a snowboard, a board exposed to catch snow, with the accumulation measured every hour through the storm and then brushed off, a time-consuming method.

Meteorologists at Penn State seek an average reading from ten different points after the snow stops.

THE VISION THING
Q. *Why do you aim with one eye closed?*
A. Not everyone does, but those who do, do so because of a phenomenon called binocular rivalry. If you look through a sight with the left eye, what you see is not identical with what you see with the right, and the two images compete, rather than blending, as they normally do when you look at something with both eyes.

For example, if the left eye is shown only vertical lines and the right eye only horizontal lines, you might think you would see a screen pattern, but in fact you would see patches of vertical lines intermingled with patches of horizontal lines. Some people can mentally suppress the competing image, but some find it uncomfortable, so they close one eye.

In aiming, most people tend to use the dominant eye, which generally but not always has better vision. If the eyes differ in focal length, some may use one eye for long distances and the other for short distances.

TIMBERLINE
Q. *Why do the altitudes of timberlines vary from one mountain range to another?*
A. The treeline or timberline, the line on mountains and in polar regions beyond which trees will not grow, is mostly determined by temperature. Trees need a long enough and warm enough summer to ripen seeds, produce new wood and form buds.

However, temperature is not the only factor, and the altitude above sea level is not the only thing that determines how cold it gets.

For example, the mountain timberline would always be higher near the equator than it is near the poles if it were not for the abundant rainfall in the equatorial mountain regions, which lowers temperature.

The seasonal distribution of rainfall is a factor at all latitudes, as is drainage.

Local snow distribution is also involved. The area must be clear enough of snow for long enough to allow seeds to germinate and seedlings to become established.

High winds tend to stunt woody plants, creating a "shrubline," particularly in tropical mountains. Other factors determining tropical treelines are incompletely understood.

SOUTHERN SUNDIALS

Q. *Would a sundial made for the northern hemisphere work in the southern hemisphere?*

A. Yes, you can take your garden sundial to the same latitude in the southern hemisphere, but the numerals would have to be reversed in a mirror-image way. That is, for example, the displaced sundial would show 1 P.M. when it was 11 A.M.

While the sun's apparent path across the sky moves from east to west in both hemispheres, it stays generally to the south of directly overhead above the equator and generally to the north of directly overhead below the equator.

When a sundial is used in the northern hemisphere, the raised tip of the gnomon, the wedge-shaped device that casts the shadow, points toward the north. It is positioned to cast a shadow at the center of the dial at noon, and the hours run clockwise.

In the southern hemisphere, the tip of the gnomon would point in the opposite direction, so the hours would have to run counter-clockwise.

"WEIGHT" OF EARTH

Q. *How much does the earth weigh?*

A. What we think of as weight is the gravitational pull of the earth

itself on a person or object. Therefore, asking the earth's weight is
essentially meaningless, because it
has weight only in relation to another object.

However, the mass of the
earth, the quantity of matter in it,
can be estimated by calculating its
gravitational effect on the motion
of an object of known mass. Basically, if the earth had one mass,
it would make things move one way, but if it had another mass, it
would make things move another way. Most scientists give a figure
for earth's mass of around 5.98 times 10 to the 24th power kilograms, or 598 followed by twenty-two zeros.

Before the space age, the estimation process was extremely
complicated. The first reasonable figure for the earth's mass was
obtained by Nevil Maskeyne in 1774. He estimated the mass of a
mountain in Scotland and calculated the approximate effect of its
gravitational pull, as opposed to the pull of the earth, on the motion of a swinging pendulum.

These days, better estimates are derived by observing the
motion of man-made satellites around the earth.

EARTH'S MASS
Q. Is the earth gaining mass from meteorites, etc., or losing it
when things are launched into space?
A. Easily it's gaining. A large number of small meteorites strike
the earth every year, while the amount of material thrown out into
space is comparatively negligible.

Most of what is launched returns to earth as man-made meteorites. Everything that is sent into orbit remains in the range of
earth's gravitational pull, which keeps it in the range of the earth's
upper atmosphere. Even though the gases are extremely thin, the
friction is enough to slow and heat the object. As its orbit decays
further, it gets closer and closer to the earth, eventually returning

in flames. Everything comes back eventually, except stuff sent to the moon, the planets or beyond.

Highest Temperature

Q. Is there a maximum temperature that corresponds to absolute zero?

A. There is no maximum temperature, because there is no limit to the amount of energy you can put into anything.

Absolute zero, minus 273.15 degrees Centigrade (minus 459.67 on the Fahrenheit scale), is theoretically the temperature at which all molecular activity ceases. It represents an absence of energy.

There is the concept of a lowest temperature because any given body has a lowest energy state, when all possible energy has been extracted.

You can also talk about a maximum temperature for any given body, because at some point it will be hot enough to break up, melt or disassociate, so that at that point it would not be the same body. However, since there will always be some object or substance that will still exist, the concept of temperature does not have an upper limit, because more and more energy could still be added.

A cosmologist might say that this question is like asking "What is the shortest time?" Things have been cooling since the big bang, so a millionth of a second later, approximately as far back as our physics will take us now, would theoretically be the hottest known temperature, but a billionth of a second after the big bang would be still hotter.

Radio Reception

Q. Why does standing in a certain place near a radio or touching it sometimes improve the reception?

A. Standing near and touching the radio probably represent two different phenomena.

In addition to traveling from one point to another, radio waves are being reflected and absorbed by objects in a room, and the pattern of reflection can cause interference as the spurious signal interferes with the original signal. Standing in the path of the unwanted reflection can change the pattern at the antenna and improve the reception of the desired signal. Only a tiny amount of the signal may be affected, but that can be enough to improve reception. A good radio receiver can distinguish between the primary signal and the weaker reflected signal and reject the unwanted reflection.

On the other hand, by touching the radio, you really are being an antenna. The body is filled with salt water, which is not a terrific conductor of electricity, but does conduct it.

VISIBILITY

Q. How is visibility determined in weather reports or at the airport?
A. Daytime visibility is defined as the greatest distance at which it is possible to see and identify, with the naked eye, a prominent dark object against the sky at the horizon; daytime visibility reports are estimates based on local landmarks and conditions.

Nighttime visibility is the greatest distance at which it is possible to see a known light source of moderate intensity.

For a pilot making a nighttime takeoff on a runway, visibility can be measured with equipment like a transmissiometer, a narrow light beam focused on a photoelectric cell 250 feet away. The photo cell's output depends on the amount of light it receives through the atmosphere. The weakening, or attenuation, of the light beam is a measure of how well the atmosphere transmits light and is related to what the human eye (that is, the pilot's eye) can see.

If the light is not attenuated by atmospheric conditions, the visibility is said to be unlimited. If the light is attenuated 100 percent, the visibility is less than 250 feet, the distance from light source to sensor.

LOGIC OF FAHRENHEIT

Q. If the centigrade (or Celsius) and Kelvin temperature scales are based on natural phenomena like the freezing and boiling points of water and absolute zero, what is the logical basis for the Fahrenheit scale?

A. Daniel Gabriel Fahrenheit, who devised the scale, wanted natural reference points, but he did not choose wisely. Fahrenheit, an instrument maker born in Danzig in 1686, developed three different temperature scales as his knowledge of natural phenomena increased. He chose points like the freezing temperature of water and the underarm temperature of a healthy adult male. His last scale closely corresponds to the modern scale bearing his name.

Casting about for the coldest temperature possible for the zero point on his scale, according to historians, Fahrenheit visited Ole Romer, a fellow instrument maker in Copenhagen, who had calibrated his mercury thermometer based on the coldest temperature of the winter of 1708–9. Thus, Fahrenheit's zero was nothing but a particularly cold day in Copenhagen.

IX TIMES XXXVII

Q. How did the Romans use Roman numerals to do complicated calculations?

A. Not a great deal is known about Roman mathematics because they were not terribly interested in it. Doing arithmetic probably played a much smaller role in the everyday lives of Romans than it does in ours.

The Romans had signs for 1, 10 and 100, etc., but they did not have a place value system, so a sign had the same value no matter where it occurred. This made complex arithmetical operations very cumbersome.

We do know they used the abacus or counting table. This would not necessarily have resembled an Asiatic abacus, but could simply have been a table or smooth slab with the surface ruled into columns headed by values: units, tens, hundreds, etc. The counters had different values depending on which column they were in.

The Romans might also have used a system of successive doubling to do multiplication. For example, to multiply 9 by 7, set up two columns, one headed by 9 and one headed by 1. Double 9 to get 18, double 18 to get 36. In the right-hand column, double 1 to get 2 and 2 to get 4. Using the right-hand numbers that total 7, add the corresponding left-hand numbers. They total 63, or 9 times 7. This system was used by the ancient Egyptians and was also used in Russia into the nineteenth century.

MINES AND GRAVITY

Q. Would I weigh more at the bottom of the deepest mine shaft than I did at sea level?

A. You would weigh very slightly less. If you assume that the earth is a perfect sphere with a uniform mass throughout, and you went below the surface of the sphere, only the mass within your radius would contribute to your effective weight.

The radius of the earth is 6,371 kilometers. If you were able to dig a shaft a kilometer deep, your effective weight would be 6,370 divided by 6,371, or a fraction slightly less than 1 of your effective weight at the surface.

It works like that all the way to the center of the earth. If the effective radius is zero, your effective weight is zero. At the center of the earth, all the gravitational forces of the earth would be acting on a person simultaneously, so they would cancel each other out.

CENTER OF THE EARTH

Q. If a hole of, say, 3 feet in diameter were dug straight through the earth, and an object, such as a brick, were dropped into the hole, how far would it go?

A. Theoretically, it would go all the way through and then back, oscillating back and forth forever.

The brick would be exactly like a mass on a spring pulling it toward the center of the earth. Momentum keeps it going through the center, but after that the spring is slowing it down. The object goes all the way through to the center, picking up speed until it reaches its maximum at that point, then roars right through the center but starts slowing down.

When the brick got to the other side of the earth, it would reverse direction, and if you didn't stop it at that point, it would go back and forth forever. The trip from one end of the tunnel to the other would take about forty-five minutes.

If the hole were slanted, between New York City and London, say, the one-way trip would still take the same forty-five minutes. The distance would be shorter but the accelerating force of gravity would be weaker.

The explanation assumes that the hole goes from pole to pole, so that the earth's rotation would not be a factor, that it is lined with a vacuum tube, so there would be no air resistance, and finally that the brick is resistant to the heat of the earth's interior.

MEASURING MOUNTAINS

Q. *How do scientists measure mountains like Mount Everest?*
A. The simplest way, and one that is still in use with the aid of satellites, is just an elaboration of how scouts are taught to measure the height of trees, by constructing a triangle with some known values and then filling in the blanks.

In the surveying method called triangulation, a baseline of a known length is established. To determine the distance between any two points, they are made the vertices of a triangle. The an-

gles of the triangle and the length of its other two sides can be determined from observations made at the ends of the baseline.

In surveying a large area, a series of triangles is constructed upon the baseline; each has at least one side in common with adjacent triangles. In fact, Mount Everest was named for Sir George

Everest, a director of the nineteenth-century Great Trigonometrical Survey of India done by this method.

A 1987 Italian expedition to confirm the height of Mount Everest made multiple observations from four ground stations on the mountain and with repeated signals from four Global Positioning System satellites. The signals were picked up by receivers that measured the exact time the coded signal was received and computed the time difference between transmission and reception. This time, multiplied by the speed of light, yielded the ground station's distance from the satellite. Four such measurements define the station's latitude and longitude and, with further calculations, determine its elevation above sea level. The Italians then followed regular triangulation methods to measure the height of the summit from these carefully plotted baselines.

The result: 29,108 feet above sea level, but it may be slightly higher now. The Indian and Eurasian plates, colliding to form the Himalayas, are still pushing the chain up by half an inch or so a year.

SEA LEVEL

Q. *What is "sea level"? Are all the world's mountains measured from the same point?*

A. Sea level, actually mean sea level, is calculated as the average height of the sea surface taking into account all stages of ocean tides (as measured at various locations by a network of tide gauges) over a nineteen-year period.

Scientists have long recognized the inaccuracy of these tide measurements, and satellites are offering more precision, showing from the vantage of space that even calm ocean surfaces have large, constantly changing hills and valleys. But for now these tidal measures are the standard for measuring all things up and down, including mountains. Mount Everest is said to be the tallest, just over 29,000 feet above sea level.

But another way of measuring mountain peaks is by their distance from the center of the earth. On this basis, Ecuador's Chimborazo, at 20,561 feet above sea level, would be taller than Everest by a whopping two miles. This is because the earth bulges at the equator (near Chimborazo) and flattens toward the poles. Using the center of the earth as a benchmark, "sea level" at the equator is 14 miles higher than at the poles.

Airplane Speed

Q. How do airplanes know how fast they are traveling?

A. A hollow tube called a pitot tube is mounted on the surface of the nose. As they board, passengers may be able to see this tube on the nose toward the bottom of the plane.

The tube is parallel to the air that comes over the plane, and measures what is called the total pressure of the air. This increases as the plane moves faster. Meanwhile, another measure is taken of what is called static pressure, the local thermodynamic pressure of the air, which varies in pressure along with the temperature.

From these two readings, what is called the local air speed is determined. As air flows over the nose and then over the rest of the plane, the pressure changes, so different figures for each area of the airplane are used to determine the ratio of local velocity to the actual speed of the plane.

Many airplanes also use an inertial guidance system, like that used on the space shuttle or an intercontinental missile. It measures the acceleration of an airplane on an absolute basis, by keeping exact track of the loads exerted on spinning gyroscopes, with a factor subtracted to account for gravity. These devices can be set very accurately at takeoff so that they indicate not only speed, but the exact location of the airplane in space with respect to where it took off.

THE METER BAR

Q. *Is the official standard for the length of the meter still a metal bar kept in Paris?*

A. For many years, the international standard for defining all units of length was the meter as defined by the distance between two scratches on a platinum-iridium bar stored in a vault at the International Bureau of Weights and Measures at Sèvres, near Paris. In 1960, the basis of the standard was changed to the wavelength of orange light emitted by the gas krypton 86.

In 1984, the General Conference on Weights and Measures in Paris switched once more, to a standard based on the speed of light. Under this system, one meter is defined as the distance traveled by light through a vacuum in 1/299,792,458th of a second. That definition will remain in use for the foreseeable future, according to the National Institute of Standards and Technology, formerly the National Bureau of Standards.

? ? ? !

Industrial Secrets

BATTERY DRAIN

Q. *Which drains a battery faster, using it for four hours straight or using it for four one-hour periods?*

A. Using a battery-operated device continuously for four hours would run down a battery faster than using it for an hour on, then an hour off, for four cycles. The reason is that batteries have a tendency to recover a little bit if not used for a time.

A battery's current comes from electrons that are a byproduct of a chemical reaction between two substances, and how those substances are physically arranged affects how the reaction proceeds. They actually move from one side to another. The rest period time allows the ingredients to equalize and lets the liquids get where they are supposed to be.

There is some recovery with continuous use, but if a battery is used until it is completely dead, you get more service with intermittent use than with continuous use. The difference between intermittent and continuous use is greater with a device that makes a heavy drain on a battery, a toy with a motor that runs wheels, for example, than with a clock with very light hands that runs continuously.

The physical arrangement helps explain why rechargeable batteries made with nickel and cadmium may exhibit what has been called a memory effect. For example, if a battery designed for an hour of use is used for ten minutes and then recharged, and if this process is repeated several times, the next time the battery is needed for a full hour, the power drops off fairly quickly, as if the battery had a memory of what was expected of it.

MAGNETS

Q. *Why does a magnet lose its power over time?*
A. Newer magnets are made of materials that are far less likely to lose their magnetism over time than the old horseshoe magnets.

Magnets are composed of many little magnetic regions called domains. The magnetic field of the whole magnet runs opposite to the direction of the domains that cause the field. That tends to make the domains reverse their magnetism. In modern magnets, the domains are energetically stuck, more or less, making them less vulnerable to this effect. Such a magnet will lose its magnetism only if it is heated to a high temperature or subjected to vibrations.

The new magnets use materials like alnico (an aluminum-nickel-cobalt compound) and cobalt samarium that have internal structures that prevent the deterioration of the magnetic circuit. They are divided into many little particles, each of which is one domain.

In contrast, the old horseshoe magnets had domains that were much bigger, solid pieces of iron, with the domains bounded by little impurities made of iron carbide. Paradoxical as it may seem, small particles of an optimum size are more energetically stable than large ones in magnetic substances, a discovery made only in the last few decades.

A COLD GLOW

Q. *How do the glowing plastic necklaces sold at fairs and carnivals work?*

A. The necklaces and other temporary chemical lights work by imitating the chemical reaction called bioluminescence that allows fireflies to light up.

The reaction in the plastic tube is oxidation, as in burning, but the chemicals involved, called luciferins, produce more light than heat.

When the proper chemical is mixed with diluted hydrogen peroxide from a glass ampule in the tube, it generates dual carbon dioxide molecules, a compound called dioxetane dione. This compound reacts in the presence of a fluorescer, or glow-producing chemical, to generate light plus carbon dioxide. The reaction can continue until all the active components are consumed.

The nontoxic fluorescers used in American Cyanamid's Lite-Up lightsticks are proprietary formulas.

People can prolong the light from their necklaces and bracelets by keeping them in the refrigerator, the company says. As with all chemical reactions, chilling slows down the reaction and makes it last longer.

STEEL HARDNESS

Q. *What do knife makers mean when they give a Rockwell number for the steel in their blades?*

A. The scale of relative hardness, developed by Stanley P. Rockwell around 1920, runs from C20 to C80.

Each point on the Rockwell scale represents 80 millionths of an inch of depth when the steel is tested with a sharp point and a standardized weight. The higher the number, however, the harder the steel. In general, the harder the steel in the knife, the sharper the edge it takes.

There are other hardness scales, but the Rockwell scale is especially suited to the rapid inspection of parts.

In one device, the part to be tested is put under a diamond

penetrator, ground to a curved conical point. First the minor load, a weight of 10 kilograms, is applied, and the zero point is determined. Then the major load, a weight of 150 kilograms, is applied for two seconds. The device displays the hardness number, based on how far the point penetrates. The minor load is applied first to get down into the material a little bit, to get beyond surface irregularities that might influence the hardness test.

THE NIGHT MIRROR

Q. How does the night position on a car mirror work?

A. A rearview mirror with a night position is actually two reflective surfaces. One is a shiny mirror that is about 90 percent reflective. Over it is a wedge of glass that is only about 4 percent reflective. The wedge is very thin and angled only a few degrees.

In the daytime, the mirror is angled so that the shiny side reflects the outside light. The less shiny side is pointing somewhere at the driver's pants leg, but all the driver sees is the reflection from the shiny back surface of the glass, through the wedge. There is also a 4 percent reflection from the wedge, but the driver doesn't see that, because so much light is coming in from outside.

At night, a lever switches the mirror to a different angle, and the process is reversed. Now the shiny side is reflecting nothing but dark roof of the inside of the car, where there is very little light. But when the bright beams of a car hit the less reflective glass wedge, the light can be seen without blinding the driver.

CHEWING GUM

Q. Is it bad for you to swallow chewing gum? Does it get digested?

A. The nonsoluble gum base of chewing gum is not digested, but neither are parts of many foods, like popcorn or lettuce, scientists in the food industry say.

Gum typically contains five ingredients: sugar, corn syrup, softeners, flavors and a nonsoluble gum base. The first four ingredients are soluble and are extracted as the gum is chewed. The gum base moves intact through the normal digestive process in a few days, much as roughage does.

Makers do not advocate swallowing, but it would not hurt more than eating a big bag of popcorn. Some manufacturers use various forms of latex as a base, and it passes safely through the digestive system, much as a rubber band would. Like toothpaste, chewing gum is defined as a food for the purpose of Food and Drug Administration regulation.

The original formulations of many gums might predate F.D.A. regulation, but as each new ingredient, like a modern synthetic gum base, is added, the regulators take into consideration that it could be swallowed. The amount that would normally be swallowed must be safe for people.

Small children should not be allowed to chew gum because they might choke on it, medical authorities advise.

THE DIAL TONE

Q. Why is the dial tone an A on the musical scale all over the country?

A. It isn't really a pure A, but a composite of two frequencies: 350 hertz, or cycles per second, and 440 hertz. Most symphony orchestras tune to an A of about 440 hertz.

The tone was apparently not intentionally selected to make life simpler for musicians with no tuning fork, but rather evolved relatively early in the history of dial telephone equipment, when national standards were being set.

Various tones from about 160 to 480 pulses per second were needed for audible signals to subscribers and operators. Some were interrupted to convey busy signals and other information.

When touch-tone service was introduced, the dial tone had to be altered slightly because it confused the touch-tone equipment, reducing the sensitivity of the receiver at the central office to the first tone dialed. The new frequency is similar enough to the old tone to be accepted by customers as a dial tone.

COUGH MEDICINE

Q. *Why do so many medicines, especially cough preparations, contain alcohol?*

A. Alcohol is the safest solvent for drugs that do not mix well with water, as pharmacists have known since ancient times. Safe, that is, for the general population. For an alcoholic or anyone else who does not want to ingest spirits, a pharmacist will recommend a tablet or lozenge, or for a severe cough, a spray with a very small amount of alcohol that mostly evaporates.

There is some pharmacological activity in the alcohol in cough syrup, but normally the concentration is very low. For example, a teaspoon of something that is 15 to 20 percent alcohol has only about 1 milliliter of pure alcohol, as against about 15 milliliters in a shot of bourbon.

HOT WATER

Q. *Why does hot water work better with dishwashing detergent than cold water?*

A. For two reasons. First, hot water melts fats and softens other food particles, making it easier for detergent to penetrate them. The active ingredients in dishwashing detergent, known as surfactants, are chemicals that bind fat and water together so they can be removed from the dish. That is why grease can be cleaned off a plate without detergent, but the water would still leave a greasy residue.

Second, hot rinse water removes more of the thin film of dishwater residue that is left behind after washing, again because it melts fat and softens other kinds of dirt. This residue causes rinse water to puddle on dishes. When the water evaporates, it leaves behind deposits of salts and other minerals, causing spots.

FROZEN STOCKINGS

Q. *Does putting nylon stockings in the freezer make them last longer?*

A. There is no data to support the belief that freezing nylon hose makes them more durable.

Nylon is a fiber made from petroleum derivatives. Properties such as strength and resistance to fatigue (stress from flexing) and abrasion do not differ depending on temperature, particularly by the time nylon is in a finished article. By then, the filament has been through processing that has heated, cooled and relaxed it, etc., so that there is not much left that can be done to it that will make a difference.

Du Pont, which developed nylon, suggested a possible source of the belief, however. At nylon plants, comparison samples from each batch are frozen as a strict scientific control, to rule out any slight changes, such as shrinkage, that might take place in samples stored in a closet. However, such changes would affect only the filaments themselves, not the finished product.

CALCULATOR BATTERIES

Q. In a battery-operated calculator, what determines the amount of energy used: the length of time it is turned on, or the complexity of the computation?

A. The central processing unit, the microprocessor that actually performs the calculations, is what takes the most power when the calculator is running.

The more calculations the machine is asked to perform, the more power it would draw. Just being turned on would take only enough of the calculator's battery power to light up the display.

SHINY FOIL

Q. Why is ordinary aluminum foil shiny on one side and dull on the other?

A. The shiny and dull surfaces result from the final rolling step in the manufacturing process and make no difference when the foil is used.

In foil mills, heavy-gauge aluminum foil is rolled like clothes put through a wringer to get a thinner gauge of foil for consumers.

In the final rolling, the foil is put through the rollers in two layers, so that more foil can be processed at one time. The side that is in contact with the highly polished steel rollers becomes shiny, and the other side, which touches the other layer of foil, comes out with a dull or matte finish.

SHRINKING CLOTHES

Q. *Why do clothes shrink?*

A. The answer has to do with the chemical and physical properties of fibers from natural sources, especially cotton, wool and linen.

The individual fibers in yarns are made of long polymer chains, or strands of giant molecules. In their natural state, the chains are scrolled up or crinkled. In preparing them for spinning and weaving, the first step is usually a straightening of the fibers by processes like carding wool.

However, the fibers try to go back to their natural state. Moving from one state to another requires crossing an energy barrier. It even takes energy to get back to the lowest-energy, most disordered state. Hot temperatures in laundering give the fibers the energy that allows them to change state so that the long polymer chains scroll back up again. There is little shrinkage in synthetic fibers, because their polymers can be designed the way the makers want, and they start off in a straightened state.

TIME CAPSULES

Q. *How do time-release medications work?*

A. The first time-release medication was probably just a sugar-coated pill; the coating did not dissolve and release the bitter medicine until it was safely past the mouth. Many time-release medications, like Contac, introduced in 1961, are based on that fairly simple idea: small amounts of the medication are coated with varying thicknesses of soluble material; the thicker the coating, the longer it takes to dissolve in the body. If exactly the right number of pellets of exactly the right thicknesses is in each capsule, the dose is released gradually over a fairly predictable period.

However, the release actually takes place in tiny spurts, not continuously. Some drugs that can be absorbed through the skin, like nitroglycerine, can be put in patches that release the drug both slowly and constantly. One system to deliver scopolamine to fight seasickness uses a disk with an impermeable backing, an ultrathin reservoir holding the drug, a membrane with microscopic pores to control the drug release and an adhesive surface to hold it on the skin. Some drugs, like hormone implants used as birth control, use a similar system in pellets implanted in fatty tissue under the skin.

A recently patented timed delivery system for a drug that does not dissolve in water uses a pair of separated compartments. One compartment contains a polymer that draws water into the pill through a semipermeable membrane. The inflow of water increases pressure within the pill, pushing medication out of the other compartment through a tiny hole.

CATCHING COUNTERFEITS

Q. *How do bill changers tell that the money isn't counterfeit?*
A. Many of the specific techniques machines use to detect counterfeit money are closely guarded secrets, since once counterfeiters know how the machines work, they try to foil them. But two common means of identifying paper money are magnetic sensing and optical sensing.

Inks used to print notes have certain magnetic properties, which can be sensed by a magnetic head in a bill changer. A computer can recognize the electronic signature of specific tracks along the money and accept or reject it.

In optical sensing, light is passed through or reflected from a bill. Some inks absorb light and others reflect it. The computer can analyze these patterns and determine if the bill is acceptable.

In either case, the scanning takes about one second.

DRY CLEANING

Q. *Is dry cleaning really dry?*
A. It is dry in the sense that the solvents used have no water. Al-

though they are liquid, they have the ability to remove soil without affecting fabric as water would. They also evaporate quickly and leave dry clothes behind.

About 95 percent of what is used for general cleaning is perchloroethylene, or C_2Cl_4, a compound that is 14.48 percent carbon and 85.52 percent chlorine. It is also used to degrease metals. It is very volatile, and is used in closed cleaning machines so that the evaporated solvent does not escape.

In addition to general cleaning, in which clothes are gently agitated in the solvent until soil and some oily stains are released, what is called dry cleaning can involve spot removal using solvents to dissolve stains; lubrication to penetrate and lift stains; chemical action to change stains into other substances that are invisible or soluble; and digestion by an enzyme to make stains form a soluble sugar.

DRY ICE

Q. *How is dry ice made?*
A. At room temperature and pressure, carbon dioxide, or CO_2, is a common gas, about 0.05 percent of the air at sea level by weight. It is also a product of combustion and the respiration of all animals. When chilled below minus 109 degrees Fahrenheit, it becomes a solid, called dry ice.

In the commercial production of dry ice, liquid carbon dioxide is chilled below minus 109 degrees Fahrenheit and compressed. The material is sprayed into a square chamber with a nozzle. It forms "snow," and powerful hydraulic rams form it into a very dense solid block of dry ice, weighing 240 pounds. It is then cut into four 60-pound blocks for shipment.

Dry ice is also formed into nuggets, by forcing the snow through stainless steel dies with round holes that are one-eighth to three-quarters of an inch in diameter. The nuggets break off in random lengths of 1 to 2 inches.

Dry ice does not melt, but vaporizes, passing from a solid state to a vapor without going through a liquid state. This is called sublimation. The time this takes depends on temperature, air movement and whether the dry ice is in an enclosed area.

Dry ice is what is called an expendable refrigerant, which leaves nothing behind when it evaporates, so it is desirable for shipping and storing a variety of foods. It is also used for manufacturing processes, like shrink fitting, in which a plastic part is chilled with dry ice so it shrinks, inserted into another part and then allowed to warm up and expand for a tight fit.

TINY BUBBLES

Q. How do they get all that shaving cream into an aerosol can?
A. Shaving cream is basically soap and water. It is put into the can along with compressed butane gas. Without the gas, all you have is soapy liquid. When the valve is pressed, some of the gas mixes with the soap and water, escapes and expands to make foam.

The filling process is just like filling a tire, or even a balloon. As long as the pressure is maintained in a closed system and the gas from a pressurized source is not allowed to escape, it takes up a very small space. The fact that any pressurized gas expands when the pressure is released means that a very little soap and water can make a lot of foamy bubbles.

FABRIC SOFTENER SHEETS

Q. How does a fabric softener sheet work?
A. A sheet put in the dryer works much the way a liquid fabric softener does, but includes agents that disperse very small

amounts of softening and anti-static components throughout the warm air that permeates the damp fabrics.

Fabric softening agents are surfactants, chemicals that reduce the tension at the surface where two different materials meet. (Soap and detergents are surfactants that reduce oil-water surface tensions and thus help wash out oily dirt.)

Surfactant molecules have two components, one soluble in oil that resists water and one soluble in water. Those used to soften fabrics have a high proportion of fatty material, generally long fatty chains, with water-soluble groups that may be anionic (negatively charged), cationic (positively charged) or nonionic (uncharged).

The fatty agent puts an extremely thin coating of oil at the interface of two moving surfaces, so they slip by each other easily and without friction. Cationic or nonionic solubilizing groups help reduce static buildup resulting from the presence of negatively charged ions.

Dimethyl tallow ammonium chloride is a typical cationic soft-ener and polyethylene glycol monostearate is a typical nonionic softener.

SECTION TWO:

The Softer Side of Science

? ? ? !

A Modern Bestiary

GIRAFFE HYPERTENSION

Q. *Is the blood pressure of a giraffe extremely high to get blood to the head? Do giraffes get hardening of the arteries and strokes?*

A. In an adult giraffe, the systolic blood pressure, the pressure when the heart contracts to pump blood through the body, is about 200 millimeters of mercury at the level of the heart, about twice that of an adult human being.

During exercise, the blood pressure at the level of the giraffe's feet might be double what it is at heart level because of gravity. At the head, it is comparable to the blood pressure of a human being.

Stroke and hardening of the arteries can occur in most mammal species, but is not a notable problem with giraffes. The giraffe's circulatory system has evolved with special adaptations for both high and low pressure.

For example, because the blood pressure in the lower part of the body is so high, the artery walls in the legs are very thick, much thicker than in the neck, to prevent edema, or leakage of fluid out of the vessels. The skin and tissue under the skin on the limbs are also very tight to prevent leaks.

In the large veins of the neck, there are valves to restrict the flow of blood so that it does not flow backward and pool in the head when the giraffe puts its head down to drink or eat.

DOLPHINS AND DOLPHINS

Q. *When dolphin is on the menu, am I eating a Flipper-type superintelligent dolphin?*

A. No. The true dolphin is a mammal, any one of about thirty-three species of cetacean mammals in the family Delphinidae, characterized by a pronounced beak-shaped mouth. The dolphin on restaurant menus, Coryphaena hippurus, is a fish with gills, iridescent colors and firm flesh. It is called mahimahi in Hawaii and dorado in South America.

The dolphin fish is a fast-growing species that can reach 5 feet in length. It is not an endangered species and in fact is raised for the market.

Dolphin mammals, like all cetaceans, breathe air directly, instead of extracting oxygen dissolved in water as fish do. Unlike fish, dolphins must return to the surface periodically to take air. They have a large brain relative to body size and a high degree of folding of the cerebral cortex, comparable to that of primates. Other cetaceans are several families of whales and the true porpoises, which belong to another family, Phocoenidae.

Orca, the killer whale of motion picture fame, is actually a kind of dolphin, and so is the familiar bottle-nosed dolphin, like Flipper, the television star. The dolphin fish is not an entertainment figure.

DEATH BY PYTHON

Q. *When a cormorant catches a fish, it appears to swallow it alive. What kills the fish? Does the same thing happen to a python's victims?*

A. The cause of death is, in all probability, suffocation. If not, the acid in the stomach compartments in the cormorant would interfere with oxygen transport in the gills.

Pythons, boas and other constrictors kill their prey before they feed on it, by constricting and suffocating it before they swallow it. In other types of snake, the prey suffocates once it is in the animal's stomach. It is a combination of suffocation and drowning.

WHY SLUGS?

Q. *What use are slugs?*

A. It may surprise someone whose vegetable garden has been munched by voracious shell-impaired land snails, but slugs do have some fans. Among them are their predators, like snakes, toads and starlings, another pest. Some slugs are edible by humans, too.

Most of the worst garden pests are foreign invaders. Domestic varieties like the nine-inch banana slug (*Ariolimax columbianus*) of the Pacific Northwest content themselves with fungi and decaying vegetable matter in the woods. They were part of the diet of Indians and of early German immigrants, who batter-fried them.

And at least one scientist, Dr. Alan Gelperin, a research scientist at Bell Labs in Murray Hill, New Jersey, found slugs to be excellent guinea pigs. He used the brains of slugs in his research on the neural mechanisms of learning.

FRIED FISH

Q. *Why don't fish suffer from the high pressures deep in the ocean? And what prevents fish from being electrocuted when lightning strikes?*

A. All fish have internal pressures that are equal to the pressures outside their bodies at their normal depths. This is true of both tissues and the gas-filled bladders in the abdominal cavity that many fish have.

They would only be in trouble if they changed depth greatly. If they come up a great deal, they might explode. If they went a great deal deeper, they might implode.

Most deep-sea fish do not have gas-filled bladders, which is a good thing, because gases expand and contract much more than fluids or tissue.

As to electrocution, fresh-water fish need have little fear because fresh water is not a good conductor of electricity. Because of its salt ions, however, sea water is a fairly good conductor.

But even ocean fish are relatively safe.

If lightning strikes the water surface, you get a high density of current right at the point where it strikes but current is free to flow in all possible directions, and it spreads out tremendously because of the great volume of conductor. Thus, depending on the size of the lightning strike, the strength of the current at any single point is not high.

If a fish stays completely underwater, so current could flow around it, and a few meters away from the point of incidence, it would probably be safe, but if it goes too close, it would be fried, of course.

DRINKING LIKE A FISH

Q. *What do whales and other marine mammals drink? What about fish?*

A. Marine mammals depend primarily on the water content of the food they eat, rather than on drinking sea water.

Whales, for example, eat mostly shrimp-like krill and fish. A high percentage of the body tissue of fish is water.

Toothed whales eat larger fish or squid, while the baleen whales, which are larger, take big gulps of sea water and strain the food through the bony baleen structure, an efficient sieve-like mechanism.

As for fish, they absorb water through body surfaces. They have gills and membranes that allow a transfer of water osmotically.

Marine fish must process sea water, which has a higher concentration of salt than fluids within their bodies. They have semipermeable membranes, which allow water in but keep most of the salt out. Then the fish must conserve the water they have processed, so they produce a very concentrated urine, expending little water in the waste process.

ONE-EYED ANIMALS

Q. *Are there any one-eyed animals?*

A. There are no mammals, birds, reptiles or amphibians that naturally have only one eye. Flatfish like the flounder, commonly thought of as having only one eye, in fact have two; one migrates to join the other on the right or left side.

However, there are several orders of one-eyed animals among the invertebrates. Among them are some "water fleas," which are actually crustaceans.

Another one-eyed crustacean, appropriately named the cyclops, is a common inhabitant of pond scum in stagnant bodies of water. It has compound eyes like those of the fly, but only one per customer.

SQUIRRELS' NESTS

Q. *Do squirrels actually build nests? One seems to be doing so in my London plane tree.*

A. There are nearly three hundred species in the squirrel family, and some of them, called tree squirrels, are expert tree nest builders. Some other species dig burrows and build nests there.

Tree squirrels belong to the

genus Sciurus. Their nests are called dreys. The common gray squirrel, *Sciurus carolinensis*, is a tree squirrel. Its natural habitat is the oak, hickory and walnut forest of the eastern United States. It has been observed taking fine strips of bark to make its drey or to line dens in hollow trees.

Tree squirrels do not hibernate, though they may stay in their nests for days at a time in bad weather, huddled together for warmth. The mother's nest may be home to young squirrels even after they are weaned, and adult squirrels may share nests.

ASLEEP IN THE DEEP

Q. *How do the large marine mammals manage to sleep without drowning?*

A. Some sleep out of the water, and some may not sleep at all.

The furred or hairy aquatic mammals in the pinniped suborder (seals, etc.) have a variety of interesting adaptations that permit them to spend a comparatively long time underwater, sometimes at considerable depths. However, they rise frequently to breathe and emerge from the ocean to sleep, relax, molt, mate and reproduce on a handy beach, rock, ice floe or snow cave above the water. Diving tends to be reserved for hunting purposes.

The situation is less clear for cetaceans (whales, etc.) and sirenians (sea cows and manatees). The whales evolved from land animals that returned to the sea millions of years ago. Though whales come to the surface to breathe air into their lungs, they can spend a remarkably long time between breaths, up to an hour in some species, and spend nearly all their lives underwater.

However, whales learned to hold their breath so well that they lost their involuntary breathing mechanism and must be conscious to continue to breathe. Not only would a reflex have to take care of breathing, it would have to take them to the surface for air. Also, the blowhole automatically closes and must be opened voluntarily by the whale. Whales would drown if they fell asleep or were knocked unconscious.

The animal must think about each breath. It cannot have an

unconscious sleep as we know it. There are theories that the whale has the ability to rest half of the brain and control breathing functions with the other half, but they are just theories.

Sea cows and manatees tend to live in warm, calm, shallow, vegetation-rich waters where they can float lethargically at or near the surface. They have an extremely low metabolic rate, do not expend much energy to regulate body temperature and require little oxygen. Manatees may sleep or rest supported by the bottom. When they hold their breath, large blubber deposits and natural buoyancy let them float at the surface and engage in a resting behavior, though not an unconscious sleep.

BATS IN THE BELFRY

Q. What should you do if a bat gets in the house?

A. Relax and enjoy it might be the best advice.

A one-ounce brown bat, the kind most likely to show up in a North American house, is capable of eating five hundred mosquito-sized insects an hour all night, but is virtually incapable of doing any harm to a human being. Its only defenses are tiny teeth and a fierce appearance. A frightened bat makes a chirping sound and tries to look ferocious.

If you feel that you must try to get rid of it, turn on the lights; bats have very good vision, and the extra light will help it find the way out. Close off the room from the rest of the house and open windows or doors to the outside, then stand against the wall, out of the bat's flight path. Chances are the bat will leave if it is there by mistake.

On the other hand, bats may choose your house because it is a likely hunting ground, in which case it would be wise to let them stay. They are only there because there is enough food to feed them. Besides mosquitoes, bats like Japanese beetles, gypsy moths and other night-flying insects, especially the ones that vex gardeners.

Bats are also site-faithful, which is why artificial bat roosts may or may not attract them. They prefer places with vertical temperature gradients, like chimneys, attics and shutters.

SHARKS' SENSES

Q. *Does a shark really smell blood from a long way away in the water?*

A. Definitely. Sharks have an extremely sensitive sense of smell for blood in the water. A few molecules can be enough to draw a shark.

A shark has nostrils, called nares, connected to olfactory bulbs that go back to the brain. Just by studying the brain, scientists concluded that the shark was heavily dependent on olfaction, with 70 percent of a relatively small brain, by weight and volume, devoted to smell.

There is a difference between the sense of smell and the sense of taste, although the molecules being sensed are very similar. The organs doing the sensing stimulate different hormonal and physiological chains of response, generating very different kinds of behavior.

Smell can trigger emotional or behavioral responses ranging from sexual behavior to searching for food, whereas the reaction to taste is simply to accept or reject the food.

In fact, there is strong evidence that most shark attacks on people are cases of mistaken identity or reflex action. Many such attacks occur where visibility is low, at night or in turbid water.

The smell of blood might stimulate a shark to try to feed on a person it mistakes for a turtle or sea lion, but the taste of neoprene rubber or suntan oil might lead to rejection.

Many more people are attacked by sharks than are eaten by sharks. But who wants to be tasted?

RED-BLOODED FISH

Q. *Do fish have blood, and if so what color is it? Why don't I see blood when I clean a fish?*

A. Fish do have blood, and it is red.

Other cold-blooded animals, like amphibians and reptiles, also have red blood.

Fish have a circulatory system with blood and a heart as the pump just like that of humans, and just like that of humans, fish blood is red because it contains hemoglobin, the iron compound that carries oxygen.

If a fish is fresh and is cut near major vessels, you will see blood. In muscle tissue, which becomes fillets, the vessels are so small that the blood may not be evident, or if the fish is not fresh, the blood may have coagulated or collected in one part of the body.

Fish from the fish market may have already been gutted and beheaded and so may be drained of most blood. Even so, you might see blood around the spine, because a major blood vessel goes right under the arches of the vertebral column.

SAFE DIVING FOR WHALES

Q. Why don't whales get the bends?

A. Luckily for deep-diving whales, they have an entirely different system from that of humans for handling the air they breathe before diving and their oxygen needs while diving.

When pressure is released on gases dissolved in the blood, the bends result. Whales are taking in air breathed at the surface and carrying it to the bottom, not breathing pressurized air underwater. Besides, they don't carry much with them in the first place, because they don't need it while diving.

The bends, also called decompression sickness and caisson disease, appears in divers who breathe compressed air in caissons and diving apparatuses after a rapid reduction in air pressure when they come back up. Symptoms include skin itching, joint pain and nervous system impairment. Severe cases, if untreated, can lead to partial paralysis or degeneration of bones and joints.

The symptoms result from the formation of bubbles of gas in tissues during the ascent; bubbles may block blood vessels and start a cascade of problems. Trained divers avoid the bends by allowing gas to escape slowly in a gradual ascent.

Whales have some special breathing adaptations for diving.

First, before and during deep dives, whales expel most air from the lungs, and instead use oxygen combined with the hemoglobin of the blood and the myoglobin of the muscles for most of the supply for prolonged dives. Meanwhile, their arterial networks seem to act as shunts to maintain a normal blood supply to the brain but a reduced supply to the muscles. Also, the heart rate decreases for a further saving of oxygen.

Any free gases they do carry to the bottom are absorbed under pressure into rigid, thick-walled parts of the respiratory system.

Another underwater adaptation that humans do not have allows whales to avoid nitrogen narcosis, or rapture of the deep, which comes from breathing nitrogen under increased pressure. Whales can dissolve nitrogen in their blubber, so that it does not affect brain cells and lead to the intoxication and euphoria that have doomed many divers.

HOMING SQUIRRELS

Q. If I catch the squirrels that have taken over my bird feeder and take them to the woods several miles away, will they make it back to my yard? In other words, do squirrels have a homing instinct?

A. They do have such an instinct. It is not well understood by science, but they will often return several miles.

For example, an informal experiment was conducted at the Brooklyn Center for the Urban Environment in Prospect Park, which conducts extensive environmental education programs for schoolchildren and adults. Some years ago, a classroom in the park's Picnic House was invaded by squirrels that would distract the children. So the Center trapped the squirrels alive and transported

them to the Dyker Beach Golf Course near the Verrazano-Narrows Bridge, which is about seven miles away from Prospect Park as the crow flies.

There is no doubt that the same ones were back in three to four days. They had somehow found their way for more than seven miles, through urban backyards and busy streets, to their preferred habitat.

SLEEPING DINOSAURS

Q. *Did dinosaurs sleep? If so, was it standing up or lying down?*
A. Dinosaurs probably did sleep, though it's all speculation, because scientists don't know enough about their physiology.

The speculations are based on their structures and diets and on the habits of the presumably most similar living species, like crocodiles and birds, which do sleep.

Carnivorous dinosaurs like *Tyrannosaurus rex* and *Deinonychus* would probably have slept a lot, based on the analogy of predaceous animals of today, which (whether warm- or cold-blooded) get their meals in big chunks after a quick pursuit, then go back and rest. Lizards often rest after dining on mice, and lions and cheetahs spend most of the time lounging around between hunts.

Herbivorous dinosaurs probably did not get a chance to sleep as much, because they would have spent more time eating continuously throughout the day.

As for their sleeping positions, scientists suspect that two-legged dinosaurs would have slept lying down, whereas sauropods like the brontosaurus (or apatosaurus), with their long necks and tails and their elephant-like stance on four straight legs, would have been the best candidates for sleeping standing up. It is hard to imagine that *Tyrannosaurus rex* could get much sleep standing up.

ANIMAL LIFE SPANS

Q. *What is the longest-living animal species? What about mammals?*
A. For most animals the idea of an expected life span is meaning-less, since so many die shortly after birth and so few die of old

age, except in captivity. However, reliable longevity records for individual animals have been kept.

The animal with the longest recorded life span is the Marion's tortoise of the Seychelles Islands in the Indian Ocean. One tortoise lived to be more than 152 years old and found its way into *The Guinness Book of Animal Facts and Feats*.

The quahog, a type of clam, is in second place and can survive 150 years if it avoids the dinner table.

The mammal with the longest recorded life is man. Some human beings live more than 110 years. After humans, the Asiatic elephant lives the longest; one elephant lived to be 78 years old.

The shortest-lived mammal is the pocket gopher, which typically lives for 20 months.

TALKING TO BAMBI

Q. *Can animals of different species understand each other?*

A. In some cases, yes. In research on the complex signals gulls send to each other within the same species, scientists found that birds in mixed flocks can respond to each other's alarm calls, and that

this could be a matter of learned behavior or an inborn instinct.

It is possible that deer might take warning from bird calls, like Bambi, but there are no Bambi-like interspecies conversations in the forest.

The communication is on the level of simple signals of danger or expressions of anger, but there is no doubt that when a wolf snarls when cornered, it conveys a defensive threat, and the signal can occur across species lines.

There are cases where different species use communication deceptively. For example, hungry female fireflies of one species might imitate the flashing signals that the females of another species make when responding to a love call. In this way, they can lure a male of the other species within range, pounce and eat.

BABY TEETH

Q. *Do other mammals lose their baby teeth the way humans do? Why?*

A. Baby teeth are more scientifically called deciduous teeth, because they are shed like leaves. They are also called milk teeth, which is a clue to the answer.

Mammals, with a few exceptions, have two sets of teeth. The key to mammalian success is specialized teeth for many different foods, and two sets, often with different mixes of types, provide for even more adaptability as the animal grows and changes diet.

There are three basic kinds: incisors, to bite and gnaw, like the beaver, whose hard-worn teeth grow all its life; canines, to stab and seize, like the dog or tiger, and molars and premolars, to grind and chew, like the cow.

While mammals are little and growing, the initial source of food is milk, and they do not need teeth at all. The first teeth emerge and develop as needs change; they may have some utility for eating solid foods. Then, as the animal gets a full-sized jaw, it loses the baby teeth and the second set of teeth emerges for the adult diet.

Some mammals have more than two sets and some have none. The baleen whale's teeth never erupt above the jaw. Anteaters do not need them for their diet of termites and ants. Some herbivores have one set of molars that continue to grow through life. And elephants, with their diet of coarse vegetation, have six sets of molars to last them through their long lives.

SNORING ANIMALS

Q. *Do any animals besides people snore?*

A. Yes, some animals do snore, according to anecdotal reports and personal observations. Just a few snorers that zookeepers and pet owners have observed are dogs, gorillas and bears.

The mechanism of snoring in these mammals probably resembles what happens in people. In human beings, snoring is noisy breathing through the open mouth produced by vibration of the soft palate, the back part of the separation between the oral and nasal cavities. It is more common while people are sleeping on the back, as the lower jaw tends to drop open. Snoring is encouraged by anything that hinders breathing through the nose.

ANIMAL GOURMETS

Q. *How discriminating are the palates of wild animals? Do wolves wolf down their food because they can't taste it, for example?*
A. Animals' sensitivity to taste varies widely by species, but animals do have food preferences and many have taste buds.

Animals also seek out food based on consistency, color and smell. Certain snakes that have poor eyesight have powerful receptors for the heat of their prey and make their choices based on that, and some animals seek out special nutrients.

Because the diet of zoo animals like lions is prepared to provide certain levels of vitamins and minerals, their preferences are not the best guide to what a lion would eat in the wild. That would usually be what they can catch, for example, small hoofed stock like antelopes.

Animals may sense whether what they are about to eat is rotten, but whether they will select against it, we don't necessarily know. They usually prefer fresh.

As for wolves, they are close relatives of the domestic dog, and it is assumed that their taste buds are somewhat similar. The gusto shown, however, depends on when they last ate.

CITY PIGEONS

Q. *There seem to be no pigeons in the countryside, only in cities. Why?*
A. Pigeons, or rock doves, are actually fairly common in agricultural areas. There they find niches in barns and lofts that resemble the

rocky ledges that are their natural nesting sites, as well as plentiful supplies of their favorite food, small grains.

However, pigeons do seem to prefer cities to small towns and wilderness. There are probably two reasons. The first is food. City pigeons feed on anything, from bread to popcorn, and they find more food strewn on big city streets than on small-town lanes.

The other reason is nesting sites. Rock doves live only in open areas, not densely wooded places, and only near a suitable roosting or nesting site. This usually means a manmade structure. Cities offer a multitude of suitable sites, on the ledges of tall buildings, under bridges, etc. In the nonagricultural countryside, there are fewer such opportunities to set up housekeeping.

Rock doves, the same species used as homing pigeons, are not native to North America. They were carried around the world from Europe, perhaps as food, and the date of their arrival here is not certain. They are believed to have been around since the late 1600s, almost since the Mayflower.

WOODPECKERS
Q. How do woodpeckers know where to peck to find food?
A. They have an extremely good sense of hearing. For example, the hairy woodpecker and pileated woodpecker can actually hear those carpenter ant larvae and get right into a nest of them quite efficiently.

Woodpeckers also tap tree trunks to find the hollow places where insects might be.

ROBINS AND WORMS
Q. How do robins detect worms?
A. All the studies point to their doing it entirely visually, not by hearing or smell. When robins run along the lawn, cocking their heads, it looks like listening, but actually it is just looking. What the robin usually sees is the castings or pellets of mud at the entrance to the worm hole.

However, worm detection methods vary from one species to another.

Shorebirds like sandpipers have sensitive tips to their bills so they can feel worms that they may not see, and kiwis actually have nostrils at the tip of the bill and a very good sense of smell, allowing them to find earthworms and other food.

BIRDS AND PERCHES

Q. *Why don't birds fall off their perches when they sleep?*

A. Birds don't have to work at not falling off their perches. Tendons on the bottom of their feet, called flexor tendons, respond to pressure from a branch or other perch by causing the toes to wrap around the perch automatically.

Humans would have to expend energy to hold on, but birds would have to exert effort to unclench. It's the relaxed position, as can be plainly seen in dead birds, which have their toes clenched up.

THE ANCIENT ALBATROSS

Q. *What is the longest-living bird species?*

A. The wandering albatross is often listed as the longest-living bird in the wild, but it is not known exactly how long its life span is. The information from bird bands returned to ornithologists indicates that both royal and wandering albatrosses, the two largest species, are around for at least forty years.

Ornithologists know they live longer than that. They are thought to live to be eighty in the wild. (As with any species, individuals might live longer in captivity, safe from predators.) The problem is that the albatross outlives its band; the bands recovered after forty years are in really bad shape.

Most banding is done on songbirds, using an aluminum band, and songbirds have an average life expectancy of only eight months in the wild.

The albatross enjoys such a long life because of its habits. It nests on remote islands in southern seas in and around Antarctica, far removed from most predators.

Albatrosses have a bizarre breeding cycle. The young are fed until they become huge, the nestlings actually weighing more than the adults. The adults take off and ride the ocean winds, soaring and following them around the edge of the ocean for about a year. The young stay in the nest, living off their fat reserves, until the adults return.

The former nestlings then rejoin the flock as adults, ready for courtship, which is also accomplished in an offbeat way. Most birds sing, but albatrosses rattle their bills with each other, like two buccaneers in a saber fight, clapping them together extremely fast.

BIRD NAVIGATION

Q. Why don't birds hit branches when they fly through the forest?
A. Some do, but most are very maneuverable. They also have excellent vision, and the flight pattern and style, musculature and aerodynamic characteristics, and even how fast they fly, are adapted to the environment in which they fly.

Birds that live in the forest and fly through the canopy are agile and small, and they fly more slowly and change direction more quickly than birds that fly in the open.

SEA GULLS

Q. I thought sea gulls were coastal birds but now I see them far inland. Is this a change of habitat?
A. First of all, they are gulls, not sea gulls. "Sea gull" is something of a misnomer; while these birds were mostly coastal in the past, there have always been some inland.

Now, many gulls' habitats have shifted inland, primarily because they like to scavenge in garbage dumps. They will eat almost anything, making them goats with wings.

On the seashore, gulls consume mollusks, dropping the shells to break them and eating the seafood inside.

The early Mormons in Utah were saved from invading locusts by Franklin's gull, which was always an inland gull, found in the

Canadian prairie provinces and the northern plains states. Bonaparte's gull spends the winter on the Great Lakes.

The two most common gulls, the herring gull and the almost identical but smaller ringbilled gull, also have inland distribution, with their distribution being affected as open landfills become less and less common.

REUSABLE NESTS

Q. *Do birds often reuse their nests? And when they do, as a pair of phoebes seems to be doing in my back yard, is it the same pair from year to year, or their children, or the same female with a new mate, or what?*

A. Birds often do reuse their nests, not always and not all birds, but the phoebe is a perfect example of a species that uses the

 same nest from year to year. It is usually the same pair of adult birds, but if misfortune happens to one, the other will probably find a new mate and return to the old nest.

It is unlikely that the occupants would be their young, because they typically disperse somewhat as they mature and move out into the world.

The subject is not fully studied, but the supposition is that they are in the same neighborhood, but not in the same "building."

FLYING BLIND

Q. *When birds fly in the rain, why doesn't it hurt their eyes?*

A. Birds have a sort of thin extra eyelid called a nictitating membrane that protects their eyes and may do so in the rain. The membrane is not entirely transparent, so the birds may not see clearly, but they can probably see light and dark.

As in cats, dogs and other animals, this membrane can flick over the eye very quickly to protect it. It guards against collisions when birds are crashing through brush, and in birds of prey like the peregrine falcon, it closes immediately before impact with victims, covering the eyes as the bird grabs its prey.

BIRDS IN HURRICANES

Q. *What do birds do in a hurricane?*

A. A number of authorities agree that birds do not get any special storm warnings before a hurricane that allow them to avoid it.

In fact, bird-watchers find that oceanic birds often fly before the winds of a hurricane and end up far from their tropical homes. For example, sooty terns may be swept from Florida and the Caribbean and deposited on Long Island. After flying for days without feeding, the birds drop as soon as the hurricane reaches land, often exhausted and starving.

As for land birds, all have their own territories, even in winter, and tend to stay there, seeking any shelter they can find, as they would in any storm. A migrating bird may turn back to land when it hits the bad weather on the fringes of a hurricane.

There is almost certainly an increase in mortality in a hurricane because of exposure to heavy rains. In terms of the survival of bird species, only late nesters would be in serious trouble. By the time fall hurricanes arrive, most birds have completed the raising of their young.

NESTING BOXES

Q. *How can I find out what kinds of birdhouse attract which birds?*

A. The key is not a manufacturer's custom design but a simple box of the proper size. If you put up nest boxes of the proper dimensions, you will typically get a wren or a chickadee; a flicker or a red-bellied woodpecker; a screech owl; and perhaps a titmouse, for a usual maximum of four species a back yard.

But bird authorities urgently warn that if a box larger than one for a chickadee or a wren is put up, it must be opened periodically to make sure it houses the birds you invited. European immigrants, house sparrows and starlings, will get in if they can, kill the birds inside and build their own nests. (Contrary to myth, the invited tenants won't mind a quick peek.)

To create a demilitarized zone in this war, try building a nesting box that is attractive only to the smaller birds. It should have a floor 4 inches by 4 inches, inside dimensions; walls 8 to 10 inches high; and a hole 1 inch in diameter, 6 to 8 inches above the floor. It should be placed about 4 feet off the ground for easy observation, and should have holes near the top of the walls, to let hot air escape, and in the bottom, to let rain out.

FEEDER DENIZENS

Q. When I am out of town, will the birds I feed starve because they have become dependent on my feeder?

A. Unless you live on a farm in the middle of Nebraska and the nearest house is thirty miles down the road, birds do not become dependent on you as a sole source of food.

Birds come to feeders for supplemental food. They prefer to eat natural food, and given the choice between ant steak and sunflower potatoes, a chickadee will go for the steak. But they can be enticed to a feeder for the pleasure of the watcher, and the watcher should always remember that he is not feeding birds for altruistic reasons. Therefore, the feeder should be kept clean.

If you go on vacation, take the feeder down, both for sanitary reasons and because birds can get their heads caught trying to get the last few seeds from some feeders. If the feeder is missing, the birds will quickly go elsewhere for snacks, but once it is put back up, the birds will be back in a week.

DUST BATHS

Q. Why do birds take dust baths?

A. The gestures that birds make when they put dust on their feathers and then shake and preen it off look like the movements they make when bathing in water, but the purpose is not exactly the same.

Birds take dust baths to rid themselves of all sorts of parasites that crawl in and between their feathers. Lice and mites are common to birds and infest them in great numbers, particularly birds away from water, like quail and others that live in relatively dry areas.

For birds, taking a dust bath is much like rubbing your hands with sand to get grit and grime off. The abrasive dust helps the birds remove parasites. Some authorities have suggested that the purpose might be to keep the birds' plumage fluffy by removing excess moisture and oil, but others say there is no convincing evidence to support that theory.

FASTING PENGUINS

Q. *Male emperor penguins sit on the eggs for months without food. How do they survive?*

A. They build up big fat reserves and slowly burn them off. At fifty or sixty pounds or more, emperors are the largest penguins, and their size means they can withstand cold better than smaller species and can "nest" the farthest south. They breed on the frozen Antarctic Sea, where temperatures may reach minus 60 or 70 degrees Fahrenheit.

However, they do not actually build nests, but balance the eggs on top of their feet. The males have a special pouch that drops over the egg to protect it, so they can waddle around during the incubation period. They basically stand around for the whole two-month period.

The males may lose 45 percent of their body weight while they fast. But first they gain large layers of blubber-like fat from a diet containing mostly fish and squid. Then they start to fast while they conduct what may be a two-month courtship. The single egg is laid in May, and the incubation period begins. (The female goes to sea to feed and recuperate from egg-laying and returns to give the males a respite after the egg is hatched.)

Luckily, the chicks depart in December, when they are two-thirds grown, leaving the rest of the Antarctic summer for building up body weight again.

DEAD PIGEONS

Q. *Why do you so seldom see a dead pigeon in the city?*
A. There are plenty of dead pigeons around, if you look carefully, but there are lots of things around that clean them up, scavenging animals of all sorts, including rats, and even gray squirrels.

Insects probably do not have a major role in pigeon disposal. It might take a week for the various carrion beetles to do their job on a pigeon carcass, and a larger scavenger would probably get there first.

Pigeons hit by city cars are often hit by more and more cars until they disappear in dust. But a bird that feels unwell tends to huddle by itself and die out of sight, in an out-of-the-way place where there may be few people, but plenty of scavengers.

MIGRATING BIRDS

Q. *How do birds know their migratory path?*
A. Birds are known to use a combination of things, including land-

marks, the angle of the sun, stars, odors, even the magnetic field of the earth, as they migrate.

However, scientists still do not know exactly what they use for a map and compass, let alone exactly how they use them.

A flock of birds, for example, is not just headed to a general geographical area like Central America, but to a very specific location. How do they know when they get there? They may have an intimate knowledge of the local area, but how they are able to navigate so precisely, even over the ocean at night, is not known.

What might seem an obvious explanation, that birds who have migrated before might lead the way, is not the answer. Ornithologists know this because in many cases the parents bail out first before the end of the year, and the young continue to feed until they are developed enough to leave, then migrate unassisted.

It appears that birds know where they are going, though they have never been there before, because it is programmed in the genetic material. Most of the research has been done on the compass. For example, even on cloudy days, there is a plane of polarized light that lets birds tell where the sun is, and they derive directional information from that.

But if you are plunked down in the woods from outer space, a compass won't help you decide where to go, and one hundred years of research on the homing pigeon still has not answered the question of how a bird carried a hundred miles in a covered box immediately orients itself and heads accurately for home.

SURVIVORS

Q. *Why didn't whatever killed the dinosaurs kill everything else, too?*
A. There have been many mass extinctions over the millions of years since life began, each sparing a remnant of living things.

Survivors of the extinction that killed the dinosaurs tended to be widespread, adaptable and, perhaps most important, small, paleontologists say.

There are many theories about exactly why the dinosaurs died and over what period, but whatever it was wiped out about three-quarters of the species on earth at the time, according to paleontologists. And whatever it was tended to spare species that had relatively small food requirements, lived in many places and were adaptable.

Among the theories about the dinosaurs' demise about sixty-five million years ago, a common one is that a cosmic or volcanic event darkened the earth so much that food for big hungry dinosaurs was hard to find, or even so much that sunlight-fueled photosynthesis stopped for months.

According to fossil studies, widespread species are more likely to survive any mass extinction, while specialized species adapted to a smaller area are especially vulnerable. It has also been suggested that weedlike species like the rat and cockroach that can survive in many habitats are more likely to survive human destruction and fragmentation of habitats. Changes in climate, sea level, oceanic oxygen levels and ocean currents have all been suggested as possible culprits in extinctions, either together or separately.

Domestic Animals, Pets—and Cats

FIDO'S CAVITIES

Q. *Do animals get cavities?*

A. Yes, and for the same reason that people do, even without a sweet diet. Bacteria build up on the teeth and cause decay, although they may be different bacteria from the ones that cause human cavities.

It is recommended that pets have their teeth cleaned. In a relatively recent development, a few veterinarians specialize in dental care for animals, but most veterinarians do some dental care. Pets may also need periodontal treatment for gum disease.

ANIMAL DREAMS

Q. *Do animals dream?*

A. That depends on what is meant by dreaming, and obviously you cannot ask an animal if it has had a dream. But experts cite strong suggestive evidence that mammals like dogs and cats experience something people would recognize as dreams.

Such animals have the same brain processes during sleep as humans. They experience both rapid eye movement sleep, or REM sleep, and non-REM sleep. REM sleep is when dreaming is known to occur in adult humans. While it is going on, the brain is very active but biochemical controls prevent the body from acting on the mental images.

In experiments with cats, if the inhibition of motor activity is removed by surgery, when animals go into REM sleep, they may walk around the room and generally act as though they were acting out a "dream."

A cat might demonstrate every behavior involved in chasing mice, for example.

But is the dream a series of vivid, discrete, integrated images? We don't know if an animal is capable of that in wakefulness. There is controversy over whether human infants dream, for the same reason.

GOLDFISH METHUSELAHS

Q. How long do goldfish live? Is it true that they will grow bigger in a pond? Do they change color?

A. The common aquarium goldfish, *Carassius auratus*, can live thirty years or more under ideal conditions. An aquarium limits their size, but a pond lets them achieve their maximum growth. Some reach up to two feet in length.

Goldfish often change color as they age and develop their full color patterns. In fact, one of the skills of goldfish breeders is to predict which fish are going to develop the best colors.

Goldfish are closely related to the carp family and are quite hardy. As long as the pond does not freeze over completely they can withstand very cold temperatures.

Another pond fish, the koi, is even larger and more elaborate. It is very closely related to the wild carp, *Cyprinus carpio*, but has long been bred to achieve fantastic colors and shapes by fanciers in Japan, where prize fish are auctioned for large amounts of money. The koi is long-lived but not as hardy as the common goldfish.

ANIMAL COLOR VISION

Q. How do scientists find out whether animals have color vision?

A. It is not as simple as seeing whether a bull charges a red cape, scientists say, and some of the evidence is indirect.

Indirect research methods include examining the behavior of the animal in its natural world.

One way is simply to look at whether the animal itself has colors. You can assume that if the animal has color that is meaningful to it in some way, it probably has color vision. For example, brightly colored bird species may have color differences between sexes, and some primates can tell when the female is receptive to mating by color changes.

Or you can see if the animal uses color choice for food, telling the difference between ripe and unripe food, for example.

These pieces of evidence do not by themselves prove that an animal sees colors. Another step is to do anatomical work on the animal's eyes, looking to see if they have cones, the color receptors in the retina that strongly suggest color vision; but this kind of research involves killing an animal.

There is also electrophysiological research, in which anesthetized animals are presented with a color stimulus of a specific wavelength to see if there is an electrical response in the brain.

Then there is laboratory research with unanesthetized animals, in which an animal might be trained to expect a reward from pressing a food bar if it chooses the right color. Such experiments have to be designed so the response is to color, not brightness, saturation, texture or some other visual variable.

It is also possible for an animal to see color but not to attend to it. However, if you motivate an animal whose brain is wired to be able to make sense of color information, it will react to color. Domestic cats don't attend to it much, and given their lifestyle, this is not that surprising. They are nocturnal, and go after gray and agouti-colored mice. (Agouti refers to animals that have bands of dull colors on each hair.)

Studying feline color vision usually involves putting a cat on a stand about four feet high with a choice of colored squares to land on. If the cat is rewarded when it jumps onto a red square, for example, it can learn to distinguish it from a blue square. An animal like a monkey might learn to do this in only ten or twenty trials, but cats take a much longer time. On the other hand, a cat learns quite quickly to distinguish between things like straight and wavy stripes.

WIGWAG SIGNALS

Q. *Why do dogs wag their tails? And what happens when they make eye contact?*

A. Tail motion and eye contact are parts of a complicated inborn system of communication among dogs. The signals let dogs figure out who is top dog in a group or when meeting a stranger. They can also communicate emotional states.

Tail wagging may simply indicate excitement. Position is important, too. The tail held high is a signal of dominance, which may be challenged or not, and a tucked tail shows a dog is kowtowing or accepts lower status.

The social signals can best be observed in wolves. One of the things they do when they challenge each other is to monitor the autonomic signs, such as heart rate and blood pressure, that signal emotion.

Some of these signs are read indirectly, through changes in pupillary light. If the pupil becomes wider, it generally means fear or at least ambivalence. If wolves' pupils narrow, on the other hand, based on other bodily postures and signs, it generally means they are angry, and you had better take them seriously.

Signals by domestic dogs are more ambiguous because owing to human intervention in their breeding, they are divorced from the original meanings and can signify anything from "come and play" to "watch out."

CATNIP

Q. *Why do cats like catnip?*

A. The active substance of catnip, *Nepeta cataria*, is a chemical called nepetalactone that sets off in the cat's brain the behavioral patterns usually connected with a variety of pleasurable or exciting things.

The playing, hunting, feeding or sex neurocircuits are randomly triggered, in no particular order. Lactones are chemicals present in certain body substances, like sweat. They are oil soluble and carry chemical messages within the body.

Cats under the influence of catnip may engage in activities related to the sexual response, such as rubbing and rolling; the playlike response, such as leaf chasing, batting and tossing; and hunting or feeding behavior.

For example, they will grab catnip and give it a killing bite, or hold it with the front paw and scrape it with the back paws, like a cat with its prey.

About 50 percent of adult domestic cats are affected by catnip, and the sensitivity is hereditary. Scientists have determined that it is smelling of the substance that causes the reaction, not ingestion. But exactly what it does to the brain, they have no idea. They are also still trying to find out why only members of the cat family are sensitive to catnip.

Catnip is in fact related to marijuana, and some people might get a little high when they smoke catnip, but marijuana gives no pleasure to cats. In fact it makes them sick, so people can smoke catnip, but cats can't smoke marijuana.

FELINE RABIES

Q. *Why do I have to have my cat vaccinated against rabies if it never goes out?*

A. First, it is a legal requirement in more and more states, and second, there aren't any cats that never go out, there are only cats that aren't supposed to go out.

Eventually, any cat leaves the safety of home to visit the veterinarian, to be boarded, to leap or fall out an unguarded window, etc. There was even one case in which a New York City cat was bitten by a rabid bat that flew in through a window.

A rabies vaccination is an insurance policy against the owner's having to worry about rabies at all. The vaccination is intended to create a barrier between wild animals that might have rabies and human beings. It is much more likely, for example, for a lost pet that accidentally wanders into the woods to have contact with a rabid bat or skunk than for its owner to meet a rabid wild animal directly.

The initial vaccination for a kitten is good for a year. Boosters are available that confer immunity for one year or three years.

DOGS' NOSES
Q. If a healthy dog has a cold, wet nose, does a warm, dry nose mean the dog is sick?
A. The dog's wet nose is relatively misunderstood. It is not an invariable indicator of health, good or bad.

It is normal for a dog to drain some fluid out of the nose, and the nose may be wet and cold because of evaporation. And it is true that a dog with a high fever may have a dry, warm nose.

However, many factors, especially the environmental temperature, may also cause a healthy dog to have a warm and/or dry nose. Just feeling the nose is no substitute for taking the temperature and a medical examination.

KNEADING CATS
Q. Why do cats "make bread" with their paws?
A. The kneading motion with the forepaws, often done when the cat is in a pleased or expectant mood, probably imitates the kneading of a mammary gland by a nursing kitten, stimulating the release of milk; it is also called milk-treading.

However, there are also scent glands on the feet, and scratching or kneading with front or back paws may also be involved in scent-marking, whether done on a favorite person or object.

CANDY, DRUGS AND PETS

Q. *What is it in chocolate that hurts dogs?*
A. Two things: The first is the worst, a chemical called theobromine. The second is rather high levels of caffeine. A small amount of chocolate is unlikely to cause much harm, but in large amounts theobromine can be very dangerous.

Eating an entire box of chocolates is more dangerous to a dog than to a human because of the difference in their body weights. In addition, the combination of the two stimulants can be worse than either one alone.

Chocolate can cause diarrhea, abdominal pain, muscle tremors, fever and lack of coordination. Brain effects can range from depression of alertness to seizures and convulsions to coma and death.

If you see your dog wolf down some chocolate, immediately take it to the vet. There are no antidotes, but quick treatment may help. It involves getting the dog to vomit as much as possible or possibly using a stomach pump. Medication is given to stop the poison from being absorbed, and supportive therapy, like anticonvulsants, treatment for heart arrhythmia and intravenous fluid to wash the chemicals out.

Other common substances can also hurt pets. Aspirin is not as bad for dogs as for cats, but should still be given only under the advice of a vet, because of side effects like serious stomach ulcers.

As for cats, they have a double problem with aspirin. It is toxic to them, and they cannot metabolize it, so it stays in the body. One dose may last several days.

And do not give your cat Tylenol instead. Acetaminophen is thousands of times worse. One dose can kill a cat, though dogs tolerate it pretty well.

CIRCLING DOGS

Q. *Why do dogs make a tight little circle before lying down to sleep?*

A. Scientists would find it difficult and perhaps pointless to try to

prove an explanation, but can make some educated guesses.

All canids, that is, wolves, coyotes, dogs, etc., typically circle before they lie down, though not every single member of all species will do this. The old assumption was that it was to stamp down grass, but of course it would also work very well to make a little depression in dirt, or particularly snow, to get under the surface for protection from high winds in winter.

Or the circling might be preparatory activity, simply feeling out the ground for sticks or rocks or checking for enemies. Dogs often circle, lie down, stand up and move someplace else. It is not a rational process, but instinctive experimentation, because dogs apparently don't have the brain power to look and think, "This looks comfortable, I guess I'll lie down here." Instead they feel it out with their feet.

SWIMMING SHEEP

Q. *Do sheep swim? If so, how do they learn?*

A. Sheep can swim, but only in dire circumstances. It's basically in-

stinctive, a life-saving device. They don't go swimming every day, but in case of flooding, or falling into a river, in essence they know how to swim.

Sheep have never been known as big swimmers, and most of the habitat where they evolved does not now have a lot of water resources. However, like many animals, they float. Then, in struggling to keep the head above water and to keep breathing, the method they use is basically fast walking, which constitutes a kind of dog paddle.

A number of mammals that do not normally swim, like a migrating caribou or a wildebeest in Africa, know they want to cross a river, get in and dog-paddle across. American bison even swam across parts of the Mississippi.

Other large mammals can swim too. Cattle can swim when herded across a river, as Western movie fans know. Deer can swim as well. The moose, the largest deer in the world, actually feeds in water and is a very good swimmer.

VEGETARIAN CATS

Q. Could a healthy vegetarian diet be devised for cats?

A. It would be difficult to the point of impossibility. A vegetable-based diet could be devised, but only if some chemical reagents and animal fats were added to it. That is because cats cannot synthesize some of the essential fatty acids found in animal fat.

For example, plants have virtually none of an amino acid called taurine. Taurine deficiency results in blindness and loss of hearing, an abnormally enlarged and weak heart, grave retardation in kittens and the birth of kittens with developmental abnormalities.

PURRING CATS

Q. How and why does a cat purr?

A. Most researchers agree that the purr results from vibrations in the muscles of the larynx and in the diaphragm. That's why you can feel it both in the throat and down in the stomach.

Purring, which is limited to the common domestic cat, has also been described by some as resembling human snoring, with an interrupted stream of air passing over a pair of structures in the cat's larynx that function something like an additional set of vocal cords.

Another theory, that purring somehow results from turbulent blood flow in the chest, is not widely accepted.

Scientists are not sure where in the brain the purring reflex is touched off. Behavioral studies indicate that cats purr when it is appropriate to project not just contentment but reassurance, lack of hostility or submission. For example, kittens purr while nursing, and the mother purrs back.

A cat may purr in the presence of a dominant, aggressive cat, and a veterinarian sometimes sees cats that purr when they are near death.

Purring around humans may indicate that the cat is treating us as the mother, another member of the species or an aggressor. Scientists have to study the circumstances under which cats purr with each other to know what it might mean.

BARKING DOGS

Q. Why don't dogs get hoarse when they bark for hours?

A. Unfortunately for the neighbors, such barking puts no more strain on dogs than normal conversation does on people.

We tend to think of the bark as so atonal that it sounds like the equivalent of a human scream. If we made such a sound, we would be hoarse in five minutes. But the dog has a different vocal structure, especially designed for barking, and in fact every noisy species has a characteristic means of normal sound production.

PET LIFE SPANS

Q. How long do dogs and cats live?

A. The question of potential animal longevity is complicated even among pets by the fact that many dogs and cats do not live an entire life span, because of trauma and euthanasia.

The Animal Medical Center in New York asked animal medicine

experts from around the nation at what age they consider pets to be geriatric. The consensus of these experts can be used as a rough guide to life expectancy, within a year or two in either direction.

According to the study, animal size tends to make more difference than anything else. For the giant-breed dogs, like the Great Dane, St. Bernard and Irish wolfhound, the figure is eight years or so. For large dogs, like the German shepherd, Irish setter and Labrador retriever, the figure is about ten years. Medium-sized dogs, like the beagle, Scottish terrier and cocker spaniel, might live twelve years. The smallest dogs, like the toy poodle, Yorkshire terrier and Chihuahua, live about thirteen or fourteen years.

The same thirteen to fourteen years holds true for cats. There is little difference from breed to breed among cats, although the Siamese has long been rumored to live a little longer than average.

Individual pets can differ considerably from the norm, and as every pet owner suspects, there may be more exceptional pets than average pets.

Why size makes such a difference for dogs may have to do with the types of disease the larger breeds get or with chronic stress. But genetics probably plays more of a role in health and life span than any other factor. For each breed, susceptibility is absolutely tied to the genetics of the stock they started with, and some pure breeds have a tendency to live a very long time, probably because they have fewer inherited disease patterns.

As for mixed breeds, veterinarians speculate that they might do better than purebreds as a whole because with different types of stock there is less likelihood of getting matching genes for a defect from both parents.

CATS' EYES
Q. *Can cats see in the dark?*
A. They cannot see in total darkness, but they require much less light than people and some of the animals they hunt because of the structure of their eyes.

A cat's pupil is a vertical slit when it is constricted and becomes a large round or oval when it dilates. The slit-shaped opening protects the eye in bright light, and the large opening lets in as much light as possible while the cat is hunting at night, anatomists say.

A cat's eyes shine in darkness because there is a special reflective layer beneath the retina called the tapetum lucidum. It is positioned mainly in the upper half of the eye. The function of the tapetum is to reflect any light not absorbed during its first passage through the retina back for a second opportunity to be absorbed.

A cat's light sensitivity is estimated at nearly six times that of man's, and this is probably mainly because of the tapetal reflection.

Both dogs and cats have better night vision than human beings because their retinas have a higher percentage of rods, cells for dark vision, as compared with cones, which are for day vision and sharp color vision.

DOGS' TONGUES
Q. *Is a dog's tongue cleaner than a person's? And does it hurt my dog to lap muddy water in the woods?*
A. A dog's tongue is not cleaner than a person's, and judging by all they lick, it may not be as clean.

Dogs, like people, harbor various kinds of germs in their mouths, and dogs' tongues have no special antiseptic properties.

Different species of animals do have different levels of resistance to the many different microorganisms. Some disease germs are highly specific, like hog cholera, while others, like rabies, can infect virtually any warm-blooded animal.

As for mud, a little dirt suspended in water would not in itself be harmful. Dogs lick mud off themselves all the time, just as children eat mud and dirt all the time without harm. Any danger would come from some other ingredient, like microorganisms or toxic materials.

THE CAT'S MOUTH

Q. *If a dog's mouth isn't any cleaner than a person's, what about a cat's?*

A. Whether dog, cat, human or cow, they are all probably pretty similar. It's certain that there's not a whole lot of difference as far as bite wounds are concerned. Mouths contain germs that can cause infections, and it would be dangerous for a child to bite a cat as well as for a cat to bite a child.

The cat's tongue, which is used for grooming, is not any cleaner or dirtier than a dog's tongue, although it is scratchier because of the special comb-like structures that clean the fur.

KITTENS' PARENTAGE

Q. *Can a litter of kittens have more than one father?*

A. Yes, and so can a litter of puppies. In fact, any of the species that have litters and can be bred multiple times during one heat cycle can have offspring with different sires. The scientific term for such breeding is superfecundation.

Female cats are induced ovulators and need to be bred before they release eggs from their ovaries. In general, they are bred several times before they ovulate, so there could be sperm from different males in the reproductive tract before the eggs are released.

But having multiple sires is probably not very common. In the wild state, one dominant male will generally breed the female, so all the kittens usually have the same father, and owners of pedigreed cats make sure that only one tomcat is allowed to mate with a queen.

Determining the sires of a litter of kittens would require paternity testing involving their DNA.

A Cat's Extra Sense

Q. *When my cat stalks her prey, she opens her mouth and seems to pant. Why?*

A. Cats, like many other animals, have an extra olfactory organ, called the vomeronasal organ or Jacobson's organ, that helps them sense scents and excretions from both other cats and their prey.

The organ is very well developed in some animals, like reptiles, and almost vestigial in humans. In cats, it is a pouch above the hard palate that communicates with the nasal and oral cavities through a duct that opens behind the incisor teeth.

The organ is believed to perceive pheromones, the chemical odors in urine and glandular secretions, and possibly the secretions of other organs, as well as the residual scent marks that cats and other animals leave in the environment.

At mating time, males may show an open-mouth response to the urine of a receptive female. Called the Flehmen response, it involves exposing the teeth by retracting the upper lip and sniffing.

Many cats, both male and female, exhibit this response when the vomeronasal organ picks up the scent of a chemical in catnip called nepetalactone. Some may also show the response as they pick up the scent of animals they are pursuing.

Dachshunds and Wolves

Q. *Are all dogs descended from wolves? If so, how did so many very different breeds develop?*

A. The best evidence indicates that all modern dogs are descended from an ancestral wolf species.

Darwin originally thought dogs were so diverse that they must have been descended from more than one form. And Konrad Lorenz, the expert on animal behavior, popularized the idea that dogs like huskies and German shepherds were descended from wolves, and dogs like terriers and hounds were descended from jackals.

However, this idea doesn't hold water. In terms of behavior and genetic affinities, there is no evidence for more than one ancestor, probably an Asian wolf. As for the dog's huge variety, genetic variability is built into a species so it can adapt if conditions change. In wild forms, the coyote and wolf, there are what are called buffering systems, so that all the genes they have are not necessarily expressed. In domestication, however, the system of genes that buffer differences from the norm are bred out. Dog breeders have selected away from the buffering system, so all possibilities can appear, and dogs can freely show all their genetic variability, from dachshund to wolfhound. There is a tremendous choice in variables like coat, leg proportions and nose length, and without the buffering genes, breeders can select desired characteristics and, over time, develop a particular breed.

Domesticated cats, on the other hand, still have their buffering system, and so are more of a natural species than dogs. Human beings also have a buffering system, so that while humans, like felines, are free to choose their own mates, the mismatches tend to average out; all humans, from Pygmy to Zulu, and all cats, from Persian to Siamese, tend to have the same basic body plan and are recognizable as members of their own species.

? ? ? !

Insects, Bugs and
Creepy-Crawlies

INSECT SENSES

Q. *Do insects see color, smell and hear?*

A. Insects definitely see color, smell and sometimes hear, but not the way people do.

Our eyes see a wide range of wavelengths, but many insects have vision tuned into a specific range to find resources like food and shelter. For example, because of filters in their eyes, quite a few insects see leaves as yellow, so pest control experts can use color vision to fool foliage-seeking insects into thinking they are landing on foliage when in fact they are landing on a sticky yellow trap.

More than three hundred different odors can lure insects to traps. Some of these odors can be smelled by humans and some can't, but most individual lures use such a small amount that a person could not smell it.

Many insects use sound to communicate. Grasshoppers and crickets, for example, have a tympanum, a body surface that vibrates with sound, rather than a true ear.

Bottoms-Up Insects

Q. *Why do insects turn over on their backs when they die?*

A. Some do, some don't, and some may not be dead at all. Collectors usually do not find many dead insects in the field, because they are so quickly scavenged by other creatures.

As for what position they end up in, it depends on the shape of the insect. They tend to fall on the biggest flat surface. The insects that are higher than they are wide tend to end up on their sides when they die.

For those that are wider than they are high, the legs may have been keeping them from rolling onto a flat surface. When the legs crumple under such insects, they may roll over onto their backs as well as falling on their sides.

And finally, there are many insects that may feign death, drawing up their legs and holding still. Some fall on their backs once their legs are out of the way, while those of other shapes may fall on their sides.

If they are feigning death, they eventually move, then feign death again if the threat is renewed.

Another way to tell whether insects are alive or dead is to note the position of the legs. If they are feigning, they hold the legs tight to the body. If they are dead, the legs go every which way.

Lovebugs

Q. *In South Carolina, I saw flying push-me, pull-you insects, attached by a filament. The locals called them lovebugs. What are they?*

A. They are in fact lovebugs on a nuptial flight, Bibionid flies of the species *Plecia nearctica*. They come out in huge numbers, emerging in a synchronized fashion twice a year, especially in fall, when the clouds of them are so thick they impair driving visibility.

They fly around with the tips of their abdomens connected. During the nuptial flight, sperm is transferred from males to females. The flight lasts for a prolonged period of time, probably hours.

Bibionid fly species are primarily coastal. They live in the ground, burrowing in leaf litter.

USEFUL WASPS

Q. *Do wasps have any useful role?*

A. "Usefulness" is a subjective term, but wasps, which with bees and ants make up the order Hymenoptera, are extraordinarily well adapted to certain human ends. Almost all are predators or para-sites of injurious pests, and some act as pollinators of valuable plants.

With varying degrees of success, wasps of different species have been bred, imported or encouraged to fight these problems:

Corn ear worms and tobacco bud worms, which attack at least one hundred plants, including corn, cotton, soybeans and tomatoes; the eucalyptus longhorn borer beetle; the alfalfa weevil; flies plaguing tourists on Mackinac Island, Michigan; the gypsy moth; tomato hornworms; hemlock scales; wood-boring insects; and the Colorado potato beetle. Other wasp species fight Mexican bean beetle larvae, which attack snap and lima beans and soybeans, and the cereal leaf beetle, attacking wheat, oats and barley.

Fig trees and several species of the ornamental ficus tree also depend on specific wasp species for pollination.

KATY DID OR DIDN'T?

Q. *An insect with papery wings is holding call-and-response sessions in my tree in New Jersey until 4 A.M. Is it a cicada? Or a katydid? How can I tell? What does it eat?*

A. It is probably a katydid, and it is probably feeding on the tree foliage, but it will probably not do the tree tremendous harm.

Katydids and cicadas have different sounds and schedules. The male katydid, a relative of the cricket, does its chirping beginning at dusk in the mating season, which is early fall. It is a distinctive three- or four-part call, traditionally transliterated as "Katy did" and "Katy didn't." There are hundreds of bush- and tree-dwelling katydid species. A common species east of the Rockies, *Pterophylla camellifolia*, is roughly grasshopper-shaped, with very long antennae, but it is more often heard than seen.

The cicada, noisier by day, makes a prolonged "ch-ch-ch" noise, sometimes sounding like the clicks of the gears of a ten-speed bicycle or like a windup toy. The hum lasts many seconds and can be deafening if a lot of males are doing it at the same time.

There are also hundreds of species in the Cicadidae family. They are brownish and chunky, with a wide blunt head, prominent eyes and large, lacy forewings.

Adult cicadas suck juices from limbs and twigs of trees, and the nymphs, which spend their time underground, nibble on tree roots. But neither stage has a noticeable effect on the trees; as with the katydid, the main damage comes from the egg slits the female makes with a swordlike ovipositor.

CANNIBAL SPIDERS

Q. *Are some spiders cannibals?*

A. Yes, there is a group of spiders sometimes called cannibal or pirate spiders, members of the family Mimetidae, that feed on other spiders, creeping into their webs and killing them. Many authorities believe the pirates never spin their own webs and feed exclusively on other spiders.

The black widow spider is comparatively abstemious, with the female only occasionally consuming the male or some of her young.

About a dozen mimetid species occur in the United States. Many are about a quarter of an inch long or smaller. They are delicately marked with dark lines and spots. On the front pairs of legs they have distinctive rakes of long and short spines. They are slow-moving and stealthy, and some prey on specific species.

One cannibal species, *Ero furcata*, enters the web of a larger *Theridion tepidariorum*, or domestic spider. It carefully clears a space of threads without alerting the host. Then the infiltrator pulls at a line, and the web-spinner hurries to the spot to find its own meal. Instead, it encounters another spider, which grasps its legs and body, holding on firmly using its spines.

The attacker quickly bites the femur of the victim's front leg and uses a virulent venom that brings a complete collapse. It then systematically sucks the body juices of the larger spider. Only rarely is the pirate defeated and victimized by its prey.

SNOW FLEAS

Q. *What are snow fleas?*

A. They are not fleas, but tiny insects of several species that thrive on glaciers and snowbanks, feeding on even smaller specks of plant debris. A common North American species, also found in Europe, is also called a scorpion fly. It is only about a tenth of an inch long. Wings are vestigial or missing, and it resembles a grasshopper nymph.

A tiny wingless springtail also swarms on snow around the world, even in Antarctica. A springlike mechanism on the abdomen allows it to leap dozens of times its own length.

A stonefly that emerges in late winter is also sometimes called a snow flea.

BUTTERFLIES' WORK

Q. *Do butterflies and moths do a significant amount of pollination, or are they just lightweights that let the bees do all the real work?*

A. Significant pollination of many plants is done by butterflies and moths, sometimes exclusively, and they are not the only animals other than bees that work at pollination.

124

Bees of various kinds, especially honeybees, and other social insects are the most familiar and important pollen carriers. However, beetles, moths, butterflies and flies are involved in pollinating a wide variety of plants, including many of economic importance. For example, anise and black swallowtail butterflies are drawn to carrot, parsley and dill plants, and the giant swallowtail likes citrus flowers. Many ornamental flowers, like honeysuckle and many orchids, depend on the ministrations of butterflies or moths.

Flowers pollinated by insects are often positioned, colored, scented and shaped to attract specific ones. The sweet fragrance of night-blooming flowers draws moths, for example, and their fragrance usually disappears after pollination. The pollen grains are often clumped, sticky and textured like Velcro, with spines, hooks and other protuberances to make it easier for even light insects to pick up pollen.

Flowers that offer nectar to specific pollinating insects often hide it in vessels that require made-to-measure mouth parts to reach it. A famous example is a Madagascan orchid found by Darwin in 1862, called *Angraecum sesquipedale*; its nectar is in a tube eleven inches deep. It was not until 1903 that a long-tongued sphinx moth was identified as its pollinator. An orchid that would require a moth with a fifteen-inch tongue is known, but such a moth has not yet been identified.

Yucca moths and yucca plants have an exclusive interdependent relationship; the moth is the plant's only pollinator, and its fruit is the only food for the moth larvae. The female moth gathers a pollen ball with a special tentacle and inserts it into the stigma of a yucca flower, usually on another plant; it also lays its eggs in the base of the flower, and its larvae feed on some, but not all, of the seeds in the developing fruit.

Wasps, hummingbirds and even bats (which pollinate the agave plant, source of tequila) are also important pollinators. Some plants are self-pollinated; water pollinates some plants; and many rely on wind-borne pollen.

FLYING ANTS

Q. In July, a swarm of something that looked like flying ants congregated on the air-conditioner in my high-rise apartment window. What were they, termites after the piano?

A. In all likelihood, they were not termites, but an ant of some type at its reproductive stage. Some ants, both males and females, or queens, have wings at mating time, and July is a time when several species would be flying. Termites would be more likely to swarm in spring or fall.

As for what they wanted, inspect the air-conditioner for excess moisture, which might attract them.

If they were termites, they would probably not attack the piano, but might seek out structural wood, roofing materials, or anything else with cellulose in it, including books and paper. Termites have been found even in the top floors of tall steel and concrete buildings where there was a moisture problem and spaces and cracks in the structure that allowed them to penetrate.

SIGNIFICANT DOTS

Q. What are the three dots I see on the heads of many insects?

A. Chances are, they are the simple eyes, or ocelli. Many insects

have both compound and simple eyes. A compound eye is the familiar faceted bulge on the fly, for example, but a simple eye is just one little hexagonal surface.

They are not believed to generate an image, though we do not really know what an insect sees. They are believed to be receptors sensitive to light and dark.

FLIES AND MOSQUITOES

Q. Where do flies and mosquitoes go in the winter? And where do the large flies that show up in the house with the first warm days come from?

A. Many adult flies die off with the arrival of cold weather, but others live through the winter. Among these flies are cluster flies, so called because of their habit of clustering. Relatively large flies, they are not from the same family as houseflies, but they also like houses, and are probably the ones that show up fully grown in the spring. *Pollenia rudis* is a common species.

Cluster fly larvae are parasitic on certain earthworms, and the adults pollinate a horrible-smelling vine in the milkweed family called the black swallow wort. The vine is native to southern Europe, as are the flies and the earthworms. The flies probably came here with the earthworms, which are the ones most commonly raised for fishing. In the larval stage, they are found in the worms' body cavities.

With the first cold days, some of the adult cluster flies go into houses, seeking out any little crack or hole. They become active on a warm day in winter, because to them it's spring.

There are many species of mosquitoes, and they all hibernate, or, more properly, overwinter. In the Westchester County, New York, area alone, forty-two kinds of mosquitoes have been found.

Some overwinter as adults, hiding out in basements and other damp, dark areas. In early spring, they are just starting to come out of nooks and crannies, looking to go outside, get a blood meal and lay some eggs.

Other species overwinter in the egg stage. The eggs are laid sometime in summer and sit there, frozen, until the warm spring rains come. Then they thaw and hatch. A few overwinter as larvae, the aquatic wiggler stage. They seem to be able to withstand freezing.

JUMPING BEANS

Q. *What makes Mexican jumping beans jump?*

A. Mexican jumping beans, actually seeds of plants in the Croton family, are invaded by larvae of a moth, *Cydia saltitans,* and it is the larvae that make the beans move.

The larvae are aroused by the warmth of someone's hand, making the "beans" jump.

The insect, commonly called the Mexican jumping bean borer, is native to Mexico and is now found in Arizona and Florida. Plants in the Croton family are chiefly weeds. The moth is related to some serious pests, like the codling moth and the hickory shuck worm. The feeding habits of its larvae could be of economic concern in Mexico, but the larvae are not yet known to threaten any crops in the United States.

INSECT MUSCLES

Q. *Do insects have muscles?*

A. Yes, and they are extremely strong. An insect can lift twenty or more times its body weight, while most people can lift their own weight or a little more.

Insects have their "bones" on the outside, but the attachment points for muscles are on the inside. The muscles are linked

to little inward extensions of cuticle, the layers of skin. The strength comes from the cross-hatching of muscle fibers.

The musculature can be very complex. The wings, for example, may be worked by five groups of muscles that pull on different parts of the body, like points on a pentagon. This enables an insect to move its wings not just up and down, but in twisting patterns to angle them properly against the air.

MOTHS IN THE CLOSET

Q. *Do moths actually eat wool, or something on it? Does cedar keep them away?*

A. Some moths do eat wool and digest the fibers, especially if the wool is soiled. They can also damage synthetics, though they get no nutrition.

However, the two main species of clothes moths, the case-making moth and the webbing moth, are unjustly blamed for holes in sweaters caused by carpet beetles, which are probably more destructive than moths. About three beetle species are known to feed on tapestries and other fabrics.

In all cases, the pests lay eggs that develop into hungry larvae. The adults do not feed on fabric.

From 2 to 4 percent of red cedar wood is made up of a natural volatile oil. It will kill newly hatched or young larvae of clothes moths if the cedar chest or closet is tight enough to retain the oil and is kept closed; most are not. The active ingredient in red cedar may last a few months or years before it dissipates.

FLY ON THE WALL

Q. *Why don't flies and ants fall off the ceiling?*

A. In terms of weight in comparison to volume, flies don't weigh much, so very little force is required to keep a fly from falling. That force is exerted by structures on the tarsi, the tips of the fly's legs.

First, there is a set of claws, which can be seen with a very good hand magnifier. There are also spongy pads that have ridges like a ruffled potato chip, providing for greater contact or adhesion. They are cushions, not suction cups. These body parts allow the fly to stay in place and move with confidence. When the fly moves, two of its six legs can be out of contact with the surface at any time.

Ants tend to rely more heavily on their claws, which are relatively larger than those of flies, than their pads, which are relatively smaller.

Some are not as good at climbing as you might think. Ants that live on the ground where the soil is rough might not be able to climb well on smooth surfaces or upside down, the way tree-dwelling ants do.

The ones that get into houses, of course, usually have that ability. They are very small, so they have even less of a weight problem than flies.

COBWEBS

Q. What makes those gray strings on the ceiling in my house, things I have always called cobwebs? They don't look much like traditional spiderwebs.

A. Cobwebs are made by spiders; "cob" is derived from the Middle English word for spider, coppe, and cobweb is often used to refer to any spiderweb. The dusty strings that do not look like the circular Halloween spiderwebs, which are made by only some species, are instead probably an accumulation of abandoned draglines.

Draglines are made by almost all spider species. A spider pays out the dragline behind it as it moves from place to place, attaching the line at intervals to any available base, using sticky disks. It is used for escaping predators by dropping gently away from a web or perch while leaving a line to climb back up. Weavers of orb webs use it as a way to detect the presence of insect prey in the web. It can serve as a bridge between trees or plants or across a stream.

Several strands of dragline silk are also spun to catch the wind when a spider feels the urge to go sailing through the air, or "ballooning."

TICK SURVIVAL

Q. If a deer tick got into the house accidentally, how long could it lurk in the rug without feeding?

A. The deer tick, which often carries the Lyme disease microbe, requires very humid surroundings and would probably not survive longer than forty-eight hours in the dry air of a house.

The deer tick belongs to the hard-bodied tick group, but certain other kinds of ticks can live for long periods under adverse conditions. One species of soft-bodied tick that carries relapsing fever bacteria, found mostly in the western United States, is an extreme case. The Federal Centers for Disease Control investigated an outbreak of relapsing fever among guests in cabins on the North Rim of the Grand Canyon in 1973. The ticks collected were kept in the laboratory, and fed a blood meal every two or three years. In 1992, they were still around.

BEESWAX

Q. *What exactly is beeswax?*

A. Beeswax is secreted by four pairs of glands under the abdomen of worker bees. It has more than two hundred chemical components. Most are fairly high molecular-weight hydrocarbons similar to a plastic. The wax is naturally white and is stained by the pollen, gums, resins and other things that bees collect.

Beeswax is akin to human earwax. All insects secrete some protective wax, to coat their wings, for example. Beeswax is simply the product of more specialized glands that enable bees to produce honeycombs.

HONEY

Q. *How do bees make honey?*

A. Honeybees collect the nectar secreted by flowers to attract pollinating insects and convert it to honey through two chemical changes and one physical change. The changes add up to a product that is digestible by bees or humans, easy for the bees to store and free of microorganisms that can cause spoilage, like bacteria or yeast.

The nectar is largely water and sucrose, a sugar with twelve carbon atoms. First, bees add an enzyme called invertase, which converts the sucrose into two six-carbon sugars, glucose and fructose. A second enzyme, glucose oxidase, converts a very small amount of the glucose into gluconic acid, which makes honey as acidic as wine or vinegar. The very low pH protects the honey against bacteria. Both enzymes come from glands in the heads of the bees.

The bees also use something like a factory process to reduce the water content of the honey to 18 percent or less. They spread droplets of it throughout the hive and fan their wings to move large amounts of air over it. The water reduction saves storage space and creates a high osmotic pressure. This strong absorptive power of the condensed honey further protects it because microorganisms shrivel and die as water flows out of their cells into the surrounding honey.

If the stored honey becomes diluted, the glucose oxidase is reactivated to produce hydrogen peroxide, which also kills microorganisms.

It's a Jungle Out There:

Plants

AUTUMN LEAF DISPLAY

Q. *What factors determine whether there will be a particularly brilliant autumn leaf display?*

A. The leaf color changes of autumn result from a complex interplay of factors of temperature, sunlight and moisture, all dependent on timing. Not all the processes are predictable, but it is known that sunny days and cool nights in late summer and early autumn make for a particularly bright display of reds.

The yellow display operates separately from the red display, though both result from a shutdown of photosynthesis. Shorter days signal the development of a layer of cells at the base of the leaf, called the abscission layer, that cuts off the water supply and later severs the leaf. This stops production of chlorophyll, the green chemical at work in photosynthesis. The chlorophyll breaks down, unmasking pigments already present in a leaf that will "turn" yellow: the xanthophylls, or yellows, and carotenes, the same orangey-yellow chemicals found in vegetables like carrots.

Still another class of pigment, the anthocyanins, is manufactured more quickly as summer ends. As the leaf is cut off from its circulation, its sugar is trapped in the leaf and turns into anthocyanins, which depending on the species can be red, purple or maroon. Cool nights in autumn inhibit the loss of sugar from the leaves, but brilliant sunshine promotes the maximum sugar synthesis and its transformation into anthocyanins. A mild to moderate drought also stimulates anthocyanin production.

(Drought or stresses like insects early in the season have comparatively little effect on the eventual nature of the color display, but can cause premature browning and leaf loss.)

LIGHTS ON TREES

Q. Does it hurt living trees to be strung with holiday lights in the winter?

A. Strings of lights do not harm a tree unless it is brought inside in a pot and exposed to warm dry air and then suddenly taken back outside into the cold, or unless the lights are actually hot enough to cause burns.

Light does affect the growth cycle of trees, but chiefly in combination with temperature changes; the two are closely related in the natural world. In the winter, the outdoor cold has more effect on a dormant deciduous tree than light does.

Leafless groves hung with small white lights, like the famous one at Tavern on the Green in Central Park in New York City, stay dormant because there are no leaves to absorb the light. Light will not affect the trees until they are also exposed to the warmer temperatures of spring.

Evergreens will react somewhat to extra light in winter, but they are also more sensitive to temperature, and their processes, like photosynthesis, proceed all year long at a much lower rate than for deciduous trees, with very slow uptake of water and transpiration. That's why they're evergreens.

PLANT VIRUSES

Q. *How do viruses kill a plant?*

A. Viruses attack living cells like soldiers taking over a factory.

The processes a plant relies on to survive, like growth, metabolism and photosynthesis, take place in cells. Viruses can subvert the cells' functions to their own ends, eventually killing the tissues that the cells make up.

First, the virus attaches itself to the external wall of a cell, eats a hole through the wall and injects its genetic material into the cell. Then the viral genetic material directs the host cell to stop whatever it is doing and start making viral genetic material.

When several hundreds of thousands of viral particles, or fragments of genetic material, have been produced, they coat themselves with a protein and produce an enzyme that digests the cell from inside out.

As the cell is destroyed it releases all the thousands of viruses, which go to other cells and do the same thing.

INDOOR SUNLIGHT

Q. *Do lights for growing plants indoors work? Is the ultraviolet radiation harmful?*

A. All plant functions, from germination to photosynthesis to blooming, can be accomplished under light in wavelengths ranging from 300 to 700 nanometers (billionths of a meter). Therefore, indoor gardeners need either incandescent "grow lights" or a combination of "cool" and "warm" fluorescent bulbs that give off light in that range.

Regular incandescent lights give lots of light at the long, red end of the spectrum, and plants grown under them tend to grow tall and gangly. Under short wavelengths of blue-green light plants tend to produce a short growth of a weird dark color.

As to the ultraviolet light given off by bulbs, the amount is very low, less than sunshine in some bulbs, and does not harm plants.

COCONUT SEEDS

Q. *Can I grow a coconut palm from a coconut?*
A. Yes, if it is an unhusked coconut. The ones usually sold as food have had their tough fibrous outer coating removed.

The hairy kernel of *Cocos nucifera* encloses an insignificant embryo amid a large endosperm of meat and liquid. An unhusked coconut, still filled with milk, will sprout if the seed is buried horizontally and kept wet. Germination may take months.

THE BIGGEST SEED

Q. *Which plant has the largest seed?*
A. A tall palm tree called *Lodoicea maldivicia*, which grows only in the Seychelles in the Indian Ocean, produces the largest single seed known in the plant kingdom.

The two-lobed seed can be twenty inches long. It grows in huge fruits that look something like two coconuts joined together in an almost heart-shaped arrangement.

To the European sailors who first saw the seeds floating in the ocean, the shape was suggestive of female buttocks. To the tourists who eventually followed, they looked like wonderful souvenirs, and the trees are threatened in the wild because local residents collect the seeds to sell.

The seeds are also much sought after by amateur palm growers, but they are not easy to cultivate. They have a very slow germination time of several years. Eventually a shoot grows out of the seed and then goes underground.

POISON IVY

Q. *Why is poison ivy poisonous? What natural enemy might it repel?*
A. Sometimes there are nice correlations between an organism's defenses and its enemies, but in the case of poison ivy, any such connection is a puzzle. Poison ivy is toxic to humans and a few

higher primates and that's it. As close a relative as the rhesus monkey, for example, is normally not sensitive to it.

Fossil ancestors of poison ivy predate human settlement of North America by millions of years. It is almost as if nature anticipated that it would be a good thing to keep humans off beaches.

Poison ivy acts as a soil binder and grows especially well in very sandy areas. It was even imported into the Netherlands to bind some of the dikes. In late summer, its white berries are an important food for migrating birds. In fall, the leaves turn a brilliant salmon color when conditions are right, and it has attractive white seed heads that have lured some flower arrangers and given them a rash.

The chemical that produces the rash is an oily substance in the sap called urushiol. It flows in special channels, and the leaves and stems must be bruised to release the oil. Contrary to folklore, merely being close to poison ivy is not dangerous unless the plant is burned, so that the volatile oil moves into the air.

When urushiol binds with skin layers, the body detects a foreign agent and sends white blood cells rushing to defend the area. The white blood cells overreact and attack the skin cells, too. The whole area becomes inflamed as the white cells release cell-destroying substances. Where the oil is concentrated, blisters form.

Poison ivy belongs to the same family as cashews and mangoes. The apple-like cashew fruit has nuts in a green shell hanging out from one end, and it is full of volatile irritating oils that must be roasted out. Biting into a mango's skin can also cause blisters around the mouth.

TOADSTOOLS

Q. How does toadstool poison kill?

A. There are several types of poison associated with different kinds of poisonous mushrooms. The chief mechanism is the destruction of the liver, the filtering system for poisons in the body.

The toadstool toxin inhibits an enzyme called RNA polymerase, which synthesizes the genetic material messenger RNA.

Without the messenger RNA, the liver cells stop synthesizing normal proteins and so cease to function. Jaundice sets in. The process lasts four to seven days. With the filtering system gone, vomiting is frequent before the victim dies.

Frequently, by the time symptoms appear, major irreversible damage has been done. In a few cases, liver transplants have been attempted to save people who have eaten poisonous toadstools.

Wild mushrooms require expert identification. Among fungi, many make you sick, some make you very sick and some are hallucinogenic. Only a few are fatal.

The most famous fatal toadstool is the death angel, or *Amanita phalloides*. In this country it is found chiefly on the coasts. It is not native to North America and was probably imported with nursery stock.

Native poisonous species are *Amanita verna*, *Amanita bisporigera* and *Amanita virosa*. They are usually found in woodlands, associated with various trees.

DEADLY OLEANDER

Q. *How poisonous is oleander?*

A. It is extremely toxic, one of the most toxic plants on anyone's list. Even a few leaves falling Into a small ornamental pool could poison a dog who lapped water from the pool.

All parts of the plant are considered toxic, with the seeds usually the most toxic, the leaves a little less and the flowers least, but still dangerous. Even the stems are dangerous, and there are anecdotal reports of children poisoned by hot dogs roasted over a fire of the stems. Adults have been poisoned by consuming one leaf.

The widely used ornamental bush comes in two species, *Nerium oleander*, the common pink oleander planted in California in the space dividing interstate highways, and the yellow oleander, *Thevetia peruviana*.

Both contain cardioactive glycosides, which are similar in effect to digitalis but much more toxic. They can be quickly fatal.

Besides disrupting the heart function, they cause gastrointestinal symptoms like vomiting and diarrhea.

Extreme care should be taken with oleander plants and trimmings around people or animals. Well-fed animals will not usually seek out oleander leaves, but some may accept them despite their bitter taste and consume enough to be harmed. Those most at risk would be naïve animals new to an area, or perhaps a horse who is attracted to trimmings thrown over the pasture fence.

INTRUSIVE IVY

Q. *Does ivy destroy the mortar between bricks chemically? Or is it just a physical intrusion? How often do you need to cut it down?*
A. Experts say it is possible for ivy to damage walls both physically and chemically, but botanical gardeners usually advise that the chief danger is to masonry that is already in bad shape.

There are two schools of thought. One sees ivy as a likely threat to a wall. The other believes that if the mortar is in good condition, ivy will not destroy it, but if it isn't, ivy becomes an avenue to destroy it further.

Ivy climbs by attaching little disks with protruding rootlets. In 1982, when ivy was being stripped from some hallowed "halls of ivy" at Harvard University, botanists said the particularly dense growth of ivy trapped moisture against the walls. Then the decay of the adhesive disks and other organic matter yielded humic acid, which is capable of dissolving carbonate rock, like marble, and lime mortar. It was not the live ivy but the decay of the deciduous plant material that caused the problem, and there were masses of ivy. The Ivy League ivy had had decades to grow, and on very old walls, to reach a dangerous state.

SAP AND SYRUP

Q. *What makes sap rise?*
A. Water and dissolved minerals are taken up through cells called the xylem, and food manufactured in the leaves is distributed to the rest of the plant through cells called the phloem.

The rise of sap is essentially concerned with the xylem. It is a system of very fine tubes that continuously connect the extremities of any plant with the tips of the roots, where the water and minerals are absorbed. The tubes consist of individual cells arranged end to end, with one or more openings at the end.

These capillary tubes are so fine that the molecules of water within them move through the entire tube as a single unit.

The leaves have pores for the exchange of gases necessary for photosynthesis. When the pores are open, there is a loss of water, known as transpiration. As water is lost, a pull is exerted on the column of water.

Two forces are at work to sustain this tremendous pull and keep the stream of water intact. The first is the adherence of water molecules to the cell wall, which can occur only in a very fine tube. The second is the strong coherence of water molecules to each other.

In experiments, these forces of adhesion and cohesion are more than strong enough to carry water as high as the tallest trees, the California redwoods, 350 feet or more.

The sap we call maple syrup is a special case involving stem pressure.

In daytime in late fall through spring, when the leaves are not out, cells in the stem start metabolizing. The process, which is not fully understood, produces carbon dioxide, which collects in the spaces between the cells. The pressure forces the sap out when a hole is made.

At night, the carbon dioxide is dissolved into the sap, creating a small vacuum, which pulls more water in from the roots.

Once leaves start coming out in the spring, the normal circulation takes over, the pressure in the stem is not as great, and the maple syrup stops running.

STREET TREES
Q. How do street trees survive with only foot-square holes in the pavement?

A. Many of them don't. The average life of a street tree surrounded by concrete and asphalt is seven to fifteen years. Many do survive, but decline rapidly.

Many factors underground determine whether a tree will make it. If the soil is so compacted that the roots can't get in, it will surely die. If they can get in there is a better chance of getting the water and nutrients needed to survive.

Another question is whether adequate water supplies are getting into the growing area. Some of the water comes from underground sources and some from rain, and it is hard to measure where the tree is getting it.

Of course, if the roots get into sewers, they can get everything they need.

If a street tree does survive, it is because its roots have been able to explore a big volume of soil. Just as with any plant, if the pot is too small it won't grow well. The roots are very superficial, occupying only the top three feet of soil. Tree roots spread out, not down, if given the chance.

People can help street trees with mulch, water during dry periods and protection from things like dogs and garbage dumpers, which can compact the soil, and bicycle chains, which can rub the thin bark that covers the tree's growth layers. Other threats that are directly toxic to the roots are bleach water from the scrub bucket or waste from changing a car's oil.

The soil can be very gently loosened in the tree hole to make sure there is no crust to prevent absorption.

REHABILITATING KUDZU

Q. Traveling through Georgia, I saw a vine called kudzu that seemed to be taking over everything. What is it? How do you get rid of it?

A. Kudzu, often called the vine that ate the South, is a Chinese and Japanese fodder and cover crop with an edible root.

The original Japanese pronunciation was kuzu. The Latin name is *Pueraria lobata*, but it was called *Pueraria thunbergiana* until 1947.

An American consul in Japan in the late nineteenth century, Thomas Hogg, exported kudzu to the United States, where an excess of its virtues as an erosion-control planting eventually made it into a famous pest. Its twining vine stems can grow as much as a foot a day and may reach a length of more than sixty feet.

But for decades, county agents and soil conservation scientists enthusiastically recommended kudzu as a ground cover, and it has many other virtues. It is a very nice pot plant, with sweet-smelling purple flowers. It was grown as a porch vine, to keep the sun off. Kudzu starch, a fine-grain starch, is extracted from the roots and used in Japanese cooking. It can be made into noodles. For two thousand years, the Japanese have extracted an antifever medicine from it.

Kudzu can also be put up as an excellent hay, though modern haying equipment has a hard time handling the long vines. Its appeal to grazing animals can be used to control it.

Watch What You Put in Your Mouth

POPCORN, ETC.

Q. *Why does popcorn pop? Do other foods pop?*

A. Popcorn pops because of a delicate balance between a moist interior and a dry coating. The exterior cells, the pericarp, are hard and relatively impermeable. The interior cells are soft and contain moisture. When the seed is heated, the moisture turns to steam. The pressure builds up to the point where the hard outside pops, letting the kernel explode.

The same thing can occur with other foods, like potatoes, that are filled with soft starch. If no holes are pricked in a potato's tough coating before it is baked, it too will explode.

If the pericarp of a popcorn kernel is scratched through, it lets the steam out and prevents popping. If popcorn is too dry, there is not enough moisture inside to pop; if too wet, the pericarp does not hold the steam. Homegrown popcorn should be allowed to mature on the cob so that the sugar inside is converted to starch, garden experts say. Further drying may be necessary after harvest. A moisture content of about 13.5 percent to 14 percent is ideal. Popcorn should be stored in airtight containers to protect the moisture balance.

BACKYARD MUSHROOMS

Q. Is it safe to eat giant white mushrooms that sprout near a tree trunk in the backyard? If a squirrel eats one, does that mean it's safe?

A. Don't count on either safety or succulence. It is probably a harmless but not so tasty mushroom, but the squirrel is probably no better judge of its safety than a layman.

The squirrel's physiology is close enough to ours that if a mushroom is deadly to us, the squirrel would probably die too. A poisonous mushroom destroys liver function in mammals, but you would have to watch the squirrel for several days to be sure it was not affected.

A sizable pale gray mushroom that looks like layers of thick fans and grows near an old tree stump is probably a species called hen of the woods, or *Grifola frondosa*. It may be relatively safe to eat it, because there are not too many that look like it, but its flavor is not that great. And don't trust a squirrel, get a mycologist.

QUININE IN TONIC

Q. Is there enough quinine in quinine water to have a medicinal effect?

A. It would not be much help against its original target, the fever of malaria.

Quinine, derived from the bark of the cinchona tree, must be administered in very high doses to reduce fevers. Because high doses cause many side effects, including ringing in the ears and other hearing problems, the artificial substitute chloroquine is generally used.

When the British in India used quinine to treat malaria, they made it palatable by adding sugar and lemon or lime, not to mention gin. The British developed a taste for this "Indian tonic," and in 1858, Erasmus Bond, an Englishman, patented a version. But in modern tonic water, quinine is essentially just a flavoring element.

PLASTIC TASTE

Q. *Should you worry if you taste plastic in water from a plastic jug?*
A. A person who can taste the very few molecules of plasticizer that might escape from a food container probably has an extrasensitive sense of taste but need not worry about being harmed.

The plasticizers used to make the plastics flexible in containers intended for food are very slightly soluble in water and slightly more soluble in oily substances, but they are not metabolized, food scientists say, and studies have found no biological activity.

Scientists warn against using containers not specifically for food or those that have held toxic substances.

ELIMINATING ALCOHOL

Q. *How long after a person stops drinking does it take for all alcohol to be removed from the body?*
A. The National Institute on Alcohol Abuse and Alcoholism of the National Institutes of Health estimates that alcohol is cleared at a rate of approximately one hundred milligrams per kilogram of body weight per hour, or about half an ounce of pure alcohol every two hours, so that if a person ingested approximately three drinks in a half-hour period, it would take about six hours for that alcohol to leave the body. The speed could vary widely, as much as threefold, because of the range of individual variation in factors like body weight, absorption rates and blood alcohol levels.

DUSTY FRUIT

Q. *What is the dusty film found on fresh grapes, plums, etc.?*
A. It is a natural protective substance secreted by cells in or near

the skin of the fruits. Composed of many kinds of waxes and lipids, the film helps waterproof the fruit. It prevents cracking because of moisture loss and also prevents moisture from entering the fruit from outside.

The waxes in the film are hydrocarbons, some of them not unlike paraffin. The film also forms on many other fruits, including apples and blueberries. For some fruits, like the blueberry, the waxy bloom makes them look blue and appetizing rather than black and dull.

Some fruits and vegetables, like apples and cucumbers, may be waxed artificially in stores to help keep them fresh. Like the natural waxes produced by the fruits, the coating would pass through the digestive system without causing any harm.

SMALL END DOWN

Q. *Why are you supposed to store eggs small end down?*

A. It keeps eggs fresh somewhat longer.

An egg's freshness is judged by candling, using a light to see the position of the yolk. The nearer the yolk is to the center, the fresher it stays, because the surrounding albumin, or egg white, has antibacterial properties to protect the embryo, or the yolk in an unfertilized egg. The big end of the egg also has an air cell that could deteriorate when the weight of the contents rests on it.

Birds' eggs have a pair of cords, called chalaza cords, that attach the yolk to the shell lining membrane at each end. The yolk is high in fat, so it tends to rise in the egg white. The small cord is at the big end and the big cord is at the small end. If the small end is down, it allows the bigger cord to hold the yolk better. It would rise too easily the other way.

VARIED VEGETABLES

Q. *Do varieties of the same fruit or vegetable have different nutritional values? Would plants of one variety differ if grown in two kinds of soil?*

A. Varieties of fruits and vegetables can differ widely in nutrition.

For example, a New York State McIntosh apple would have about 3 milligrams of ascorbic acid, or vitamin C, per 100 grams, while a Cortland would have 11 milligrams, a Jonathan would have 17 and a Cox orange would have 19.

One kind of winter squash, called aiguri, has 1,340 micrograms of carotene (precursor of vitamin A) per 100 grams, while the variety designated 81-568 has 2,628.

The amounts of most nutrients do not depend on the soil a vegetable grows in. Broccoli has a distinctive way of being broccoli, regardless of soil fertility or cultivation methods. A given variety assembles the same building blocks of carbon dioxide, water and a few minerals into a characteristic product, whether the source is the soil or fertilizer.

Fertilizer can affect yield, and for some nutritionally important minerals, like zinc and iodine, the levels in the soil may be reflected in the composition of the plant. However, the proteins, fats, vitamins, etc. in a fruit or vegetable depend on the genetics of the plant variety, the maturity of the plant at harvest and processing and storage.

VITAMIN LOSS

Q. *How much of a food's vitamin and mineral content is lost in cooking?*

A. Some but not all, and the amount varies widely. Minerals are fairly stable in cooking, but different vitamins are susceptible in different degrees to various factors, including heat, light and air.

Generally, water-soluble vitamins like riboflavin, thiamine and especially vitamin C are more susceptible to losses in heat and water than are fat-soluble vitamins like A, D and E, which are more susceptible to oxidation. Another factor is food acidity, which preserves vitamin C but degrades vitamin A.

Vitamin C and thiamine are the most delicate vitamins. In conventional canning using high heat, 33 percent to 90 percent of vitamin C might be lost, and 16 percent to 83 percent of thiamine.

A food that loses some vitamins even to high-heat processing is not an empty food, it just has lower levels of nutrients, and it may still be nutritionally valuable.

Storage as well as processing causes losses, and because of the preservative powers of canning and freezing, properly prepared preserved foods, even those processed with heat, may offer amounts of vitamins and minerals comparable to fresh foods, unless they are taken directly from the garden and stir-fried.

In one study, a bowl of peas on the table retained a similar share of vitamin C whether prepared from fresh peas (45 percent), frozen peas (40 percent) or canned or freeze-dried peas (both 35 percent).

In the frozen peas, some vitamin C was lost in processing, but it was not heated as much in the final preparation, while the fresh peas were exposed to more heat in cooking.

TOO MANY CARROTS?

Q. How many carrots would a child have to eat to consume a dangerous level of vitamin A?

A. It is possible to get a toxic dose of vitamin A, but not from carrots. Probably the worst thing that would result from eating a large number of carrots is an alarming-looking yellowing of the skin called carotenemia. It is apparently harmless.

Carrots contain an orange pigment, called beta carotene, that the human body converts to vitamin A, or retinol, normally stored in the liver. Excess amounts of beta carotene are stored in fatty tissues, especially the skin. The skin may turn a deep yellow, especially the palms and soles. The eyes remain white, so the condition is distinguishable from jaundice, and it quickly disappears when carrots and other carotene-rich foods are eliminated from the diet.

But according to medical authorities, the body will never synthesize enough vitamin A from food sources to reach toxic levels.

Food supplements containing vitamin A, on the other hand, may pose a problem. Prolonged excessive intake of pure retinol can result in a condition called hypervitaminosis A. It has serious symptoms, including headache, fatigue, nausea, loss of appetite, diarrhea, dry itchy skin, hair loss and irregular menstruation.

The recommended daily dietary allowance of vitamin A, revised in 1980 by the Food and Nutrition Board of the National Academy of Sciences, is 1,000 retinol equivalents for men and 800 for women. One retinol equivalent is 1 microgram (millionth of a gram) of retinol or 6 micrograms of beta carotene.

One medium carrot contains about 2,025 retinol equivalents of vitamin A, so less than one carrot a day will keep the doctor away and will certainly avoid alarming parents.

Vitamin A is also measured in international units of 0.344 micrograms, equal to about one-third of a retinol equivalent. Standard pharmaceutical reference works estimate that taking 50,000 international units of retinol a day for longer than eighteen months or 500,000 international units a day for two months constitutes a chronic toxic dose. An acute toxic dose is more than 1 million international units.

VITAMIN E

Q. I bought a cereal that says on the package, "natural vitamin E was used to preserve freshness." How does that work?

A. Vitamin E is an antioxidant, interfering with the chemistry of oxygen interacting with other chemicals. Both human bodies and food are degraded by oxidation, so the same chemistry that helps protect humans can protect foods. Vitamin E is a broad term for a member of a group of chemicals called tocopherols, which have vitamin E activity in the human body. Synthetic antioxidants like

BHT (butylated hydroxytoluene) and BHA (butylated hydroxy-anisole) are chemically related to tocopherols.

Vitamin E used as a preservative is not used in therapeutic amounts, however, and the kind people take as a vitamin is itself protected against contact with oxygen until it is consumed.

GELLING GELATIN

Q. *Why does gelatin gel?*

A. Gelatin is a tasteless, odorless substance extracted by boiling collagen, a jelly-like fibrous protein found in animal bones, tendons, hoofs and connective tissues. When dried gelatin is mixed in warm water, the fine-grained particles do not actually dissolve, but rather become evenly dispersed and remain suspended in the liquid.

When cooled to 95 degrees Fahrenheit and below, the gelatin particles absorb five to ten times their weight in liquid, expanding into a coagulated semisolid state or gel. The cooler the environment, the more water is absorbed.

POPEYE'S SPINACH

Q. *Why does eating spinach make your teeth feel funny? How much would Popeye have to eat to get his daily requirement of iron?*

A. Spinach often grows well in sandy soil, and unless It is very well rinsed it may feel gritty.

Spinach contains some oxalic acid. Rhubarb, which is sour enough to set your teeth on edge, owes its sour taste to oxalic acid, which can be gritty. However, the variety of spinach that accumulates the most oxalic acid has only 7 percent by dry weight, much less in the form of raw spinach, and it is not grown commercially.

Oxalic acid was formerly thought to prevent absorption of the iron in spinach by binding to it, but the latest measurements by the United States Department of Agriculture's Plant, Soil and Nutrition Laboratory indicate that it does not seem to bind the iron, so Popeye was right, the laboratory says.

The recommended daily requirement of iron is 10 milligrams for men. Popeye would have to eat quite a bit of spinach to get the daily allowance. Raw spinach has about 2.7 milligrams of iron per 100 milligrams, or about two cups of chopped spinach. Popeye's favorite, a half cup of canned spinach, including the liquid, has about 1.85 milligrams of iron.

Other good vegetable sources of iron are dandelion greens, Swiss chard and kale. Some dried fruits, like peaches, apricots and raisins, are also good sources of iron, but organ meats like liver are even better.

NUTRIENT INTERACTION

Q. Are there any important interactions between vitamins and minerals that would mean some must be taken separately and some together?

A. Any vitamin or mineral taken in excess could interfere with the absorption, metabolism or storage of some other component of the diet, but interactions are usually not a problem.

Nutritionists basically recommend that people should derive their nutrition from food, not food supplements, and that they should choose a well-balanced diet including a variety of fruits and vegetables.

Difficulties in the interaction of dietary supplements come only when people take unreasonable amounts. In a nutritious meal, vitamin and mineral interaction is minimal, and normal-strength multivitamin supplements should present no problem.

It is true that certain nutrients do interact if they get into the body in very unbalanced amounts. For example, iron does compete with the absorption of zinc, and the therapeutic amount of iron for someone with anemia might lead to an imbalance, but the amounts in a normal diet would not create difficulties.

Vitamin and mineral interactions are quite different from the dangerous interaction of one drug with another, like alcohol with barbiturates, and it is mostly long-term dietary imbalances that would cause trouble.

Nutritionists suggest staying away from high-potency supplements, especially of just one or two nutrients, unless a doctor suggests a specific one. Anything in excess, if not balanced by other nutrients, could result in a deficit of something else.

As for combinations, again it is the total dietary picture that counts. For example, vitamin D does enhance calcium absorption, but it is not necessary to take the vitamin and the mineral at the same time.

BEAN PROBLEMS

Q. *What is it in beans that increases flatulence?*
A. The problem is oligosaccharides, or "several-unit" sugars, which are produced by legumes, especially in the final stages of seed development.

The oligosaccharides, called raffinose, stachyose and verbascose, are used by the seeds to store energy. The human body lacks enzymes to break them down, and so cannot digest and absorb them as it does the simple sugars. Instead, they are digested in the colon by normal intestinal bacteria. In their metabolic process, the bacteria produce various gases, including carbon dioxide and hydrogen.

The problem sugars are also found in cabbage-family vegetables, among many others, and in whole grains, brans and some other seeds.

Soaking beans with frequent water changes and boiling them will help break down the sugars, as will germination into bean sprouts and fermentation into tofu. A commercial product called Beano, containing the enzyme alpha-galactosidase, which breaks up the sugars, may also help.

CALCIUM IN VEGETABLES

Q. *Is it possible for the child of strict vegetarians to get enough calcium from a diet that does not include eggs, meat, fish or milk products?*
A. It might be difficult, but it is not impossible. The recommended

daily allowance of calcium for children is 600 to 1,000 milligrams, depending on age. Many fruits and vegetables contain significant and sometimes surprisingly large amounts of calcium, according to estimates from the United States Department of Agriculture and nutrition experts who work in the food industry.

A cup of cooked frozen collard greens contains 357 milligrams of calcium and a medium spear of broccoli has about 205 milligrams, making them comparatively rich sources. Five dried figs contain about 126 milligrams of calcium, and a medium orange has about 54 milligrams.

It might be easier to get a child to eat blackstrap molasses. Two tablespoons would deliver about 274 milligrams of calcium, more than 25 percent of the recommended allowance.

A cup of cooked fresh spinach has about 245 milligrams of calcium, but it also has oxalic acid, which interferes with calcium absorption. Oxalic acid is also present in calcium-rich beet greens, chard and rhubarb, cutting their value as calcium sources.

ROTTEN PEACHES

Q. Peaches seem to go bad faster than other fruits. Why?
A. Peaches spoil faster than fruits like apples or pears for several reasons. First, they have a different surface structure, with no natural waxy coating or thick epidermis to protect them from bruises. Second, unless a fruit is completely dried out, normal metabolism continues and the fruit burns up sugar reserves; the peach respires at a higher rate because it is burning its sugars faster. The higher the temperature, the faster the process.

Leaving peaches out at room temperature not only speeds ripening and aging, it also increases the rate at which rot organisms develop.

Another factor that may make peaches rot faster than they did just five or six years ago is the reduction in the use of chemicals to retard spoilage.

GREEN TO RED PEPPER

Q. *What is the chemical change when a green pepper becomes red?*

A. The change is the same kind that occurs in any other ripening fruit that changes color. Chlorophyll breaks down or degrades, and other pigments are exposed or formed.

The complex ripening process is under the control of plant hormones like ethylene, a growth regulator that makes chlorophyll break down, and auxin, the hormone involved when a leaf drops. Auxin, in turn, is under the control of the day length or the amount of sunlight.

At the same time that the chlorophyll fades, the fleshy part of a fruit often softens, though this happens a little later in peppers, and starches and organic acids metabolize into sugars. These changes make the fruit sweeter and more attractive to animals that eat them and spread their seed.

The whole purpose and strategy of a large fruit like that is to get its seeds dispersed, to get the products of its reproduction scattered about to find fertile ground to make new plants.

RED-HOT PEPPERS

Q. *What natural function might hot peppers' hotness serve?*

A. It may protect them from animals so they get eaten by birds. Any plant, whether it is a shrub like a pepper, a tree or an herb,

that has bright red or orange fruit with a number of small seeds in it, and in which the fruit does not fall to pieces, but is removed whole, is almost always taken by fruit-eating birds.

The seeds of those plants are adapted to being dispersed by birds, and many peppers, especially wild ones, are very attractive to birds. Therefore, scientists suspect that the compounds in hot peppers that cause the burning sensation serve to keep other animals from eating the pepper fruits and to preserve them for the birds.

One example that grows wild in the southwestern United States and Mexico is in fact called bird pepper, or *Capsicum annuum aviculare*, because birds greedily devour the fruits. In wild peppers like this one, the birds seem to have no aversion to eating the fruits and are not affected by the substance that causes horrendous burning in us.

However, the jalapeño pepper and practically all the others in the food market are not wild varieties, but have been bred for different colors, shapes and degrees of hotness, or simply for larger fruits. The ones the birds favor have many small fruits on a plant, each about the size of a pea.

PEPPERY CLIMES

Q. *Why do people in hot climates eat hot peppers?*

A. There is not a perfect correlation between the amount of hot foods eaten and the warmth of the climate. In Honduras, for example, hot pepper is not a major part of the cuisine, as it is in nearby Mexico and Thailand.

A regional fondness for pepper may simply arise because meat and other foods tend to go bad quickly in a hot climate, so that people tend to use spices and spicy condiments to cover an off taste. This was one traditional explanation for relatively chilly northern Europe's lust to retrieve the spices of the Orient in the days before refrigeration.

As for direct physiological effects that might be beneficial in a hot climate, it's hard to say, but one effect of both peppers and peppercorns is the stimulation of gastric juices, saliva and mucus flow. This could improve an appetite depressed by the heat.

Some medical authorities have suggested that hot spices might act as an antibiotic, but such claims have not been scientifically substantiated. The active hot ingredient in peppers, a substance called capsaicin, can also stimulate the circulation and raise body temperature, so that sweating occurs; this might make people feel cooler as the sweat evaporates.

SALT AND SAVOR

Q. My soup seems to need more salt when it is cold. Why? Would it work to chill it if it is too salty?

A. With cold soup, the fault may not be in the salt but in the absence of heat to volatilize the other flavorings so they ascend to the nose.

Flavor is both taste and smell, and most spices are also perceived with the nose, so that the perceived concentration increases as the volatiles, the gaseous form of the flavorings, rise in the steam from the soup. Cold soup might seem so bland that more salt might be added in an attempt to flavor it.

But salt is tasted solely with receptors on the tongue. In fact, it is one of the few spices that is all taste and no smell. A change in temperature has no effect on the perceived concentration of salt.

Temperature itself is not a trivial taste stimulus. Taste involves more than chemicals. Temperature and mechanical events also affect the same receptors. For example, iced coffee tastes very different from hot coffee. Volatiles are one factor, but a lot of the taste is what occurs at the tongue, including temperature and texture.

As for soup that is too salty, scientists have discovered why adding lemon juice, an old cook's trick, helps the taste. If the soup is more acidic, the acid molecules block the entry of salt ions, specifically sodium ions, right at the membrane where the salt enters the cells of taste receptors.

CANS GONE BAD

Q. Why do spoiled cans of food swell?

A. Cans of spoiled food may swell, and it is usually taken as a sign of spoilage, but canned food may be spoiled even if the can does not swell.

If cans do swell, it can be for two reasons, one chemical and one biological.

Acid foods, like tomato juice, canned pineapple or almost any canned fruit, may attack the lining of a metal can, and one of the by-products of the chemical reaction is hydrogen gas. The gas exerts pressure inside the can, causing it to swell. What food scientists call a hydrogen swell poses very little health risk, and you could probably eat the food, though it might taste metallic, but don't take a chance, because the other cause of swelling could be fatal, and a consumer has no reliable way of telling the difference.

The second reason for swelling is that inadequate processing of the canned food could have left behind living microorganisms that are capable of reproducing, especially anaerobic organisms, the ones that can live in the absence of oxygen.

The organisms give off gases, mostly carbon dioxide, that can cause the can to swell. This swelling can be a sign of very serious food spoilage that could cause illness or even death, like botulism. Other less dangerous microbes can also cause swelling, but to tell the difference, lab tests would be needed.

A rule of thumb for consumers is not to use cans that have pressure in them, on the chance that it might be of microbiological origin. When in doubt, throw the can out.

PINEAPPLE SEEDS

Q. Where are the pineapple's seeds?

A. The modern commercial pineapple is seedless, thanks to English greenhouse breeders of the early 1700s who turned a small, seedy tropical fruit into a large, fleshy object. Over generations of breeding, most of the reproductive organs of the pineapple's tight cluster of flowers were persuaded to clump into one sterile mass called a syncarp. It has one hundred to two hundred juicy, seedless "berries" fused to a fibrous stalk that extends into a crown of leaves.

The modern pineapple, *Ananas sativus* or *Ananas comosus*, is probably derived from ancestral species with seeds that were native to Paraguay. Pineapple varieties were already widely distributed in tho New World before Columbus encountered them in Guadeloupe in 1493.

The ancient type was pollinated by birds. The modern type is propagated from shoots, from the leafy crown or from suckers or branches. It is a terrestrial (earth-grown) bromeliad; most bromeliads are epiphytes, plants that grow on other plants, like Spanish moss.

The pineapple can be grown as a houseplant. Cut off the tuft of leaves at the crown, remove any flesh, let the tuft dry for a day or two, then root it in moist, coarse sand. When roots are established, plant it in well-drained potting soil and let it grow for a year or two. It may then be induced to form fruit by enclosing it, pot and all, in a plastic bag with a ripe apple for forty-eight hours. Ethylene gas from the apple stimulates fruit production. Fruit should appear in a few months and ripen from green to gold in six months.

Don't Eat the Pits!

Q. *I have been feeding apple seeds to my bird for years. Is there really cyanide in them? What about apricots and other fruit seeds?*

A. Compounds containing cyanide can be found in some fruit pit kernels and some other foods as well. Even cabbage, broccoli and cauliflower contain cyanide compounds, but not enough to make them unsafe.

Too many fruit pits can add up to a real risk, however. Apricot pits, for example, contain a compound called amygdalin, the supposedly active ingredient in laetrile, the discredited cancer drug. Amygdalin is a member of the class of chemicals called cyanogenic glycosides, meaning that it can be broken down into cyanide, glucose and benzaldehyde by an enzyme.

A study of the toxicity levels of peaches and apricots clearly shows that thirteen to fifteen raw peach pit kernels could be lethal for adults.

For apricots, the toxicity varies widely in a tenfold range, depending on variety. The wild apricot is highest, and some are quite low, but for a variety in the middle level of toxicity, about seventeen to twenty kernels could be lethal. No one has survived eating more than thirty-eight.

For children, as little as around 15 percent of the adult level could be lethal.

Apple seeds contain some cyanide, about a quarter as much as peach pits for the same weight. They are very small compared with peach kernels, but eating a cupful of apple seeds has caused cyanide poisoning. The occasional consumption of an apple seed or two is not a problem.

As for toxicity to wildlife, species differences are wide, and it is important not to translate human data to animals, or vice versa. In a study of rats, for example, they were found to be far more resistant than humans to apricot pits.

BLUE CHEESE

Q. *I have been told that Scandinavian blue cheese is toxic in large quantities. Is there any truth to this?*

A. The mold that normally produces blue cheese produces traces of toxic substances, but not enough to hurt a human being in the quantities normally consumed.

Almost all blue cheeses are ripened by the mold *Penicillium roqueforti*, which does make about six alkaloid toxins, called myco-toxins. However, two of the six, the most potentially harmful, are not produced on cheese or break down immediately on cheese.

The four that are produced are detectable in parts-per-million levels. There is no human data on their toxicity, but in rodents it takes an awful lot to do anything. Based on calculations extrapolating from the most sensitive rodent studies, it would be necessary to eat more than ten pounds of cheese a day for any harm to befall a person.

The biggest potential problem with cheese would be contamination with another mold, like aspergillus or a different kind of penicillin. Aspergillus, for example, can produce aflatoxins, the storage toxins on grains and peanuts, which are extremely dangerous, but this problem has never been reported for cheese.

NIGHTSHADE

Q. How much can you safely eat of vegetables that belong to the deadly nightshade family, like potatoes, peppers, eggplants and tomatoes?

A. Some members of the deadly nightshade family, Solanaceae, produce chemicals called glycoalkaloids, which are toxins. Normal amounts of the parts of these plants that are normally consumed are not ordinarily toxic to human beings, though the potato plant itself is very toxic, as is the tomato plant.

Consuming very large quantities of potato skins (2.4 pounds for an adult or 1.4 pounds for a child) can cause severe illness. In

some cases the potato can become toxic because of the "greening effect," in which disease, damage or exposure to light causes synthesis of harmful chemicals to occur. When this happens, the toxin levels increase about twelvefold.

For potato varieties with a naturally high level of glycoalkaloids, it would take 3 pounds of potatoes (about 6.4 baking potatoes) to make an adult ill and about 1.5 pounds for a child. But if the same potatoes were green, the toxic amount would shrink to one-twelfth that amount.

About twenty glycoaldehydes have been found in potatoes, though only two, alpha-solanine and alpha-chaconine, are a significant problem. They cause severe digestive distress and are neurotoxins, interfering with nerve transmissions. For some potato varieties, less than an ounce of the potato shoot emerging from the eye would be toxic for adults.

Tomatoes contain a glycoalkaloid called alpha-tomatine, and eggplant and red and green peppers contain solanine. However, it has been estimated from animal studies that an adult would have to eat 4.5 pounds of eggplant or pepper or 150 small green tomatoes to reach a potentially lethal dose, and fully ripe tomatoes have virtually no toxin. In contrast, less than two ounces of tomato leaves is likely to be lethal for an adult.

BUTTER VS. MILK

Q. *Why doesn't butter spoil quickly the way milk does?*
A. It has to do with the amount of free water or available water in the food. The microbes involved in spoilage require water to live and multiply. Milk has a huge amount of available water, 93 or 94 percent, and butter has much less, so bacteria, yeast and molds are less able to grow in butter. Milk lasts a matter of days, butter a matter of weeks.

Dry cheeses like Romano last even longer than butter because the cheese-making process is in large part the removal of water from milk.

Some milk is ultrapasteurized for a longer shelf life, meaning that it is treated at an ultra-high temperature to kill off the bacteria that lead to spoilage.

WILD TOMATOES

Q. *I was taught that the tomato is native to America. So where are all the wild tomatoes?*

A. Most of them are relatively small and are found close to the equator. The tomato is a New World plant, but comes from South America and Mexico, not North America. There are thousands of varieties, and new wild varieties are still being sought out in South America to enrich the limited genetic pool of the domesticated version.

One variety of wild tomato, found in the Galápagos Islands, is so hardy it can grow in sea water. It also has jointless fruit stems, a characteristic that has been genetically introduced into some commercial tomatoes to make them easier to harvest mechanically. Another variety produces a natural pesticide.

A member of the Solanaceae or nightshade family, the cultivated tomato is formally named *Lycopersicon* (or *Lycopersicum*) *esculentum*, which translates as edible wolf peach; the cherry variety is called *L. cerasiforme* or *leptophyllum*, and an even tinier Andean variety is called *L. pimpinellifolium*, or currant tomato.

The tomato is believed to have originated in the equatorial highlands of South America and to have been introduced into Europe in the mid-1500s, possibly through Turkey. The traveling variety resembled today's cherry tomato. It also reached North America, and contrary to legend was apparently not universally regarded as poisonous but was grown in some Colonial and Victorian gardens as both an ornamental and a food plant.

It does seem to be true that early cookbooks recommended extremely long cooking, up to three hours, and that some English cooks were suspicious that what the French called a love apple, or *pomme d'amour*, was a dangerously powerful aphrodisiac. However, that name may have been a corruption of the Italian name *pomi d'oro*, golden apples (yellow varieties were common in Italy), or even of *pomo dei mori*, apple of the Moors.

Sound Bodies and
Unsound Bodies

STOMACH CAPACITY

Q. *Does the stomach shrink when you eat less?*

A. New research has shown that there is a significant reduction in stomach capacity when someone reduces food intake. However, stomach capacity can also be increased by someone who eats more, which has implications for someone facing a big Thanksgiving dinner.

The research involved obese people on a formula diet of six hundred calories a day, about five cups of formula a day. After one month, there was a pretty dramatic change, a 30 percent reduction in capacity. The control group of people who were not dieting showed no change.

The research did not assess the size of the stomach itself, which is difficult to measure, but its capacity. This was done by filling an empty balloon placed in the stomach and measuring changes in pressure.

The smaller the capacity of the stomach, the bigger the rise in pressure. There was also a subjective change in feelings of fullness, with the dieters reporting they felt full much earlier in the distention of the balloon.

In the opposite direction, in bulimics who binge, stomach capacity is markedly increased, and obese subjects have a much larger capacity than normal-weight subjects.

THE SANDMAN
Q. *When you are tired, do your eyes feel scratchy because of the sand you wake up with the next day?*
A. "Sand" and scratchy eyes are not cause and effect but are both the result of irritation.

The so-called sand, or "sleep," that builds up at the corners of the eyes is actually dried mucus. If the eyes are irritated for any reason, pollution or dryness, for example, more mucus is secreted, and the longer the eyes are exposed to the irritant over the course of the day, the more mucus builds up.

Overnight, the eyes themselves stay fairly moist with tears, because the lids are closed, but the mucus collects in the corners and dries out.

LIMITS OF GROWTH
Q. *A friend of mine grew several inches after graduating from high school. Is that normal? How long can a person keep growing?*
A. People stop growing at many different ages, but for most people the age limit is about eighteen or nineteen. Thus, a person who

continued to grow right after high school would be well within the normal range.

In some unusual cases, people can continue to grow until about the age of twenty, and in people without estrogen or estrogen receptors, growth can continue well into the twenties.

164

Growth, both normal and abnormal, is under the control of a battery of hormones, including human growth hormone from the pituitary gland, thyroid hormone and the hormones involved in sexual development.

Usually, there is a preadolescent growth spurt that begins at about the age of ten in girls and around twelve in boys. It tends to reach its peak about two years later, with annual growth rates of three to four inches. The rate then slows down; by the time of a girl's first menstrual period and by the end of a boy's growth spurt, adult proportions and body shape have emerged.

HIGHER HEIGHTS

Q. *Are people getting taller on average?*

A. It depends on what people you're talking about. In a given population, physical anthropologists and public health experts believe, the trend could go either way.

Physical anthropologists point to a trend toward increasing height over time, which they call the "secular trend." The trend is borne out by measurements made since the time of Napoleon, who was the first to try to give his armies standard uniforms.

But the question is immensely complicated by factors ranging from varying diet to the mixing of populations. The secular trend has been noticed with immigrants to North America, but the reasons are not certain, and there are probably many factors involved, including nutrition and possibly psychology. Conversely, some experts have suggested that there could be "psychosocial dwarfism," as in the failure of emotionally neglected though well-fed orphans to thrive.

Some experts in anthropology and public health think that the height trend may have reached a plateau. Some have even suggested the possibility of a "reverse secular trend," based on a reversal in the trend toward a later onset of menstruation. The later it occurs, the longer girls keep on growing. It has not necessarily been observed, but the term has been brought up.

THINKING AND CALORIES

Q. *Does the act of thinking burn up calories?*

A. The brain's activities do expend energy, and fuel is burned, but in very small amounts. In the sense of actually breaking down fatty tissue so that one might lose weight, thinking would play a very minor role.

Extensive studies of brain function have been made and the varying levels of energy use at different levels of activity and in different areas of the brain have been mapped by PET scans and magnetic resonance imaging. It is known that signal transference involves energy-using processes at the cellular and molecular levels, but very little heat is produced.

The most significant role of the brain in weight loss would probably involve the state of mind and motivation of a person who had decided to diet or exercise to lose weight.

WAYWARD HAIR

Q. *Why does humidity make some hair curly and some hair straight?*

A. Because, as each hair owner suspects, hair has a mind of its own, a natural curl pattern. Any change in relative humidity can make the hair fiber assume or exaggerate its natural state.

As each hair fiber is formed in the follicle, the sac it grows from, it emerges with a distinct curl pattern, determined by different protein structures. In general, if hair is very curly, the cross section tends to be more flat than round; straight hair is more round than flat.

In a normal water set, wet hair is wound around a rod and takes that shape as it dries. Upon exposure to high humidity, however, water goes into the hair fiber, acts on the proteins, and lets them change back. A change from high humidity to low takes water out of the strand, also allowing change.

The natural curl can naturally change with age, perhaps from straight to curly; after the loss of hair because of chemotherapy, it may grow back more curly than it was.

CRACKING KNUCKLES

Q. *What happens when you crack your knuckles? Does it cause arthritis?*

A. The bones and the series of ligaments that form the knuckles and many other joints have a little elasticity. In cracking a joint, what basically happens is that you separate the two bones by pulling or bending. This abruptly creates a space between the bones, a vacuum. Then the fluids normally present in the surrounding tissues rush into that space with the sound of a tiny explosion.

The fluid is gradually reabsorbed, so there is a time lag before that joint can be cracked again.

Knuckle cracking is apparently innocuous except for being obnoxious, and the joint that is usually cracked, the one between the hand and the finger, is typically spared from wear-and-tear arthritis, or osteoarthritis.

YAWNING

Q. *Why do my mouth and eyes sometimes water when I yawn?*

A. Medical authorities believe the watering of the eyes may result from pressure on the main tear glands, at the outer margins of the eye sockets, because of the facial contortions involved in yawning. The involuntary act of yawning usually includes opening the mouth very wide while slowly taking in a deep breath.

The same contortions might also put pressure on the salivary glands, especially in a stifled yawn, when the yawner struggles to keep the mouth closed while opening the throat wide.

There are three pairs of salivary glands: two over the angle of the jaws; two in the floor of the front of the mouth, and two toward the back of the mouth close to the sides of the jaws.

It is still not known exactly why people yawn or why yawning is contagious. One theory suggests that yawning is triggered by increased levels of carbon dioxide in the blood, but other studies have contradicted this.

SLEEPING BABIES

Q. *Why do babies sleep so much?*

A. One reason is that human growth factor, made by the pituitary gland, is secreted during sleep in higher concentrations than when the baby is awake.

How the body and brain coordinate the process is not fully known, but for the first few months of life, a baby sleeps most of the day, with short periods of waking, and grows quickly. As the sleeping time gradually decreases, growth slows.

A baby who weighed seven pounds at birth would typically weigh fourteen pounds at five months, twenty-one pounds at eleven months and twenty-eight pounds at twenty-four months, so you can see that the weight gain curve flattens out tremendously.

GOOSEBUMPS

Q. *I understand why you get goosebumps when you feel cold, because each bump is where a hair is standing on end the way fur would. But why do you feel cold and even shiver when something else, like chalk screeching on a blackboard, gives you goosebumps?*

A. Just as an animal's fur stands on end when cold, it stands on end as a response to threatening noises or sights. This bristling is thought to occur to make the animal look larger, and therefore more formidable, to an opponent. Bristling fur as a response to cold keeps the animal warmer by increasing the amount of air between hairs, which traps body heat.

The reflex to threatening stimuli, which humans may have also retained from their furrier days, is part of a more complicated fight or flight reaction. As the body prepares to respond to a physical threat, among other things, vision sharpens and becomes more focused, the heart rate increases and blood rushes to the muscles to provide them with additional oxygen.

As a result, blood rushes from the capillaries in the skin. Reduced blood flow in the skin results in less internal body heat being transmitted to the body's surface, hence a feeling of coldness or chill.

A disquieting sound, such as chalk screeching across a blackboard, can provoke this reflex, if only for a moment.

SQUINTING

Q. Why does squinting sometimes improve vision?

A. It has to do with the way the rays are focused on the retina more than a change in the shape of the eyeball.

Ideally, the eye receives rays of light and bends them so that an image is resolved on a small point of the retina. If the rays focus in front of the retina, the person is nearsighted and cannot see distant objects clearly. If they focus at a point behind the retina, the person is farsighted, and nearby objects are blurred.

The shape of the eyeball and the focusing power of the lens and cornea help determine focus, but the angle at which light rays hit the eye plays a role.

Light comes into the eye from all directions. Rays entering the eye at an angle from above or below would tend to focus somewhere before or behind the center of vision. Those rays coming in essentially perpendicular to the eye, on the other hand, would tend to be focused more directly on the retina, providing a clearer image of what one is looking at.

The basic impact of squinting is to reduce the number of superficial or peripheral rays of light that enter the eye, so only the rays coming directly in are focused on the retina. This cuts out a lot of the rays that are out of focus and eliminates a lot of what would otherwise be a blurred image.

You can't solve vision problems by squinting your way through life, but squinting might help someone who has lost his glasses and needs to see a road sign.

HOLD YOUR BREATH

Q. How long can a person hold his breath?

A. On average, a healthy young person can hold his breath about three minutes. With training, that might be extended some, but beyond that, a person might start to lose consciousness, because the body does not store a lot of oxygen.

What triggers breathing is not a lack of oxygen, but a buildup of carbon dioxide in the bloodstream. When the carbon dioxide pressure in the blood gets high enough, the need to breathe gets very intense. That is because the carbon dioxide triggers breathing centers in the brain, forcing the person to take a breath.

When children hyperventilate at the side of a swimming pool, breathing deeply and rapidly for a few minutes, they think they are loading up on oxygen, but they are actually unloading carbon dioxide. They can hold their breath thirty seconds longer, but the danger is that they don't in fact have that extra oxygen. This can cause the brain to malfunction because of low oxygen pressure, so that the person starts breathing water and drowning.

The body has no strong sensors for loss of oxygen. In fact, oxygen shortage, or hypoxia, causes a temporary euphoria. That is one reason people feel a "Rocky Mountain high" when they first get to the mountains. Temporary euphoria also affected many high-flying pilots in the early days of airborne warfare, before oxygen masks.

Trying to push through the twenty-thousand-foot barrier to get above antiaircraft fire, they became euphoric, started to make bad judgments, became unconscious, crashed and died.

INFANT IMMUNITY

Q. Do immunizations of a pregnant woman give the infant any immunity when it is born?

A. A pregnant woman can pass on some kinds of immunity, whether she has been immunized or not. These maternal antibodies are very powerful, and babies are protected for several months.

That is why the measles vaccine is delayed until the age of nine to fifteen months. At earlier ages, the antibodies interfere with the vaccine.

Research is now under way to see if it is possible to use vaccination or immunization of the mother to boost the immunity of babies.

An infant's immune system does not protect against some infections early in life, though the pregnant woman's immune system does. Among the diseases are group B streptococcal diseases, which can cause meningitis in the first few weeks of life, hemophilus type B influenza and pneumococcal infections.

Pneumococcus and hemophilus B vaccines already exist, and researchers are studying how vaccines might cross the placenta into the fetus to confer immunity on the infant.

Researchers are taking a cautious approach to this maternal immunization program, first seeking to determine if vaccines are safe in pregnancy.

BIG EYES
Q. *Do your eyes grow?*
A. Yes, but most of the growth takes place early in life.

For the retina, a vast majority of growth takes place before the age of two. For the eyeball, most growth occurs before the age of six, and there is supposedly no growth at all after puberty.

Nearsightedness, which is tied to an elongated eye shape, can appear relatively late, after growth is supposed to be done; the eye remains moldable and can change its shape.

Why changes in the relative dimensions of the eye should occur is not fully understood. It is likely that the eye remains sensitive to growth factors, chemical signals that stimulate growth. But the eye has many such growth factors, and which ones are at work in the development of the eye remains to be learned.

KEEPING YOUR BALANCE
Q. *How can people stand erect if the stomach weighs more than the feet?*
A. People are indeed top-heavy, and balance, the ability to stand

upright and move around without falling over, is not as simple as it feels. It requires constant tiny adjustment of muscles as the weight shifts on the feet, much as a juggler maneuvers to balance a plate on a stick.

The adjustments become unconscious and are carried out automatically once a child learns to walk. However, balance relies on processing a constant flow of information about the body's position, sent to the brain from sensors all over the body. Signals are then sent back to the body parts to make the needed changes. The coordinator is the cerebellum, at the base of the brain.

One key set of sensors is the eyes. But even a blindfolded person can stand upright, because nerves in the skin muscles and joints, called proprioreceptors, inform the brain about the body's position. There are also important sensors in the inner ear. In the vestibule, tiny stones or crystals (called otoliths, meaning "ear stones") hang on stalks called hair cells. When the head moves, the stones move, stimulating the hair cells, which send signals to the brain. Other hair cells in the ear's semicircular canals float in fluid and move when it moves.

BODY HEAT

Q. What makes one person feel hot while another feels cold at the same room temperature?

A. It is a complex question, made even more complex by factors like the prior activity of each individual and how long each has been in the room.

Assuming that both people have become acclimatized to the room and that neither is running a fever, two important factors are the percentage of body fat, with the higher percentage retaining more heat, and the surface-to-mass ratio for each body, with the larger skin area radiating more heat.

If the room temperature is below the thermoneutral zone, so that the bodies are losing heat to the environment, the person with the larger surface-to-mass ratio feels cooler. If it were possible to obtain a population of women with exactly the same percentage of body fat as a population of men, the women would feel colder, because they have a larger surface-to-mass ratio.

If a person is running a fever, the phase of the fever determines whether he feels hot or cold. In the rising phase of a fever, for example, the person feels cold, and the peripheral blood vessels are constricted in an attempt to retain heat and raise the body temperature.

Swimming and Sweating

Q. Do people perspire when they swim? And why is an air temperature of 98.6 degrees Fahrenheit uncomfortably warm, when this is a normal internal body temperature?

A. The body may sweat during swimming, with the moisture dissipating unnoticed in the water.

You do not necessarily sweat when you swim, but if you swim long enough and hard enough so that the exercise raises the internal body temperature, then you will sweat. This can be proven by measuring body weights before and after exercise.

As to the question of discomfort when temperatures are in the nineties, the body's metabolism is continually producing heat, some of which is ordinarily lost to cooler surrounding air.

But when the ambient temperature equals the body's core temperature, it is well above the skin temperature, so the body is gaining heat from the environment, instead of radiating it, as would normally happen.

So at high temperatures, the heat builds up and we feel hot. Then the only way to dissipate the heat is by evaporating water from the surface of the skin as perspiration.

Blue Blood, Red Blood

Q. What color is blood when it is inside the body? It looks blue through the veins.

A. Blood inside the body is either bright red or dark red, depending on whether it is arterial blood or venous blood.

Red blood cells carry oxygen from the lungs to the tissues,

where the oxygen is exchanged for carbon dioxide. Each red blood cell is packed with hemoglobin, a protein that contains iron. Hemoglobin combines chemically with oxygen in the lungs, forming a compound called oxyhemoglobin, which is bright red. When the blood gives up the oxygen to the tissues and enters the veins for the return trip to the lungs, it is a darker red, closer to a purple.

The circulating blood in the veins appears blue from outside the body because of a combination of factors. First, veins are thin-walled and close to the surface, so the darker red or purplish color may show blue filtered through the layers of the skin. Another factor in the apparent color is the degree of fairness of the skin, providing contrast.

Compared with veins, arteries are thick-walled and deep in the body. Arterial blood is seldom seen unless an artery is accidentally or surgically severed.

ADAM'S APPLE

Q. *Why do men have a more prominent Adam's apple, and what is it for?*

A. The larynx, like many other body parts, is under hormonal control during development. Male hormones encourage the growth of the larynx, and the Adam's apple is the prominence made by the cartilage that creates the housing for the larynx.

The larger male larynx, the longer vocal cords and the bigger box that resonates when the vocal cords are set in vibration combine to make a deeper sound, one of the reasons the male voice is distinct from the female voice.

The hormones of puberty set off the enlargement, so the Adam's apple can be considered to be one of the secondary sex characteristics, like the beard or mustache.

AMBIDEXTERITY

Q. *Are there any truly ambidextrous people? Some people eat left-handed but play sports right-handed. How does that happen?*

A. The notion of ambidexterity is valid, and some people do show equal proficiency in various manual skills with both hands. However, hand-use preferences are on a continuum, and a mere three categories of left-handed, right-handed and ambidextrous are artificial divisions.

One researcher calls ambidextrous people ambilateral, and further divides them into the ambidextral, those with both hands as skilled as a right-hander's right hand, and the ambisinistral, those with both hands as skilled as a right-hander's left hand.

It is common for an individual to find some skills to be easier for one hand while others fall more easily into the other hand's grasp. The explanation is that two sets of factors are involved in which hand acquires which skills, the child's own capacities and hand-use preferences, which even young infants have established, and the skills modeled on the way other people do things, even contrary to their own preferences.

For example, if a left-handed child is being taught to pitch a ball, most adult pitchers are right-handed, and the way they demonstrate the skill will be affected by these preferences, so the child must adjust in order to acquire the way they use the skill. Left-handers as a group are much less strongly left-handed than right-handers are right-handed.

Researchers have discovered that it is much easier to learn a skill like knitting if the pupil's hand preference matches that of the teacher. A left-handed guitar student who has to see demonstrations by a right-handed teacher is at a disadvantage. Paul McCartney of the Beatles is a classic case. A left-hander, he had difficulty learning to play until he restrung his guitar.

TWINS AND HANDEDNESS

Q. Are there identical twins of whom one is left-handed and one is right-handed?

A. About 10 percent of identical twins have different dominant hands.

Nobody knows the causes of handedness. Left-handedness tends to run in families, but because many identical twins have different handedness, we know that is not the whole story. Other factors are presumed to be involved, such as perhaps position in the womb, but there are no definite answers yet.

Unlike fraternal twins, who develop from two fertilized eggs and are no more alike than other siblings, identical twins occur when a single fertilized egg splits to form two embryos.

When the split occurs relatively late, say ten days after conception, when there has been some cell division, you may get what is called mirror twins, identical twins that are in some ways mirror images of each other. That is because the developing embryo has begun to develop laterality, with each side a little different.

MILK SUPPLY

Q. Is there a relationship between breast size and volume of lactation?

A. No. The female breast contains fifteen to twenty lobes of milk-secreting glands embedded in various amounts of fatty tissue, which is not involved in milk production. Instead, it is controlled by hormones produced during and after pregnancy that stimulate the milk-secreting glands, and the nursing infant's demand is the key to how much milk is produced.

During pregnancy, estrogen and progesterone produced by the placenta make the milk glands enlarge and develop, but suppress the production of prolactin, the hormone that stimulates milk production. Around the time of childbirth, there is a surge of prolactin from the anterior pituitary gland, and the milk glands produce a watery fluid called colostrum, which contains protein and antibodies that protect an infant from infections. After about three days, the colostrum is replaced by milk.

As a baby suckles, there is a feedback mechanism in which nerve impulses stimulated by the sucking travel to the anterior pituitary gland, where prolactin is released and carried in the blood back to the breast, where it maintains milk secretion. At first, too much milk may be produced, but before long a balance is achieved.

HEART MUSCLE

Q. What is special about the heart muscle that keeps it from getting tired?

A. The heart muscle is a special hardworking kind found nowhere else in the body, though it can get very tired when deprived of oxygen in a heart attack and can get stronger through exercise.

The other types of muscle are skeletal or striated muscle, the kind that lets the body move voluntarily, and smooth muscle, found in internal organs and the walls of blood vessels, which is arranged in sheets and is not under conscious control.

The heart muscle, or myocardium, is called a synctial muscle or synctium, because its strands are so interconnected that they form a continuous network of cells that work in synchrony. This lets internal electrical signals be coordinated so the whole muscle acts as a unit, contracting or relaxing together. In fact, the heart was once thought not to be composed of individual cells.

The cells of the heart muscle have their nuclei buried deep within, rather than near the surface like those of skeletal muscle. They also have an abundance of large mitochondria, the energy factories inside cells, presumably because of high energy demands.

The cells are arranged in parallel columns, as in skeletal muscle, but in still another difference from other muscle cells, heart cells are joined end to end in very long fibers that branch and interconnect. The joining sites are marked by disks called intercalated disks. In between the fibers are spaces richly supplied with capillaries to supply oxygenated blood. The cells also enjoy a good supply of glycogen and lipids, potential energy sources.

Inside the cells are myofibrils, a banded contractile substance. The myofibrils have zones called sarcomeres, where thin filaments made of a substance called actin and thick filaments made of myosin contract and relax. The filaments slide by each other as they act.

MEN AND OSTEOPOROSIS

Q. *If osteoporosis occurs more often in postmenopausal women because of estrogen deficiency, why don't men get it even more often, and at younger ages?*

A. It is true that men don't have as much of the hormone estrogen as women, but the male hormone androgen, which normal men have in considerable supply, appears to exert similar protective effects on the skeleton.

Men who have an insufficient supply of androgen do get osteoporosis, the loss of bone mass that often occurs in old age.

There are other factors at work that make osteoporosis less of a threat for men, among them the fact that genetically, they have larger skeletons and heavier bones.

SALTY TEARS

Q. *Why are tears salty?*

A. Tears contain a variety of different salts, most of which probably come from the blood and, ultimately, from the diet.

Salt in food is absorbed by the intestines and enters the bloodstream. The salt probably enters tears as blood flows through the lachrymal glands, where tears are formed.

The first known chemical analysis of tears, published in 1791 in a scientific journal edited by the French chemist Lavoisier, noted that they contained sodium chloride, which is regular table salt, and other salts.

The second major salt in tears is potassium chloride, and there are also other things, like calcium, bicarbonate and manganese, that can be involved in salt formation.

Experiments in the 1950s showed that the concentration of sodium in the tears was the same as that in the plasma. Salts are also excreted in urine and sweat.

GROWING NAILS

Q. *How fast do fingernails grow? Do they grow faster in summer?*
A. Fingernail growth averages out to about a tenth of a millimeter a day. Toenails are about a half to a third slower, and drugs or disease can change the growth rate.

There are differences from finger to finger. The middle and fourth finger tend to grow a little faster than the fifth and the thumb.

Nails grow faster in summer, some research indicates, while winter and a cold environment tend to slow nail growth.

Other studies seem to find that the right-hand fingers grow faster than the left, which might be tied to handedness, and that stimulation, such as massage, helps them grow faster. People with the neurotic habit tic of rubbing a digit would find that the nail they rubbed grew faster.

Contrary to childhood myth, nails do not continue to grow after death. That is an optical illusion. Tissues around the nail tend to shrink away from the hard nail after death, giving the impression of something still growing.

MALE NIPPLES

Q. *Why do men have nipples?*
A. The presence of nipples and other breast tissue in men exemplifies the fact that the basic body plan of men and women is similar. There are exaggerations in each sex based on early development and later hormonal influence.

The nipple happens to be one of the features whose full development has been restricted in the male during early development so it never develops its full function, which is found in the female.

As far as is known, male breast tissue has no functional significance, although it is considered an erogenous zone in men as well as in women. But the tissue is still there, and actually can respond to female hormones, as exemplified by the phenomenon of gynecomastia, or abnormal enlargement of the breasts in men.

This is seen in conditions in which there is excess estrogen function in the male.

FAT CELLS

Q. *When you lose weight, do you lose fat cells?*
A. No, the fat cells simply become smaller. In people who have an excess number of fat cells, the fat cells may be even smaller than normal when they get down to a normal weight. That may be one reason it is so easy to regain weight.

The average adult has 40 to 50 billion fat cells, and some very obese people can have 120 billion or more.

The best advice is to avoid excessive weight gain at any age, because it can cause new fat cells to be made. It may be particularly easy for this to happen before the age of sixteen.

HICCUPS

Q. *What causes hiccups?*
A. A hiccup involves the diaphragm, the sheet of muscles in the chest that controls breathing and separates the chest from the abdomen, and the vocal cords in the voice box. When a sudden involuntary contraction of the diaphragm is accompanied by a quick closure of the vocal cords, the "hiccup" sound occurs.

The phrenic nerves, which run from neck to chest, normally coordinate the smooth contraction of the two leaves of the diaphragm, and hiccups may result from any irritation, mild or severe, anywhere along the path of a phrenic nerve.

The cause is usually not dangerous or even obvious. They are common after eating a big meal or drinking a lot of alcohol.

In some rare cases, the cause may be a condition that severely irritates the diaphragm or its nerves. These conditions include inflammation of the chest lining (pleurisy), pneumonia, some stomach and esophagus disorders, inflammation of the pancreas, alcoholism and hepatitis.

Attacks of hiccups are usually intermittent and brief and stop of their own accord. In the rare cases where hiccuping is prolonged, drugs may be used, and very rarely, surgery to deaden nerves to paralyze half the diaphragm may be tried.

For garden-variety hiccups, this treatment often helps: gently massaging the back of the roof of the mouth with a cotton-tipped swab for a minute or so.

OBLIVIOUS SNORERS

Q. Why doesn't a snorer wake himself up?

A. He (and a vast majority of snorers are in fact men) may be waking up hundreds of times a night without remembering it in the morning. Snoring in its worst form is a symptom of obstructive sleep apnea, in which a person's breathing passage is blocked in the relaxation of sleep, so that he cannot breathe and sleep at the same time. His oxygen levels go down, which would soon be fatal, but then he starts to wake up and breathe again.

Sufferers, who are men by a margin of twenty to one, may bounce between light sleep and something that is not quite wakefulness. They may repeat this cycle an exhausting six hundred to eight hundred times a night without ever getting into the deepest stage of sleep but may remember almost nothing.

A garden-variety benign snorer may also have a lot of sleep disruption that he does not remember.

TIRED IN THE MORNING

Q. Why do some people wake up tired after a full night's sleep but feel better as the day wears on?

A. The way a person feels when waking up from sleep, day or night, depends largely on the sleep stage the person was in just before waking up.

This "sleep inertia" affects how someone feels for a little while after waking. Waking from what is called slow-wave sleep, a deep sleep without rapid eye movement, a person is very likely to feel groggy, but one is much less likely to feel groggy when emerging from rapid-eye-movement sleep or one of the lighter non-REM stages.

Other factors that may ruin the morning include major depression, in which people feel much worse in the morning and better as the day goes on; severe obstructive sleep apnea, or failure to breathe when sleeping, which means sleep is constantly though unconsciously interrupted by waking to resume breathing; and the use of sleeping pills that are still working in the morning. Even extra sleep can leave a person tired if it represents a failed effort to make up for lost sleep.

We have no way of controlling what stage we awaken from but all of the other problems are treatable disorders.

BLACK EYES AND BRUISES

Q. Why are black eyes black? And why do bruises change color?
A. Blood released from capillaries and trapped under the skin and breakdown products of hemoglobin in the blood are chiefly responsible for the coloration of black eyes and other bruises.

In the case of black eyes, the blood is never really black, but dark purple and green. The color of the pooled blood is magnified by the loose and transparent skin around the eyes, making a bruise there darker than it is on other parts of the body.

The chemicals mainly responsible for the changing colors of bruises are a series of products of the breakdown of hemoglobin, the oxygen-carrying compound in red blood cells. An important one is biliverdin, which is green. There may also be bilirubin, which is yellow-brown.

The timing of the breakdown and the mixing of colors are not

fully predictable, but at first bruises are usually dark blue, purple or crimson. The color gradually changes to violet, green, dark yellow and pale yellow and finally disappears. In one study pathologists found that they could conclude only that a yellow bruise was more than eighteen hours old.

Runny Noses

Q. *Why does really cold weather make my nose run? I would think it would dry it up instead. And what can be done about it?*

A. A condition doctors call vasomotor rhinitis produces a runny, stuffy, sneezy nose even when no true allergy or infection is present. Many people are sensitive to things like perfume or dust, but a very common factor is cold, dry air. Although the exact cause of vasomotor rhinitis is not known, doctors suspect it is chiefly the dryness rather than the coldness of winter air that makes it worse; the colder air is, the less water vapor it can hold.

In people with the condition, blood engorges the nasal mucous membrane, sometimes turning it bright red or even purple. The sufferer sneezes and drips away, but the mucus is clear, unlike the kind present in an infection. When the nose is very dry, receptors that lie under the nasal surface activate mucus production in the glands and vessels.

Treatment aims to relieve the symptoms and is not always satisfactory. Humidified air may help, and some nose sprays may relieve the inflammation. Sometimes plain saltwater spray helps a sniffle.

However, patients should avoid drops and sprays that act as vasoconstrictors, narrowing the blood vessels in the nose, because they can cause a paradoxical effect, worsening the dilation of the blood vessels afterward.

Lead Poisoning

Q. *Does handling lead poison you, or do you have to ingest it?*

A. In general, just putting your hand on or touching lead won't hurt you. There are exceptions, like some cosmetics used in the Middle East that are absorbed through the skin, but mere skin contact is generally not a danger, unless you put your hands in your mouth or unless the lead touches something else and you put that in your mouth.

The problem is that children are inclined to do just that, and the hand is good at picking up fine lead particles. Parents who come into contact with lead and then touch their children are a threat, and so are clothes that become contaminated with lead dust.

Vapors from molten lead are also harmful.

Lead is especially dangerous to children, for three reasons: their developing nervous systems are more vulnerable to harmful agents, they are subject to greater exposure because they put things in the mouth, and they absorb a great amount of lead for a given exposure.

Adults are at risk too, but at higher levels of exposure. Several deaths have been reported in adults who drank moonshine contaminated by lead in old radiators used to build stills.

In terms of workers, the big exposures come from battery reclamation plants, secondary smelters, places where welding is done, like auto body shops, people taking paint off steel bridges, etc. Home renovation jobs involving knocking down walls containing lead paint require special precautions, like using masks and wearing disposable or separately launderable clothes, so that the dust is not taken home to the family.

SURVIVING A CRASH

Q. I have heard that drunks survive car crashes better. Does this mean you should relax when a crash is imminent rather than tensing every muscle in the body?

A. It makes no difference whether you are relaxed or tense. In fact, drunken drivers have a greater chance of being injured or killed.

Checking the National Highway Traffic Safety Administration accident files, researchers compared survival rates and serious injury rates in serious crashes for drinkers and nondrinkers and found that the inebriated fared worse. Alcohol apparently has some effect on their ability to withstand the shock of the crash.

Bracing yourself, a natural reaction to seeing imminent peril, seems to have no real effect. What does make a difference is being properly restrained.

The purpose of seat belts and air bags is not to immobilize

the body, but to lengthen the time and the distance it takes to go from whatever speed the vehicle is moving to zero speed. They also prevent a secondary impact for a body still moving at the car's original speed.

In a car crash, the body's stopping distance involves the amount the car actually crushes, that is, the amount it is shortened, plus the short distance the restraint system stretches to allow the body to slow down while the car is slowing down. The restraint system spreads the load over your body and keeps you from hitting something inside the car.

NIGHT TERRORS

Q. *What are night terrors? How are they different from nightmares?*

A. Night terrors are sudden feelings of terror, for no particular reason, that strike during sleep, with no dream or frightening scene recalled. They are most common in children three to eight years old, and it is estimated that about 1 to 4 percent of the entire population has had an attack.

During and after a night terror, a child may scream, thrash around and behave bizarrely and may sweat profusely and have an irregular heartbeat. The child may be disoriented and hard to awaken and calm, but usually returns to sleep quickly with little or no memory of the event the next day.

After a nightmare, on the other hand, the child may be frightened and tearful, but is usually not disoriented and can be reassured by a parent. However, the return to sleep may be delayed because of fear, and the child usually has an excellent memory of the nightmare the next day.

Nightmares typically come during the last half of the night, when rapid-eye-movement sleep is common. Night terrors occur in periods of partial awakening in the first half of the night or in periods of deep sleep without rapid eye movements.

The cause of night terrors is not fully known, but some families have a higher incidence, suggesting a genetic predisposition.

One study reported that a third of adults who had night terrors had had a major life event that preceded and may have initiated the episodes. Daytime stress, anxiety and irregular sleep patterns increase the risk. Sufferers may also be more susceptible to migraine headaches, sleepwalking and bed-wetting.

Occasional night terrors usually do not require specific treatment, and they may upset an observer more than they do the sufferer. Medication to reduce stage-4 sleep may help, and psychotherapy has been reported to be helpful in more severe adult cases.

EXAMINATION DREAM

Q. A common recurring dream, of signing up for a course, not attending class and then panicking when faced with the final exam, often persists decades after finishing school. Why does this nightmare situation persist rather than the far more anxiety-provoking situations encountered in later life?

A. This dream echoes the first time such an anxiety emerged in your thinking, many psychologists and psychoanalysts believe.

This is a dream that everyone has at some time in some form. Both Freud and Adler talked about the examination dream, and though they had different interpretations, they recognized it as one of the very few common dreams.

It is related to feelings of being to blame for your own failure, the guilt-inducing sense of being unprepared to meet an expectation that you put on your own self. Developmentally, such feelings come around the school years.

Earlier dreams involve things like falling, as you learn that the external world is full of hard knocks, so that if you fall off a couch it hurts. But in order to develop the feeling of being unprepared, of not doing your homework so that failure is your own dumb fault, you have to develop a certain sense of internalization, and this comes only during the school years.

Later, the feeling is echoed by many other scenarios in our life where we could have done better but goofed off and didn't prepare enough. Going to sleep worried about not preparing for a business meeting, for example, will trigger earlier memories in the same neural network or memory storage system. The new anxiety triggers the same node, going back to when the feelings were first laid down in memories.

Going to sleep with troublesome business on the back burner of the mind may first trigger a contemporaneous kind of dream, then trigger earlier and earlier examples. The one you wake up with in the morning is often the early-childhood example of the same anxiety, so your memory of your dream is often the instance most remote in time.

LOSING ALLERGIES

Q. *Do people ever outgrow food allergies?*
A. Yes, they do. Many people avoid foods to which their allergies are long gone, experts say, and many allergies disappear by the age of four.

The reason is not known, but many immune conditions are outgrown with time, possibly because the immune system needs time to mature.

Actually, only a minority of the people who think they have a food allergy are truly allergic. Many more have sensitivities, like the common one to lactose, the sugar in milk, which many people lack the enzyme to digest.

In the case of a true allergy, the reaction is inflammatory in nature and is perpetuated by constant exposure, injuring tissues more and more, so total avoidance early in life, at least in the case of food allergy, seems to make symptoms grow less severe.

There is a relationship between the severity of symptoms and whether a person will eventually outgrow the allergy. When the child reacts with anaphylaxis, the release of substances that affect muscle, leading to shock and constricted breathing, the chances of outgrowing the allergy are extremely remote.

But if a child who reacts to eggs or soybeans with eczema or diarrhea avoids the food, there is a good chance of improvement.

CAT ALLERGY

Q. *My new spouse is allergic to my old cat. Can I keep both?*

A. Depending on the severity of the allergy and the willingness of owner and cat to carry out elaborate hygiene routines, it may be possible to keep both pet and spouse.

In fact, the cat's own hygienic standards are a big part of the problem, allergists and veterinarians agree. A specific protein in its saliva and skin glands seems to be the leading culprit in allergic reactions. A conscientious cat licks and grooms its entire body, coating almost every hair, and its dander as well, with the saliva. When the hair is shed and blows about the room, saliva particles can be breathed in.

If the result is the wheezing of asthma, either cat or spouse needs a new home, as continued reexposure to allergens worsens the inflammation; the allergens can take months to disappear after the cat is gone. But if the cat's presence or contact with the cat merely brings itching, red eyes and sneezing, it may be possible to contain the allergen and make a ménage à trois possible.

First, clean the cat. The nonallergic spouse should comb the cat frequently, from head to toe, using a fine-tooth flea comb. All the fur should be combed three times in two directions, first in the direction that it grows, then backward, then smooth again. This preempts the hair that would fall out and bother the victim. Damp-mop the cat daily with a wrung-out sponge.

Some authorities also recommend washing the cat with special nondrying feline shampoos, but the latest tests are inconclusive about whether this works. Some experts even recommend an antistatic rinse twice a month, using a teaspoon of liquid fabric softener in a quart of water.

Second, clean the house. Rugs, floors and furniture should be vacuumed often.

Third, create a pet-free zone. Most importantly, the cat should be kept out of the bedroom at all times, because sleeping with leftover fur for eight hours constitutes severe exposure. High-efficiency air filters and particle precipitators can also help.

The allergic person's doctor should be consulted about the use of antihistamines, decongestants and possibly new kinds of desensitization therapy. These treatments are based on isolating the specific protein that brings about allergic reactions, then injecting increasing amounts of component molecules to turn off the patient's exaggerated immune response.

SORE MUSCLES

Q. Is there any way to accelerate elimination of the lactic acid that builds up in muscles with exercise?

A. Yes, according to exercise physiologists. Lactic acid is removed most effectively from muscle by having an active recovery period, like walking after running, rather than a passive recovery, like lying down after the end of exercise.

Lactic acid is a product of the metabolism of glucose sugar used for energy. Even at rest the process of production and removal goes on. At the beginning of mild exercise, the rate of production is equal to the rate of removal. As the intensity increases, the requirement for energy becomes very high, and the production rate exceeds the removal rate. The lactic acid builds up, possibly contributing to the "burn" many exercisers experience. Lactic acid also builds up in nonworking muscles, the arms of a runner, for example, and in the blood.

Most of the lactic acid is eventually oxidized, or burned up, but some of it is converted into other substances by a process called gluconeogenesis. It can be turned into pyruvate, another sugar that is a precursor of protein when combined with amino acids. Both oxidation and gluconeogenesis can continue during recovery from exercise.

Lactic acid does not produce the delayed soreness many people feel a day or so after exercise. What causes that is not certain, but it may be the result of small tears in the muscle.

ONLY FOUR CIGARETTES

Q. *What are the risks to a smoker who smokes only four cigarettes a day?*

A. The risk is less than for someone who smokes forty cigarettes a day, but for a particular person, it can be very hazardous indeed, a bigger environmental hazard than almost anything you can name.

Even one cigarette a day raises the risk of cardiovascular disease and cancer. One cigarette has about fourteen thousand

micrograms of tar, but the Environmental Protection Agency standard for inhalable particles is only fifty micrograms per cubic meter of air. A typical person might breathe about twenty cubic meters of air a day, so with one cigarette, the risk just from particles is about fourteen times as bad as the risk from breathing marginally polluted air.

If you add a factor to take account of the chemical hazards, it is much worse. In tobacco smoke in general there are sixty known or suspected carcinogens.

ASPIRIN AND THE HEART

Q. *Do you get the cardiac benefits of a daily aspirin from ibuprofen or acetaminophen?*

A. No, only from aspirin. Aspirin may have multiple effects, but it is likely that its impact in cutting the stickiness of blood platelets is its major role in preventing heart attacks. Acetaminophen had no effect on the stickiness of blood platelets and ibuprofen had only a transient effect.

A heart attack occurs when sticky platelets close an artery. Aspirin has its effect by blocking an enzyme by binding to it and blocks the compounds that make the platelets sticky in an irreversible way.

The same compounds, called prostaglandins, are also involved in the pain response. Tylenol and other brands of acetaminophen block pain in an entirely different way.

After exposure to aspirin, platelets can't produce the enzymes for the rest of their lives, about ten days; most cells have a nucleus, which acts as a "brain" to direct cell functions, but platelets are just little packets of cellular protein with no nucleus to tell the cells to make more protein.

About 10 percent of platelets turn over each day, and it takes a few days for platelet function to get back to normal, so an aspirin every other day works just as well for the heart.

As for who should take aspirin, some questions remain. It is known to benefit those who have had heart disease or a stroke, and there is suggestive evidence that a segment of the healthy population will benefit as well. Studies have found that even healthy men will benefit, and most of the benefit is in men older than fifty.

Studies are under way to explore the risks, benefits and side effects of aspirin for others; one study includes forty thousand women, who are taking 100 milligrams, about a third of a standard 325-milligram aspirin, every other day.

CYANIDE POISONING

Q. *How does cyanide kill?*

A. Cyanide kills by asphyxiating the cells of the body. Cyanide competes with oxygen in the body's cells. The enzyme responsible for using oxygen has more affinity for cyanide than it does for oxygen, so the presence of cyanide starves a cell for oxygen.

Cells' respiratory pathways use the oxygen in a complex process to break down glucose to produce energy for vital cell maintenance. The last step adds oxygen to hydrogen to make water. If the last step does not occur, high-energy molecules of a substance called ATP, adenosine triphosphate, are not made.

Cells use the energy from ATP to maintain their semipermeable membranes, which control their chemical balance. Without maintenance, cell membranes lose their integrity and the cell eventually dies. If enough cells in the body die, toxic symptoms or death will result.

Bee Stings

Q. *How do you treat a bee sting?*

A. There are two basic kinds of reaction to a bee sting, one requiring immediate care in the emergency room and the other less serious.

In the less serious local reaction, the chemicals in bee venom cause an immediate redness and swelling near the site of the sting and perhaps a fat, red, warm arm that gets worse for a day or two. The best way to lessen this reaction, researchers have recently found, is to remove the stinger and its sac of venom as quickly as possible, within seconds, if you can.

After that, doctors usually let the problem run its course, though antihistamines may be somewhat effective and cold compresses can help. Antibiotics are needed only for an infection, which is rare.

The more dangerous systemic allergic reaction causes a rash, hives or swelling of the body at some place distant from the sting. This crisis requires an epinephrine injection on an emergency basis. Other signs of this sometimes fatal reaction can include wheezing, throat tightness and faintness caused by a sudden drop in blood pressure. A person can be insensitive to a sting one time but hypersensitive the next.

Itching and Scratching

Q. *What causes an itch? Why does scratching help?*

A. Itching, which doctors call pruritis, can have many causes, and the exact mechanism is still a matter of controversy.

Most researchers believe the common itch starts with the release of a substance called histamine, and possibly other chemicals, from special cells called mast cells in the skin.

The release can be triggered by allergies, contact dermatitis, eczema, dry skin, medication, sunburn, parasites like scabies and many other things, and some people simply have excitable mast cells.

The chemical is believed to initiate the pathway that stimulates a nerve, finding receptors so that a sensation is transmitted to the brain. However, some researchers say that a different kind of nerve receptor is being stimulated, perhaps by physical rather than chemical means.

The process is similar to the pathway of pain, and appears to depend to some extent on the intensity of the stimulus. A small stimulus might be perceived as an itch and a greater one as pain. For example, shingles, a disease that inflames nerve endings, can cause perceptions that range from a pain to an itch.

Other kinds of itching may arise from internal diseases, like liver disease, in which chemicals are not metabolized properly so that they build up; hyperthyroidism, or increased thyroid activity; and some kinds of cancers or tumors.

Scratching may work to relieve the itching sensation at least temporarily because it acts as a competing stimulus and tends to block out and suppress the itch. That is probably why itchy rashes are worse when you are trying to relax or going to sleep at night, when other stimuli are decreased.

Mosquito Bite Cure

Q. *Why do mosquito bites itch? What is the best way to relieve the itching?*

A. A trace of mosquito saliva is injected when the mosquito bites. The saliva contains an enzyme that prevents the victim's blood from clotting while the mosquito feeds.

In humans, the enzyme prompts an immune reaction that brings mast cells to the wound. The mast cells release histamine, which produces the itching and red rash.

There is an easy remedy. The saliva enzyme is a foreign protein to the body, and the simplest thing to do is to use meat tenderizer containing papain, which breaks down protein. Papain is an edible vegetable enzyme derived from papaya.

Mix a small amount of meat tenderizer with a drop of water to form a paste and put it right on the bite. It goes into the hole made by the insect's proboscis, breaks down the protein molecules in the saliva and stops the itching right away.

To keep from getting bitten in the first place, stay inside at dusk and dawn, when mosquitoes are most active, and wear long sleeves and pants. These simple measures would probably avoid half the bites.

True Lies: Old Wives' (and Husbands') Tales and Urban Legends

EAR TO THE GROUND

Q. *When the Indians in old movies put their ears to the ground to find out if the cavalry was coming, did it work?*

A. Yes, and depending on variables like the size of the troop and the type of terrain, they may have been able to hear the troops from quite a distance.

There are many factors involved in the seismology of such a phenomenon, and only individual experiments would determine how much energy would be coupled into the ground and how far the sound would be transmitted. For example, What is the strength of the source? Are all the forces pushing on the earth together at the same time, or is it random noise? If the approaching army is on horses, it is probably random noise, while soldiers marching in step would present a different set of factors.

Another important variable is the kind of terrain. Hard rock would not carry the sound very far, because a running horse does not move the ground much, so not much seismic energy is coupled into the ground.

On the other hand, if there is a river basin with consolidated sediment, and the cavalry is on the road upriver, with the Indians around the corner on the same sedimentary formation, the soil would be a good conduit, and they could hear for quite a way.

If the soil is wet, however, the energy of the horses' hooves might go into deforming the ground, rather than vibrating it.

A listener along a railroad track might have an advantage. Seismic energy travels along a linear body, and a train is much heavier than a horse, visibly bending the track when it passes over it. Therefore, the track would carry sound well, almost like a vibrating wire.

GRAY OVERNIGHT

Q. You hear of people who go gray overnight. Can an entire strand of hair turn to gray in a short time?

A. No, but a head of hair can go gray very quickly when a person has a lot of gray already and loses all the dark hair.

Hair is made of dead cells, and you can't change the color in a dead structure unless you dye it. However, if a person is graying, the remaining dark hairs may be in the resting phase of the hair cycle while the incoming hairs are both gray and growing.

The resting hairs would normally fall out in the course of time, but after a severe insult, like a car accident or surgery or even the death of a loved one, the resulting stress can cause the resting hairs to fall out all at once.

Why graying occurs at all is not entirely clear, but it runs in families and may be treatable once the cause is found.

Mammoth Meat

Q. *I heard about explorers eating frozen mammoth. What was it like?*

A. Everyone has heard the rumor, but probably only dogs, or passing wolves, ever enjoyed a modern feast of mammoth meat. It looks like horse meat but quickly rots when it thaws.

Several mammoths were found in permafrost, preserved since the last glacial period. The most famous was found in 1901 near the banks of the Berezovka River in Siberia. An Academy of Science expedition with dogsleds was quickly sent. The expedition found a nearly complete carcass, but wolves and dogs had left the skull almost bare.

The meat was dark red, suggesting horse meat, and marbled with fat. The dogs ate it avidly; the men could not quite steel themselves to try it too. Members of the expedition said the stench was like that of a badly kept stable blended with that of offal. Members of later trips said scientists never banqueted on or even sampled the meat.

Books that describe a banquet usually lack a place and date. The rumor seems to have arisen from Siberian natives' superstitions warning against eating the meat, though the Yakut fed it to their dogs in time of famine.

Moon and Mind

Q. *Have studies been done on whether crimes, mental illness and violence increase around a full moon?*

A. Modern science offers little support for the ancient belief in lunacy, or moon-engendered madness. Despite anecdotal reports, epidemiological studies find no consistent correlation between any phase of the moon and any aberrant activity. Moreover, because of the distance of the moon, not to mention other heavenly bodies, and the infinitesimally small tidal effect it could have on an individual, scientists have found no biochemical reason that there should be such a relationship.

In one well-known epidemiological study, in 1985, Nicholas Sanduleak, then an astronomer at Case Western Reserve University in Cleveland, Ohio, did statistical research in response to a book by Dr. Arnold Lieber.

Dr. Lieber had proposed that "biological tides" were at work in the water-rich human body that could cause psychological disruption near both the new moon and the full moon, when the combined lunar and solar action is near a maximum. He said he had found an excess of homicides in Miami and Cleveland at those times in a ten-year study. Scientists who independently reanalyzed the raw data from the Lieber study said that his conclusions were invalid.

Mr. Sanduleak found no correlation between moon phases and murder when he did a similar study for greater Cleveland, using Cuyahoga County Coroner's Office statistics for 3,370 homicides in the eleven full years from 1971 through 1981, beginning when the Lieber study ended. His results "indicate with a high degree of probability that the day-to-day fluctuations in homicidal assaults are random in nature and are not correlated with lunar phase," he wrote in *The Skeptical Inquirer*. There was, however, a real and marked increase in homicidal attacks on weekends, which he attributed to increased alcohol intake.

He said his review of several similar national studies "found that no conclusive statistical evidence existed for the reality of any kind of lunar effect on human behavior."

He suggested a source for full-moon anecdotes. On a busy night in the emergency room, he said, a harried attendant might say, "There must be a full moon," planting the idea in the minds of other workers who might later recall a full-moon connection regardless of the actual phase.

Sleep Before Midnight

Q. Is it true that an hour of sleep before midnight is worth two hours of sleep after midnight?

A. No, sleep needs are much more complicated than that. The hour of rising is probably much more important in keeping sleep cycles normal.

Individuals go through a series of periods of rapid-eye-movement, or REM, sleep, and non-REM sleep, and both kinds are needed. There is no evidence that you need more of one than the other, but you do get most of the non-REM sleep in the first three to four hours of sleep and most of the REM sleep after that. The amounts of different kinds of sleep are determined by when, within a sleep cycle, a person goes to bed and gets up.

A human being's sleep cycles are also regulated by the amount of sleep needed over a period of several days. Thus, sleep is regulated both by a system based on "need" for sleep and a system designed to keep the body's time in synchrony with the time of day, so that others are awake at the same time. This system allows animal life to be coordinated with the environment, food sources and fellow animals.

The second half of the night is crucially important in setting the rhythm of sleep, and getting up in the morning is the most important act of the day to make sure our biological clocks keep the right time. It resets the clock.

Red Skies

Q. Is there any truth in the rhyme "Red sky at morning, sailors take warning, red sky at night, sailors' delight"?

A. There is some truth in it. The trick is to look at the part of the sky where the sun isn't, not into the sunset but to the east. Both sunrise and sunset are reddish, as a rule, because of what happens to the light from the sun as it goes through the atmosphere at a low angle. It scatters away most colors, so all that is left is reddish hues. But if the sky is red in the part of the sky away from the sun, some rough forecasts can be made.

The red sky rule applies to weather patterns that move from west to east.

The idea is that sunlight interacting with additional water vapor in the part of the sky away from the sun leads to red and orangeish hues, so a red sky in the west in the morning means a storm system creating the hues is moving your way. If it is red at night looking off to the east, the storm system or moisture to the east is moving away from you.

PLANT RESPIRATION

Q. My friend says it is common knowledge in Europe that sleeping with a live plant is dangerous because it uses up oxygen. Is he right?

A. There is just a grain of truth in the idea, as green plants do absorb some oxygen for use in respiration, the mirror image of photosynthesis. Photosynthesis can occur only when there is light, so at night plants are absorbers of oxygen, on balance.

However, true danger would result only from an extremely large body of plants in a very tightly closed sleeping chamber with a very limited supply of oxygen. Another person in a room would be a far

heavier oxygen consumer than one plant.

These principles of gas exchange in photosynthesis and respiration were explored in the late eighteenth century by Jan Ingenhousz, a Dutch botanist. Once Joseph Priestley had discovered oxygen and plants' role in producing it from carbon dioxide, there was a great vogue for putting flowers in sickrooms to "purify" the air.

Ingenhousz was skeptical about the benefits. His experiments showed that only the green parts of plants add oxygen, and then only if placed in strong light; flowers and other nongreen parts, as well as green leaves left in darkness, used up oxygen just as animals did, he found.

In aerobic respiration, plants use free oxygen, usually from the air, for chemical reactions that release energy from organic substances; sugar and oxygen react to produce carbon dioxide, water and chemical energy. In photosynthesis, carbon dioxide and water react in the presence of light energy to produce sugar and oxygen.

During the day, both processes occur, but photosynthesis proceeds more rapidly than respiration, and the carbon dioxide produced is immediately used in photosynthesis; excess oxygen from the photosynthesis escapes into the air. At night, however, photosynthesis ceases and respiration continues, so that green plants are absorbing oxygen and producing carbon dioxide.

THE SMELL OF SNOW

Q. My grandmother used to say, "It smells like snow," and sure enough it would snow by nightfall. Is there any scientific explanation for this?

A. Depending on what kind of snow it was, she may very well have been able to smell the wind that heralded it.

One kind of snow results from warm, moist air gliding over cold air near the ground, and that kind is typically accompanied by southerly winds. Such storms are big snow producers, and depending on geography, these winds from the south may come from areas that have a different aroma.

Each city or region has its own characteristic smell, and any number of factors could contribute to it, including industry and agricultural activity and residential pollution. In the Northeast, southerly winds often come from latitudes where there is still green vegetation and areas where there is more industry to produce ozone. Winds from areas of denser population carry the fumes of chimneys, cars and burning leaves.

In general, a southerly wind is often perceived to have a

sweeter smell and a nicer feel, and while it may not be warmer, it is often noticeably more humid.

The most prodigious moist snowstorms of the Northeast coast are often accompanied by an ocean wind from the east or northeast, with its characteristic marine smell. For New York City, a northeasterly wind would come from Boston, possibly carrying industrial smog.

Not much smell is usually associated with the second major kind of snow, brought by cold winds blowing from the north, especially from cold, dry regions of Canada where there is little industry and where most trees are bare in winter. In general, these winds bring flurries and snow showers and squalls. Unless there is added moisture from bodies of water like the Great Lakes, the snow is not as likely to be heavy.

A RED MOON

Q. Why doesn't the moon turn red as it sets, the way the sun does?

A. It sometimes does, and for the same reason: the light sent to earthly eyes (in the case of the moon, reflected sunlight) is seen filtered through a layer of polluted air, and the path through the dirty air is longest when the heavenly body is at the horizon. The larger pollution particles scatter and absorb blue light, so the red shines through.

It is an old wives' tale that when the moon is red it will be hot and humid the next day. In fact it is the attenuation of moonlight by particles that causes it to turn red. Typically the particles that are in the air when it is hot and humid are the same that are there when the moon is red, but it's the particles, not the temperature.

DEADLY CORPSES

Q. Can you really get a disease from a body taken from its grave years after death?

A. There is very little information on the transmission of infectious diseases after death, but there is probably little or no danger that most disease organisms would survive even a few weeks in the inhospitable environment of the average grave.

For survival, a certain organism needs a certain temperature, a certain level of acidity or lack thereof, a certain chemical environment and a certain oxygen level. It should be only a few days before one of these situations should disappear. Many disease organisms probably die once the blood stops circulating and cools off.

In the case of cholera, a comparatively well-studied disease, the bacterium *Vibrio cholerae* can live only four to seven days outside the body. In dead bodies, it is present in the gut only, not even on the skin unless there is moist stool on it, and once the stool dries, it dies. In stool-contaminated water, a hospitable, moist environment, it lives only a maximum of seven days.

In an unusual case, scientists recently announced an expedition to study the frozen corpses of polar explorers to see if they were killed by the 1918 influenza epidemic. There is some hope, and some fear, that disease-causing organisms from that period may have survived for study.

THICK BLOOD
Q. *Does blood thicken in winter?*
A. No. In fact, it might tend to be thicker in summer, when the body loses water through sweating and people need to drink more to remain hydrated.

Temperature is not the chief regulator of the thickness of blood. It depends on the kidneys, which sense blood volume, and the brain, which senses osmotic pressure, or the concentration of chemicals in the blood.

The kidneys regulate how much water the body excretes as urine, and the brain may signal a need for more water by making the person thirsty. Hormonal signals are also involved.

As for being able to stand the heat or the cold, which is what many people mean by thick or thin blood, the blood doesn't have as much to do with it as the very complex relationship between glands and the thermal controls in the brain.

SEA MONSTER

Q. *Does the creature Cyanea capillata, which inflicted fatal and near-fatal injuries on swimmers in the Sherlock Holmes story "The Adventure of the Lion's Mane," really exist?*

A. Yes, and it has long golden-yellow streamers of poison cells. The cold-water jellyfish might resemble a huge lion's mane, just as Sir Arthur Conan Doyle described it. Its poison acts like a neurotoxin, and the effect is paralysis.

The average swimmer need not worry about meeting one unawares, however.

It is a noticeable and colorful creature. The bell is at least three or four feet across, and the streamers drag thirty to forty feet. It does not frequent shallow waters and is most likely found only on the high seas.

LOTTERY ODDS

Q. *Are your odds of winning the lottery better if you play the same numbers week after week or if you change the numbers every week?*

A. There should be no difference. If you are flipping a coin or throwing dice, the outcome should be totally independent each time.

This, of course, depends on the randomness of the numbers. There might be some oversight in the process in some individual lottery, and you cannot analyze the problem without knowing the individual selection process. But if the numbers are truly random, each game is an independent entity, and the odds do not depend on what happened in a previous game.

SEEING STARS

Q. *Can you see stars in daylight from the bottom of a deep well?*

A. No, but you might be able to see some planets if you know where to look.

One might think, using superficial common sense, that by excluding as much daylight as possible, one should be able to see stars in the daytime, but this doesn't work. The daytime sky is bright because the atmosphere's particles, including atoms, molecules, ions and free electrons, scatter sunlight in all directions, including down. Even a tiny shaft of this scattered light is brighter than the light reaching us from a star.

If, in the daytime, you held overhead a large piece of aluminum foil with a tiny pinhole, the light pouring through the pinhole would be far brighter than the light coming from a star. The starlight is overwhelmed by the daylight.

However, it is sometimes possible to see the planets Jupiter and Venus at their brightest with the naked eye, even without going down a well. A person at the bottom of a deep shaft that goes straight down from the earth's surface is forced to look directly upward. Therefore, reported deep-well sightings of stars were actually of planets and could occur only in earth's equatorial regions, where the celestial equator is close to overhead.

SNAKES IN IRELAND

Q. *Were there ever any snakes in Ireland for St. Patrick to throw out, as legend has it?*

A. There are no snakes in Ireland now, and no fossil records of snakes are known.

This does not prove that there were never any snakes, because there is also no fossil record of the common lizard, which does occur in Ireland, but herpetologists presume that if there

ever were any snakes, they were exterminated by the last period of glaciation and have not been able to return. The glaciers receded about fourteen thousand years ago.

Ireland's cold climate is marginal for the survival of snakes, although there are a few snakes farther north on the European mainland. The few species of snakes that now live in England reinvaded after the last glaciers. There was once a land bridge between southwestern Scotland and Ireland, but snake authorities believe it was severed before any snakes could get back to Ireland.

It has been suggested that the legend of snake expulsion may have arisen because the non-Christian religion that St. Patrick threw out might have included forms of snake worship brought to Ireland from somewhere else, so that he was throwing out idolators and idols, not the models for the idols.

MOON ON HORIZON

Q. Why is the moon larger when it is close to the horizon?
A. It is not actually larger, but seems larger because of an optical illusion.

When the moon is on the horizon, it is seen next to buildings or trees, terrestrial items you are familiar with, and the juxtaposition of the two images changes depth cues. You know the building is right in front of you, and the brain compensates by assuming the moon disk is larger than it is when it is high in the sky, away from objects for comparison.

At sea, where there are no buildings or trees, this illusion is absent because there are no cues to suggest it.

Another test is to look at the moon between your legs upside down. All depth cues are completely thrown off, so the effect is lessened. When the moon is seen beside an upside-down tree, the tree is perceived as just a shape, not a tree.

A way to convince yourself that you have been fooled by an optical illusion is by measuring the size of the moon's disk in the sky. The best way is to use a piece of paper carefully positioned on a window, tracing the moon once when it is near the horizon and again when it is at the top of the sky. The head must be lined up so it is exactly the same distance from the paper for both sightings.

The atmosphere does not have a significant magnifying effect on the moon. If it does anything, it makes the full moon appear slightly shallower from top to bottom, or slightly oval.

DEATH RATTLE

Q. *What causes a death rattle?*

A. Modern medicine may have sent the death rattle the way of milk fever, the vapors, consumption and other layman's terms for the ills of our ancestors. Many pulmonary diseases that can cause noisy labored breathing before death are not the major killers they were before antibiotics. And the kind of breathing distress that would cause a death rattle would now probably call for insertion of a breathing tube, at least in a hospital.

There is a medical term, agonal respiration, for any irregularity of breathing, sometimes deep and sometimes shallow, just before death, but for most people there is no noise. If there is a sound before death, it is probably one of three kinds of respiratory noise.

First, a person slipping into an unconscious state cannot clear secretions from around the larynx, vocal cords and trachea, so the passage of air may make a staccato wheeze or rattle, mostly on expiration. This was commonly called the death rattle. But pulmonary diseases that cause such secretions, like tuberculosis and pneumonia, are now treatable, so that people are more likely to die of something else, like a heart attack or stroke.

A second airway noise, stridor, is a harsh whistle that comes on breathing in when the larynx is narrowed by swelling. Finally, the terms rales or rhonchi describe crackling sounds that occur mostly on inspiration, either because of fluid in the lung tissue itself or because of the snapping open of alveoli, or small air sacs.

NOSEBLEEDS

Q. *Can you stop a nosebleed by pinching the bridge of the nose and putting ice on the back of the neck?*

A. That is an old wives' tale. The pressure is a good idea, and in fact continuous direct pressure at the bleeding site is the only infallible remedy, but there is no use pinching the bridge of the nose, which has virtually no blood vessels. Instead, use the thumb and index finger to squeeze the fleshy sides of the nostrils together and hold them for ten to twenty minutes, while breathing through the mouth.

Don't stop and check to see if the bleeding has stopped, but leave the pressure on to give time for the clot to form. Most nosebleeds are not serious, and this simple remedy avoids a trip to the emergency room in 90 percent of cases.

For emergencies involving bleeding from lacerations of all kinds, use concentrated direct pressure immediately. There is no blood vessel in the body larger than one's index finger except the aorta, which is deep inside the body, so applying pressure with just one finger can sometimes save a life.

DEW ON THE CANOE

Q. I used to hear that morning dew on the canoe meant the rain would stay at bay. Why is that so?

A. There is truth in this idea and in a similar folk rhyme:

> When the dew is on the grass,
> Rain will never come to pass;
> When grass is dry at morning light,
> Look for rain before the night.

The effect is linked to the absence or presence of clouds. For dew to form, the grass or canoe must reach a temperature cold enough for saturation to occur, that is, the saturation point or dew point, at which air will no longer hold water vapor. When water condenses to form dew on either grass or canoe, what you have is an object losing heat to the atmosphere faster than it is being replenished. This is more likely when clouds are absent.

There is a constant exchange of energy in the form of heat radiation between the ground and the atmosphere. When clouds are present, as is the case when rain is imminent, they radiate back some of the energy an object on the ground is losing. That object warms up a little, enough so that condensation does not occur.

At most times of the year, this general rule works rather

nicely, and a wet canoe probably means that there are no clouds and that rain is not imminent. The rule would not work for a period of twenty-four to thirty-six hours, but for twelve hours there is a loose correlation.

However, the higher the clouds are, the less impact they have on the surface temperature. The rule is also less applicable in summer, when there are long periods of clear skies, especially overnight, but afternoon thunderstorms can form quickly, in a matter of an hour. Then, morning dew on the ground might still mean there was enough moisture for afternoon showers to form, particularly at high elevations.

There are other exceptions. In very cold dry air, it is hard to get down to the temperature at which the air can no longer hold water.

EGG BALANCING

Q. Is there any truth to the belief that an egg can be stood on its end during the equinox?

A. Possibly, but anyone who can stand an egg on end at that time can probably do it at any other time as well, the experts believe.

The theory is that it is possible to stand an egg on its end during the vernal and autumnal equinoxes, the two days of the year when the sun is directly above the equator. At these times, so the theory goes, the tidal gravitational force due to the sun is directed vertically, facilitating the balancing of an egg on its end, but only if the egg is at the equator. However, this effect is too small to be noticed in kitchen experiments where such other factors as air pressure, friction, light winds, vibration and the shape and texture of the egg and the balancing surface come into play. In any event, the tidal force exerted on the egg by the moon would be much greater than that due to the sun.

WHIRLPOOLS

Q. Are there really ship-swallowing whirlpools in the ocean, like the Maelstrom in the Edgar Allan Poe story?

A. No, though there are eddies, or strong currents, one hundred miles across in certain parts of the ocean. They do not suck anything down or push anything up at a speed that you would notice, and while they could overturn a small boat, they could not swallow a ship.

Perhaps the only thing comparable to the Maelstrom would be some very strong tidal currents. Sometimes, when the wind and tide are just right, the tides east and west of Scotland collide in a splashy convergence of flow. It is no threat to a large ship, but could overturn a cockleshell boat. These are not whirlpools, but simply tidal currents trying desperately to get where they belong.

The original Maelstrom, also called the Moskenstrom, is a similar strong current running past the south end of the island of Moskenaes, one of the Lofoten Islands off the west coast of Norway, which is dangerous at certain states of wind and tide.

There are also little cyclonic atmospheric features over the ocean that can pull a little water up, which could damage a ship or small boat, but these are wind effects, not ocean effects.

CURVE BALLS

Q. *Does a curve ball curve?*

A. Yes, a curve ball does travel in a sideways arc, a very small segment of a very large circle, as Dr. Lyman J. Briggs found in a

historic study in 1959. Then eighty-four, a retired head of the National Bureau of Standards, he settled the question and explained the mechanism, using an overhead camera to show the curvature of the flight path. He then used smoke streamers in a wind tunnel to study regions of higher velocity and lower pressure around curve balls.

He measured the rate of spin by using major-league pitchers throwing balls with flat tape attached, then counting the number of twists in the tape. Depending on spin and direction, Dr. Briggs found, the ball can curve downward as well as sideways.

As Dr. Briggs explained it at the time, here is how a ball that is pitched so it spins turns into a curve ball:

"Let us imagine that the spinning ball with its rough seams creates around itself a kind of whirlpool of air that stays with the ball when it is thrown forward into still air. But the picture is easier to follow if we imagine that the ball is not moving forward, but that the wind is blowing past it. The relative motions are the same.

"Then on one side of the ball the motions of the wind and the whirlpool are in the same direction and the whirlpool is speeded up. On the opposite side of the ball the whirlpool is moving against the wind and is slowed down. Now it is well known from experiments with water flowing through a pipe that has a constriction in it that the pressure in the constriction is actually less than in front of or behind it; the velocity is, of course, higher.

"Hence, on the side of the spinning ball where the velocity of the whirlpool has been increased, the air pressure has been reduced; and on the opposite side it has been increased. This difference in pressure tends to push the ball sidewise or to make it curve. It moves toward that side of the ball where the wind and the whirlpool are traveling together."

EVE'S RIBS

Q. Is there any big difference between merely the ribs of men and women that would help an anthropologist say which skeleton is which sex?

A. Not really. The idea comes from the Old Testament account of the creation of Eve from Adam's rib. However, the main sex difference is that women's ribs are a little smaller on average.

The bones forensic anthropologists really look at, the most reliable ones, are the bones of the pelvis, consisting of three bones: the two hipbones and the sacrum, which make a bony ring. The difference between males and females is related to the reproductive functions of the pelvis. In general, female pelvises are somewhat broader and more basin-like, while male pelvises are relatively narrow and somewhat constricted, especially the inner part, where a baby's head must pass in a woman.

The skull is also helpful but not quite as reliable as the pelvis. In the male skull, the brow ridges, the bones above the eyes, and the mastoid processes, the lumps of bone behind the ears, are relatively larger.

CACTUS AND SPIDERS

Q. I heard that someone bought an ornamental cactus from Arizona and that it suddenly released a lot of big spiders, tarantulas, I think. Am I in danger?

A. Almost certainly not, experts in desert flora and fauna say. Such an event is particularly unlikely to involve tarantulas, which might possibly lay eggs or build webs on, but not in, a cactus plant.

Tarantulas live in burrows in the ground, especially the female, which rarely moves around on the surface. Tarantulas take several years to reach full size.

The "spiders in the cactus" story, almost invariably heard about a friend of a friend, is one of the most persistent of urban myths. The story is often attached to the name of a well-known dealer or store. The cactus in question is supposed to have been

 field-grown or harvested wild in the desert. It starts to tremble, the story goes, and then releases its awful contents: spiders or scorpions. Sometimes the victim is said to call the dealer, who sends men with a plastic bag, just in time. However, there is apparently no verifiable instance of this having happened, and commercially sold cactuses are almost always raised in a controlled environment.

Tarantulas also have an undeservedly bad reputation. Tarantulas are very docile animals and are not easily provoked to bite. The usual prey of *Rhechostica chalcodes*, the most common species in Arizona, is insects. Its fangs are seldom used on humans and do not cause any serious complications. A Mexican variety is even sold as a pet.

Notes

THE EARTH BELOW

Transparency: Dr. Alan J. Friedman, director of the New York Hall of Science in Queens.

Silver Tarnish: McGraw-Hill Encyclopedia of Chemistry; Van Nostrand Scientific Encyclopedia.

Liberty's Complexion: McGraw-Hill Encyclopedia of Chemistry; Thomas A. Bradley, assistant superintendent of the Statue of Liberty for the National Parks Service; contemporary *New York Times* accounts.

Volcano Dating: Susan Russell-Robinson, geologist and information scientist, United States Geological Survey.

Red Clay: Bill R. Smith, soil scientist, Clemson University.

New Oil: Dr. Roger N. Anderson, petroleum geologist, Lamont Doherty Earth Observatory.

Ozone, Good and Bad: Dr. F. Sherwood Rowland, Donald Bren Professor of Chemistry, University of California at Irvine.

Glacier Ice: Dr. Mark F. Meier, director, Institute for Arctic and Alpine Research, University of Colorado.

Earth as Billiard Ball: John O'Keefe, Goddard Space Flight Center.

Dropping a Penny: Dr. Anatol Roshko, Theodore van Karman Professor of Aeronautics, California Institute of Technology.

Dustbusters: Dr. Harvey Weiss, Peabody Museum, Yale University; Dr. Alan J. Friedman.

Slippery Ice: McGraw-Hill Dictionary of Earth Sciences.

Cavernous Caves: John Scheltens, president, National Speleological Society.

A Plane Above Earth: Don Bull, director of flight planning and control for Pan American Airlines.

Real Pearls: Encyclopaedia Britannica.

Skyscrapers: C. R. (Chuck) Pennoni, president, American Society of Civil Engineers.

Dust of Ages: Vincent Pigott, archeologist, Applied Science Center for Archeology, University Museum of the University of Pennsylvania.

THE SKY ABOVE

Tornadoes and Trailer Parks: Paul G. Knight, meteorologist, Pennsylvania State University.

Moon Rings: Lee Grenci, meteorologist, Pennsylvania State University.

Thunder Snow: Fred Gadomski, meteorologist, Pennsylvania State University.

Freeze-Dried Air: Joe Lundberg, meteorologist, Pennsylvania State University.

Polar Chill: Tom Ross, National Climatic Data Center, Asheville, North Carolina.

Hurricane Season: Daniel H. Graf, meteorologist, Pennsylvania State University.

Ball Lightning: Ronald L. Holley, meteorologist, National Severe Storms Laboratory, National Oceanic and Atmospheric Administration, Norman, Oklahoma.

Double Rainbows: Dr. William Gutsch, chairman, Hayden Planetarium, American Museum of Natural History.

Hailstones: Fred Gadomski.

Weather Vanes: Paul G. Knight

Northeasters: Paul G. Knight.

By the Sea

Salt in the Sea: Dr. Harmon Craig, professor of geochemistry and oceanography, Scripps Institution of Oceanography.

Wave Damage: Dr. Tim Barnett, oceanographer, climate research division, Scripps Institution of Oceanography.

Sea Level: Dr. Eric Wood, hydrologist, Princeton University.

Double Tides: Reinhard E. Flick, oceanographer for the California Department of Boating and Waterways, Scripps Institution of Oceanography.

Melting the Ice: Dr. Richard B. Alley, glaciologist, Department of Geosciences, Pennsylvania State University; Dr. Donald D. Blankenship, Institute for Geophysics, University of Texas at Austin.

Floating Ice: Bob Park, spokesman, American Physical Society, and professor of physics, University of Maryland.

Undersea Volcanoes: Stirling A. Colgate, group leader in theoretical astrophysics and senior fellow, Los Alamos National Laboratory.

Spiraling Drains: Mark Cane, Doherty Senior Scientist, Lamont-Doherty Geological Observatory of Columbia University.

Earth's Water: Dr. Paul Warren, geochemist, University of California at Los Angeles.

Heavens! The View from Spaceship Earth

Southern Stars: Dr. Alan J. Friedman, director, New York Hall of Science in Queens.

Southern Zodiac: Dr. William Gutsch, director, Hayden Planetarium, American Museum of Natural History.

Friction on Earth: Dr. David Walker, professor of geology, Lamont-Doherty Geological Observatory of Columbia University.

Twinkling Stars: Andrew Fraknoi, executive director, Astronomical Society of the Pacific.

Earth's Tilt: Dr. David Paige, planetary scientist, University of California at Los Angeles.

Round Bodies: Leroy Doggett, astronomer, Nautical Almanac Office, United States Naval Observatory.

Moon in Daylight: Dr. Neil deGrasse Tyson, director, Hayden Planetarium, American Museum of Natural History.

One Face Forward: Dr. Alan J. Friedman, director, New York Hall of Science in Queens.

The Heat of Stars: The Facts on File Dictionary of Astronomy.

Stars and Sand: Dr. Neil deGrasse Tyson.

OUTWARD BOUND

Lunar Mapping: Patricia M. Bridges, cartographer, astrogeology department, United States Geological Survey.

Compass in Space: NASA spokesmen.

Air Supply: Dr. Randy Humphries, chief, life support branch, NASA's Marshall Space Flight Center, Huntsville, Alabama.

Space Suits: David W. Garrett, the news chief at NASA headquarters.

"Weight" in Space: Eileen Hawley, spokeswoman for NASA's Johnson Space Center.

The Slingshot Effect: Jim Wilson, NASA spokesman.

Beam Me Up?: Dr. David Goodstein, professor of physics and applied physics and vice provost at the California Institute of Technology.

Life and Death: Alcestis Oberg, author of *Spacefarers of the 80's and 90's: The Next People in Space,* and Dr. Frank Sulzman, chief, space medicine and biology branch, life sciences division, NASA.

MAN IS THE MEASURE OF ALL THINGS

What Time Is It?: United States Naval Observatory; Division of Time and Frequency of the National Institute of Standards and Technology.

Degree Days: Joe Lundberg, meteorologist, Pennsylvania State University.

110 in the Shade: Fred Gadomski, meteorologist, Pennsylvania State University.

Measuring Cups: Corning Inc.

Rainfall, Snowfall: Joe Lundberg, meteorologist, Pennsylvania State University.

The Vision Thing: Dr. Howard C. Howland, professor of neurobiology and behavior, Cornell University.

Timberline: New York Botanical Garden; Brooklyn Botanic Garden

Southern Sundials: Richard E. Schmidt, astronomer, United States Naval Observatory.

"Weight" of Earth: Andrew Fraknoi, executive director, Astronomical Society of the Pacific.

Earth's Mass: Dr. Alan J. Friedman, director, New York Hall of Science, Queens.

Highest Temperature: Dr. David Goodstein, vice provost and professor of physics and applied physics, California Institute of Technology, Pasadena.

Radio Reception: Jon Herron, director of communications for Madrigal Audio Labs, Middletown, Connecticut.

Visibility; Van Nostrand's Scientific Encyclopedia.

Logic of Fahrenheit: James Schooley, National Institute of Standards and Technology.

IX Times XXXVII: Dr. Len Berggren, professor of mathematics, Simon Fraser University, Vancouver, British Columbia.

Mines and Gravity: Dr. Thomas E. Furtak, professor of physics, Colorado School of Mines, Golden.

Center of the Earth: John Trefny, Ph.D., professor of physics, Colorado School of Mines, Golden.

Measuring Mountains: New York Times report.

Sea Level: New York Times reports.

Airplane Speed: Dr. Edward Zukoski, professor of jet propulsion and mechanical engineering, California Institute of Technology.

The Meter Bar: National Institute of Standards and Technology.

INDUSTRIAL SECRETS

Battery Drain: Roger Reece, manager of battery engineering, Eveready Battery Company.

Magnets: Dr. Charles P. Bean, Institute Professor of Science, Rensselaer Polytechnic Institute.

A Cold Glow: Dr. Bruce H. Baretz, chemist, manager of operations and new product development, American Cyanamid Corporation.

Steel Hardness: Patrick J. Farrell, spokesman, Wilson Instruments of Binghamton, New York, division of Canram Inc., maker of hardness testing equipment.

The Night Mirror: Robert J. Donohue, engineer, General Motors Corporation.

Chewing Gum: research and development department, Wm. Wrigley Jr. Company; Don Plumb, regulatory guidance department, Food and Drug Administration.

The Dial Tone: American Telephone and Telegraph Company.

Cough Medicine: Dr. Arthur H. Kibbe, director of scientific affairs, American Pharmaceutical Association.

Hot Water: Dr. Raymond L. Bendure, director of household surface care development, Colgate-Palmolive Company.

Frozen Stockings: Dr. Ebenezer D. Williams, senior research fellow, fibers department, E. I. du Pont de Nemours & Company.

Calculator Batteries: Gerald A. Erickson, research and development section manager, calculator division, Hewlett Packard.

Shiny Foil: Anne Waring, public relations manager, Reynolds Metals Company.

Shrinking Clothes: Dr. Ann Lemley, associate professor, department of textiles and apparel, Cornell University.

Time Capsules: Menley & James Laboratories, a division of the SmithKline Corporation; CIBA Pharmaceutical Company, a division of the CIBA-Geigy Corporation; the Alza Corporation of Palo Alto, California.

Catching Counterfeits: Lisa Mendheim, spokeswoman, the Maytag Corporation.

Dry Cleaning: Daniel I. Eisen, chief garment analyst, Neighborhood Cleaners Association of New York.

Dry Ice: Dewey Erzinger, director of public relations and advertising, Liquid Carbonic Industries, a division of CBI Industries.

Tiny Bubbles: Michele Szynal, communications manager, the Gillette Company.

Fabric Softener Sheets: McGraw-Hill Encyclopedia of Chemistry.

A MODERN BESTIARY

Giraffe Hypertension: Dr. Paul E. Calle, veterinarian, Animal Health Center, New York Zoological Society.

Dolphins and Dolphins: Dr. Paul Chung, saltwater ichthyologist, New York Aquarium, Brooklyn.

Death by Python: Dr. Emil Dolensek, chief veterinarian, New York Zoological Society; Paul Cowell, zoologist, reptile house, Bronx Zoo.

Why Slugs?: News accounts, *The New York Times*.

Fried Fish: Edward Brinton, research biologist, and Dr. Walter Heiligenberg, neuroscientist and physiologist, Scripps Institution of Oceanography, University of California at San Diego.

Drinking like a Fish: Paul Sieswerda, collections manager, New York Aquarium, Brooklyn.

One-Eyed Animals: John Behler, reptile curator, Bronx Zoo.

Squirrels' Nests: Encyclopedia of Mammals (Facts on File).

Asleep in the Deep: Kevin M. Walsh, director of marine mammal training, New York Aquarium, Brooklyn.

Bats in the Belfry: Heidi Hughes, co-founder, American Bat Conservation Society.

Sharks' Senses: Louis Garibaldi, director, New York Aquarium, Brooklyn.

Red-Blooded Fish: H. J. Walker, senior museum scientist, marine vertebrates collection, Scripps Institution of Oceanography.

Safe Diving for Whales: Kevin M. Walsh.

Homing Squirrels: John C. Muir, executive director, Brooklyn Center for the Urban Environment in Prospect Park.

Sleeping Dinosaurs: David Varricchio, paleontologist, Museum of the Rockies, Bozeman, Montana.

Animal Life Spans: Bronx Zoo; *The Guinness Book of Animal Facts and Feats*, compiled by Gerald L. Wood, Zoological Society of London (Guinness Publishing Ltd.).

Talking to Bambi: Colin Beer, Institute of Animal Behavior, Rutgers University, Newark, New Jersey.

Baby Teeth: Penny Calk, manager, mammal collections, Bronx Zoo.

Snoring Animals: Penny Calk.

Animal Gourmets: Dr. Robert Cook, chief veterinarian, Bronx Zoo.

City Pigeons: Steven C. Sibley, ornithologist, bird population studies program, Cornell Laboratory of Ornithology, Cornell University.

Woodpeckers: Trevor Lloyd-Evans, staff biologist, Manomet Bird Observatory, Manomet, Massachusetts.

Robins and Worms: Steven C. Sibley.

Birds and Perches: Todd Culver, ornithologist, Cornell Laboratory of Ornithology, Cornell University.

The Ancient Albatross: Todd Culver.

Bird Navigation: Dr. Pete Myers, ornithologist, W. Alton Jones Foundation, Charlottesville, Virginia.

Seagulls: Dr. Richard Bonney, Jr., ornithologist, director of education, Cornell Laboratory of Ornithology, Cornell University.

Reusable Nests: Dr. Charles Walcott, Louis Agassiz Fuertes director, Cornell Laboratory of Ornithology, Cornell University.

Flying Blind: Todd Culver.

Birds in Hurricanes: Many authorities.

Nesting Boxes: Heidi Hughes, ornithologist, Backyard Bird Society, Rockville, Maryland.

Feeder Denizens: Heidi Hughes.

Dust Baths: Dr. Pete Myers.

Fasting Penguins: Todd Culver.

Dead Pigeons: Dr. Charles Walcott.

Migrating Birds: Todd Culver.

Survivors: Dr. David Jablonski, paleontologist, University of Chicago.

DOMESTIC ANIMALS, PETS—AND CATS

Fido's Cavities: Animal Medical Center, New York.

Animal Dreams: Dr. Evelyn Thoman, professor of biobehavioral science, University of Connecticut, Storrs.

Goldfish Methuselahs: Paul L. Sieswerda, curator of fishes and mammals, New York Aquarium, Brooklyn.

Animal Color Vision: Dr. Peter L. Borchelt, president, Animal Behavior Consultants, Brooklyn; Robert L. Williams, associate professor, department of anatomy and neurobiology, University of Tennessee.

Wigwag Signals: Dr. Benson E. Ginsburg, professor of biobehavioral sciences and psychology, University of Connecticut, Storrs; Dr. Benjamin L. Hart, professor of physiology and behavior, School of Veterinary Medicine, University of California, Davis.

Catnip: Dr. Benjamin L. Hart.

Feline Rabies: Dr. Michael S. Garvey, chairman, department of medicine, Animal Medical Center, New York.

Dogs' Noses: Dr. Michael S. Garvey.

Kneading Cats: The Domestic Cat: The Biology of Its Behavior, Dennis C.
    Turner and Patrick Bateson (Cambridge University Press).

Candy, Drugs and Pets: Dr. Michael S. Garvey.

Circling Dogs: Dr. Peter L. Borchelt.

Swimming Sheep: Edward Spevak, assistant curator of mammals at the
    Bronx Zoo.

Vegetarian Cats: Dr. James Morris, professor of physiological science,
    School of Veterinary Medicine, University of California, Davis.

Purring Cats: Dr. Leslie L. Cooper, a veterinarian at the hospital of the
    School of Veterinary Medicine, University of California, Davis.

Barking Dogs: Dr. David Miller, animal behavior expert, University of Con-
    necticut, Storrs.

Pet Life Spans: Dr. Michael S. Garvey.

Cats' Eyes: Susan Kirschner, veterinary ophthalmologist, Animal Medical
    Center, New York.

Dogs' Tongues: Dr. Don Low, associate dean, School of Veterinary Medicine,
    University of California, Davis.

The Cat's Mouth: Dr. Edward C. Feldman, professor of small animal internal
    medicine, School of Veterinary Medicine, University of California, Davis.

Kittens' Parentage: Dr. Melissa S. Wallace, veterinarian, department of
    medicine, Animal Medical Center, New York.

A Cat's Extra Sense: The Cornell Book of Cats (Villard Press).

Dachshunds and Wolves: Dr. Benson E. Ginsburg.

INSECTS, BUGS AND CREEPY-CRAWLIES

Insect Senses: T. A. Green, an entomologist at the University of Massa-
    chusetts, Amherst.

Bottoms-Up Insects: Dr. Lee Herman, curator of coleoptera, American
    Museum of Natural History.

Lovebugs: Dr. Timothy A. Mousseau, assistant professor of biological sci-
    ences, University of South Carolina.

Useful Wasps: New York Times news accounts.

Katy Did or Didn't?: Louis N. Sorkin, entomologist, American Museum of
    Natural History.

Cannibal Spiders: American Spiders, Willis J. Gertsch (Van Nostrand).

Snow Fleas: Living Insects of the World, Alexander B. Klots and Elsie B. Klots (Doubleday).

Butterflies' Work: Bugs in the System, Dr. May Berenbaum (Addison-Wesley).

Flying Ants: Louis N. Sorkin.

Significant Dots: Dr. Betty Faber, entomologist and staff scientist, Liberty Science Center, Jersey City, New Jersey.

Flies and Mosquitoes: Louis N. Sorkin; Durland Fish, medical entomologist, New York Medical College; Cecile Lumer, plant ecologist, New York City Parks Department.

Jumping Beans: Dave Mills, entomologist, Arizona Commission of Agriculture and Horticulture.

Insect Muscles: Louis N. Sorkin.

Moths in the Closet: Louis N. Vasvary, urban entomologist and extension specialist, Cook College of Rutgers University, New Brunswick, New Jersey.

Fly on the Wall: Dr. Alex Mintzer, entomologist, Entomological Society of America, Lanham, Maryland.

Cobwebs: Spiders of the United States, Richard Headstrom (A. S. Barnes & Company).

Tick Survival: Dr. David T. Dennis, epidemiologist, Centers for Disease Control and Prevention.

Beeswax: Dr. Roger Morse, chairman, department of entomology, Cornell University.

Honey: Dr. Roger Morse.

IT'S A JUNGLE OUT THERE

Autumn Leaf Display: news accounts, *The New York Times.*

Lights on Trees: Jeannie Fernsworth, horticulturist, adult education department, Brooklyn Botanic Garden.

Plant Viruses: Dr. David Dilcher, president, Botanical Society of America, and professor of paleobotany in the departments of biology and geology, Indiana University.

Indoor Sunlight: Carolyn Ormsbee, staff horticulturalist, Gardener's Supply Company, Burlington, Vermont; Paul Wasdyke, engineer, Duro-Lite Inc., Fairfield, New Jersey.

Coconut Seeds: news accounts, *The New York Times.*

The Biggest Seed: Dr. Andrew Henderson, research associate, Institute of Economic Botany, New York Botanical Garden.

Poison Ivy: Dr. Stephen K. Tim, vice president for science and publications, Brooklyn Botanic Garden.

Toadstools: Harold S. Burdsall, past president, Mycological Society of America, project leader, Center for Forest Mycology Research, Madison, Wisconsin.

Deadly Oleander: Dr. Larry J. Thompson, clinical toxicologist, College of Veterinary Medicine, Cornell University.

Intrusive Ivy: Brooklyn Botanic Garden; New York Botanical Garden; contemporary news accounts, *The New York Times.*

Sap and Syrup: Dr. Stephen K. Tim and Dr. Steven E. Clements, taxonomist, Brooklyn Botanic Garden.

Street Trees: Nina Bassuk, professor of horticultural science and director, Urban Horticulture Institute, Cornell University.

Rehabilitating Kudzu: Dr. Harry Amling, professor emeritus of horticulture, and Dr. Ronald Schumack, professor of horticulture, Auburn University.

WATCH WHAT YOU PUT IN YOUR MOUTH

Popcorn, Etc.: Dr. William D. Pardee, professor of plant breeding, College of Agriculture and Life Sciences, Cornell University.

Backyard Mushrooms: Dr. Harold S. Burdsall, past president of the Mycological Society of America.

Quinine in Tonic: A.M.A. Encyclopedia of Medicine (Random House).

Plastic Taste: Donna Scott, extension associate, department of food science, Cornell University.

Eliminating Alcohol: Dr. T. K. Li, Indiana University School of Medicine.

Dusty Fruit: Robert C. Baker, retired professor of food science, Cornell University.

Small End Down: Don Downing, food science department, Cornell University's Geneva Experiment Station.

Varied Vegetables: Christina Stark, nutritionist, Cornell University Division of Nutritional Sciences.

Vitamin Loss: Christina Stark.

Too Many Carrots?: A.M.A. Encyclopedia of Medicine.

Vitamin E: Dr. Joseph H. Hotchkiss, associate professor of food science, Cornell University.

Gelling Gelatin: Dr. Robert H. Cox, a chemical consultant in Scarsdale, New York.

Popeye's Spinach: division of nutritional sciences, Cornell University.

Nutrient Interaction: Dr. Marion Nestle, professor and chairman, department of nutrition, School of Food and Hotel Management, New York University.

Bean Problems: On Food and Cooking: The Science and Lore of the Kitchen, Harold McGhee (Collier); Dr. Eric S. Rabkin and Dr. Eugene M. Silverman, Akpharma Inc.

Calcium in Vegetables: United States Department of Agriculture publications.

Rotten Peaches: Dr. Warren C. Stiles, professor of pomology, Cornell University.

Green to Red Pepper: Edward A. Cope, extension botanist, Bailey Hortorium, the plant systematics unit at Cornell University.

Red-Hot Peppers: Dr. Michael Nee, tropical collections specialist, New York Botanical Garden.

Peppery Climes: Dr. Michael Nee; Dr. Arthur D. Heller, clinical assistant professor of medicine, Cornell Medical College.

Salt and Savor: Dr. Arthur D. Heller; Dr. Linda Bartoshuk, Yale University School of Medicine; Dr. Bruce P. Halpern, department of psychology, Cornell University.

Cans Gone Bad: Dr. Joseph Hotchkiss, associate professor of food science, Cornell University.

Pineapple Seeds: Living Plants of the World, Lorus and Margery Milne (Random House); *The Plant Book: A Portable Dictionary of the Higher Plants,* D. J. Mabberley (Cambridge University Press).

Don't Eat the Pits!: Dr. Rodney S. Dietert, professor of immunogenetics and director, Institute for Comparative and Environmental Toxicology, Cornell University; Dr. Margaret Dietert, associate professor of biology, Wells College.

Blue Cheese: Dr. Rodney S. Dietert.

Nightshade: Dr. Rodney S. Dietert.

Butter vs. Milk: Dr. Joseph H. Hotchkiss.

Wild Tomatoes: New York Times accounts.

SOUND BODIES AND UNSOUND BODIES

Stomach Capacity: Dr. Allan Geliebter, St. Luke's–Roosevelt Hospital, New York.

The Sandman: Dr. Thomas D. Lindquist, associate professor of ophthalmology, University of Washington, Seattle.

Limits of Growth: Dr. Gilman Grave, chief of the endocrinology, nutrition and growth branch, National Institute of Child Health and Human Development.

Higher Heights: Tim Sullivan, Center for Human Growth and Development, Ann Arbor, Michigan.

Thinking and Calories: Harvard Medical School department of psychiatry.

Wayward Hair: Dr. Clarence R. Robbins, vice president for advanced technology/personal care, research center of the Colgate-Palmolive Company.

Cracking Knuckles: Dr. Robert L. Swezey, director of the Arthritis and Back Pain Center, Santa Monica, California.

Yawning: A.M.A. Encyclopedia of Medicine (Random House).

Sleeping Babies: Dr. Robert J. Meechan, professor of pediatrics, Oregon Health Sciences University.

Goosebumps: Dr. Henry Edinger, associate professor of the New Jersey Medical School, Newark.

Squinting: Dr. Stephen Miller, director, clinical care center, American Optometric Association.

Hold Your Breath: Dr. John G. Mohler, medical director, pulmonary physiology laboratory, University of Southern California School of Medicine.

Infant Immunity: Dr. George P. Curlin, deputy director, division of microbiology and infectious diseases, National Institute of Allergy and Infectious Diseases.

Big Eyes: Dr. Anita Hendrickson, professor of biological structure and
    ophthalmology, University of Washington, Seattle.

Keeping Your Balance: A.M.A. Encyclopedia of Medicine.

Body Heat: Dr. Carl V. Gisolfi, exercise physiologist, exercise science de-
    partment, University of Iowa.

Swimming and Sweating: Dr. Carl V. Gisolfi.

Blue Blood, Red Blood: Dr. Rao Pulakhandam, New York Blood Center.

Adam's Apple: Dr. Cornelius Rosse, professor and chairman, department
    of biological structure, University of Washington.

Ambidexterity: Dr. George Michel, associate professor of psychology, De-
    Paul University.

Twins and Handedness: Dr. David T. Lykken, professor of psychiatry and
    psychology, University of Minnesota.

Milk Supply: The Mayo Clinic Family Health Book (Morrow); A.M.A. Encyclo-
    pedia of Medicine.

Heart Muscle: Heart Talk: Understanding Cardiovascular Diseases, Dr.
    Mark V. Barrow (Cor-Ed Publishing Company); Gray's Anatomy.

Men and Osteoporosis: Dr. William Peck, president, National Osteoporosis
    Foundation, and physician in chief, Jewish Hospital of St. Louis.

Salty Tears: Dr. William Frey, director, Ramsey Dry Eye and Tear Research
    Center, St. Paul, Minnesota.

Growing Nails: Dr. Lawrence A. Norton, clinical professor of dermatology,
    Boston University School of Medicine.

Male Nipples: Dr. Bruce McEwen, professor and head of laboratory of en-
    docrinology, Rockefeller University.

Fat Cells: Dr. Judith Stern, department of nutrition, the University of Cali-
    fornia, Davis, and vice president, North American Association for the
    Study of Obesity.

Hiccups: A.M.A. Encyclopedia of Medicine; Mayo Clinic Family Health Book.

Oblivious Snorers: Dr. Aaron Sher, otolaryngologist and chairman, sleep
    disorders committee, American Academy of Otolaryngology.

Tired in the Morning: Dr. Charles Pollak, director, Institute of Chronobiol-
    ogy, and head, Sleep-Wake Disorder Center, New York Hospital–Cornell
    Medical Center, Westchester Division.

Black Eyes and Bruises: Elaine W. Gunter, head, National Health and Nutrition Examination Survey Laboratory, Centers for Disease Control and Prevention; Dr. Janice E. Ross, forensic pathologist, Cayuga County Coroner, Auburn, New York.

Runny Noses: The Merck Manual of Diagnosis and Therapy.

Lead Poisoning: Dr. Suzanne Binder, chief, lead poisoning prevention branch, Center for Environmental Health and Injury Control, Centers for Disease Control and Prevention.

Surviving a Crash: George L. Parker, associate administrator for research and development, National Highway Traffic Safety Administration.

Night Terrors: "Treatment of Psychiatric Disorders," report by a task force of the American Psychiatric Association.

Examination Dream: Dr. Rosalind Cartwright, chairman, department of psychology, Rush Presbyterian–St. Luke's Medical Center, Chicago, and director, sleep disorder service.

Losing Allergies: Dr. Donald Y. M. Leung, head, division of pediatric allergy and immunology, National Jewish Center for Immunology and Respiratory Medicine, Denver.

Cat Allergy: Dr. Peyton Eggleston, head, pediatric allergy program, John Hopkins University; Dr. C. J. Horton, veterinarian, New York City.

Sore Muscles: Dr. Karen R. Segal, exercise physiologist, associate professor of physiology in pediatrics and director of exercise physiology, department of pediatric cardiology, New York Hospital–Cornell Medical Center, New York.

Only Four Cigarettes: James L. Repace, environmental policy analyst, Federal Environmental Protection Agency.

Aspirin and the Heart: Dr. J. Michael Gaziano, director of cardiovascular epidemiology, division of preventive medicine, Brigham and Women's Hospital, Boston.

Cyanide Poisoning: Dr. Margaret F. Dietert, associate professor of biology, Wells College.

Bee Stings: Mark S. Smith, chairman, department of emergency medicine, George Washington University Medical Center, Washington, D.C.

Itching and Scratching: Dr. Lenore S. Kakita, dermatologist, Los Angeles.

228

Mosquito Bite Cure: Stuart Race, extension entomologist, Rutgers University; Dr. Ann Cali, professor of zoology, department of biological sciences, Rutgers University.

TRUE LIES

Ear to the Ground: Leonard Seeber, seismologist, Lamont-Doherty Geological Observatory of Columbia University.

Gray Overnight: Dr. Kurt S. Stenn, dermatologist, Yale University School of Medicine.

Mammoth Meat: On the Track of Ice Age Mammals, Antony J. Sutcliffe (Harvard University Press); *Exotic Zoology,* Willy Ley (Viking); *Dinosaur Plots,* Leonard Krishtalka (William Morrow); I. P. Tolmachoff account in 1929.

Moon and Mind: Nicholas Sanduleak, then an astronomer at Case Western Reserve University.

Sleep Before Midnight: Dr. Charles Pollak, director, Institute of Chronobiology, and head, Sleep-Wake Disorder Center, New York Hospital–Cornell Medical Center, Westchester Division.

Red Skies: Fred Gadomski, meteorologist, Pennsylvania State University.

Plant Respiration: The Plants, F. W. Went et al. (Time Inc.); *Botany: Principles and Problems,* Edmund W. Sinnott and Katherine S. Wilson (McGraw-Hill).

The Smell of Snow: Dan Graf, meteorologist, Pennsylvania State University.

A Red Moon: Sam Perugini, meteorologist, Pennsylvania State University.

Deadly Corpses: Dr. Laura Fisher, specialist in communicable diseases, Manhattan.

Thick Blood: Dr. Joan Uehlinger, associate director of clinical services, New York Blood Center.

Sea Monster: Harold Feinberg, senior scientific assistant, department of invertebrates, American Museum of Natural History.

Lottery Odds: Takahiro Shiota, visiting scholar, mathematics department, Harvard University.

Seeing Stars: Dr. Jerome Holzman, professor of physics and astronomy, Lehman College of the City University of New York.

Snakes in Ireland: Dr. Charles W. Myers, curator, herpetology department, American Museum of Natural History.

Moon on Horizon: Dr. Neil deGrasse Tyson, director, Hayden Planetarium, American Museum of Natural History.

Death Rattle: Dr. Mark Smith, chairman, department of emergency medicine, George Washington University Medical Center.

Nosebleeds: Dr. Mark Smith.

Dew on the Canoe: Dan Graf.

Egg Balancing: Dr. Andrew F. Cheng, physicist, Johns Hopkins University.

Whirlpools: Dr. Joseph L. Reid, professor emeritus, Scripps Institution of Oceanography.

Curve Balls: New York Times accounts.

Eve's Ribs: Dr. Clyde Collins Snow, independent forensic anthropologist.

Cactus and Spiders: Desert Museum, Tucson, Arizona; Dr. Clifford S. Crawford, professor of biology, University of New Mexico, Albuquerque; Dr. Jan Harold Brunvand, folklorist, University of Utah, Salt Lake City.

The New York Times
Second Book of Science Questions and Answers

225 New, Intriguing, and Just Plain
Bizarre Inquiries into Everyday
Scientific Mysteries

Edited by Henry Fountain

Contents

Chapter 1	REACHING FOR THE STARS	*3*
Chapter 2	DOWN TO EARTH	*23*
Chapter 3	THE WEATHER, RAIN OR SHINE	*37*
Chapter 4	FOOD, GLORIOUS FOOD	*48*
Chapter 5	FLORA! FLORA! FLORA!	*59*
Chapter 6	ALL BUGS GREAT AND SMALL	*71*
Chapter 7	IT'S A ZOO OUT THERE	*85*
Chapter 8	SECRETS OF CATS AND DOGS	*105*
Chapter 9	ANIMAL AVIATORS	*114*
Chapter 10	HOW HUMANS GET THAT WAY	*124*
Chapter 11	OUR BODIES, OUR ACHES AND PAINS	*135*
Chapter 12	THINGS YOU'VE ALWAYS WANTED TO KNOW	*155*
Chapter 13	EAT, DRINK, AND BE HEALTHY	*171*
Chapter 14	BATTLEGROUND: THE BODY	*187*
Chapter 15	WAYS MODERN AND ANCIENT	*204*
	NOTES ON SOURCES	*219*

Preface

Back when I was in college, a favorite bit of graffiti scrawled on bathroom stalls all over campus posed the age-old question: What is reality?

That must be one of the few questions that has never been asked of C. Claiborne Ray, who since 1988 has been responding to queries about science from *New York Times* readers every week in the paper's Science Times section.

Although the question has never been asked, Claiborne answers it all the time. For making sense of science is, at its heart, making sense of the real world. So when readers write to ask if the universe is rotating, or what makes the holes in Swiss cheese, or how high a housefly can fly, Claiborne's answers build up their—and our—understanding of reality, bit by bit.

Times readers are curious. They want answers to easy questions, like why plants grow straight up, and to questions that have stumped the experts for ages, like whether a guinea pig is a rodent. They want to know about creatures large (whales), small (dust mites), and in between (bears and chipmunks).

They want to know all about themselves, too: why their feet hurt and their eyes are sore, and what that thing dangling in the back of their throats is. They want to know if they can live exclusively on pizza—though why they want to know this is beyond me—and why they can't keep their eyes open after lunch.

They are curious about worlds beyond Earth. They want to know, for instance, if Pluto will ever run into Neptune, or if it's possible that alien civilizations are watching *I Love Lucy* reruns as we speak. And occasionally they ask a famous epistemological question, like: How many angels can dance on the head of a pin?

But mostly they hunger for knowledge about our world, about AIDS and the common cold, about clouds and trees and rivers and ice and hundreds of other things—225 things in total in this book.

Claiborne takes on all comers. In this she is aided by experts who are kind enough to share *their* understanding of reality. Those who aided Claiborne are acknowledged in the Notes on Sources at the end of this book.

There are no questions left unanswered in this, the second volume of *The New York Times Book of Science Questions and Answers*. But there are plenty of questions left unasked. Readers seeking answers to those will have to wait for future volumes. Or perhaps the responses that Claiborne provides here will inspire readers to go out and find some answers of their own.

—HENRY FOUNTAIN

The New York Times

SECOND BOOK OF

Science
Questions
and
Answers

CHAPTER 1

Reaching for the Stars

BIRTH AND DEATH

Q. Are stars all burning out, or are new ones forming?
A. Stars are being born as well as dying, but the rate varies greatly from galaxy to galaxy.

Stars form from huge clouds of dust and gas. If a cloud begins to contract because of its own gravity, its interior heats up as gravitational energy is converted to heat energy, reaching millions of degrees, and nuclear reactions begin that change one element into another, releasing energy.

The pressure tends to expand the cloud back out, but eventually equilibrium is reached. That is essentially what a star is—a mass of gas at equilibrium between inward pressure from gravity and outward pressure from nuclear reactions.

A star has a finite lifetime because it is burning fuel. For 90 percent of its life, it burns hydrogen into helium. When the hydrogen is used up, the pressure decreases, but gravity never disappears, so the star contracts until the temperature climbs again, this time reaching hundreds of millions of degrees, while reactions convert helium to carbon and oxygen. The star can then remain stable for a briefer time. Eventually the star dies, when the reactions no longer produce energy, but only consume it.

IN A SPIN

Q. Is the universe rotating?

A. Most astronomers would say no. There is no known mechanism that would give the universe so much angular momentum, or spin, at its beginning, and few mechanisms for adding spin later.

To know for sure if the universe rotates, scientists would need to know the velocities of millions of galaxies, over all regions of the sky and out to very great distances. Analyses of these velocities would be necessary to see if they indicated a common center about which galaxies were rotating, and a sense of direction on average.

Since it may be a while before the velocities of millions of galaxies are known, astronomers are trying to answer a simpler question: Are there regions of space toward which large numbers of galaxies are moving as a group?

Death by Black Hole

Q. What would kill you if you fell into a black hole?
A. You might not die right away, but you would eventually be pulled apart by the force of gravity. As you fell in and even afterward, you might not lose consciousness, but the pull of gravity on your feet would be stronger than on your head, and you would be stretched, then torn apart. The difference in force is called the tidal force and is like that in the ocean, except in more extreme form. The force would be less if it was a big enough black hole; in a small black hole it might kill you before you disappeared beneath the event horizon, the edge of the hole.

But even in a larger black hole, the tidal force always gets you in the end. Once you fall in, you can't avoid falling toward the center, and the force would kill you before you reached the center. How long it would take depends on how big the black hole is. If it was big enough so that the tidal force didn't kill you before you fell in, you might have an hour or several hours before being torn apart. In a small one, such as one that forms when a star collapses, you wouldn't have much time, perhaps a thousandth of a second. That would happen with a run-of-the-mill black hole, like those that might be found in the Milky Way Galaxy.

Averting Your Eyes

Q. When I look at a constellation, I can see the fainter stars better out of the corner of my eye. Why?

A. Because the eye has two kinds of receptors, cones for fine resolution and color and rods for dim light, and the rods tend to be located around the periphery, for viewing the edges of the field of vision.

Cones are extremely good at high definition and for precise positioning of pinpoints of light. Rods don't give nearly as fine resolution and don't distinguish colors, but are much more sensitive. In effect, rods serve as night-vision sensors.

The result is that when you go out at night, you can clearly see the bright stars and planets at the center of your eye, but you can see the fainter ones out of the corner of your eye. Astronomers call this averted vision. For example, if they look with the unaided eye straight at a galaxy they know is there, they may not see it, but if they look off to one side, they can easily see the fuzzy gray patch that is the galaxy.

Cameras, too, tend to give up resolution and sensitivity to color when they achieve better sensitivity to low light levels.

SEEING STARS

Q. Why can't you see the stars in photos or videos taken by astronauts?
A. Such pictures do not ordinarily show stars because the stars are not bright enough in comparison to the nearby Sun and the things it shines on.

Virtually all of the astronaut photos are of objects brightly illuminated by the Sun. To capture them on film without overexposing the image, you need a relatively short exposure, which does not provide enough time for the film to capture images of stars. If there is no other strong light source in the picture, however, a photo can show stars.

A SOUTH STAR?

Q. What is used as a pole star in the Southern Hemisphere, where navigators can't see the North Star?
A. The closest thing to a south star for navigators south of the equator is a pair of stars in the Southern Cross, Crux Australis (or just Crux to astronomers). Alpha Crucis (its brightest star) and Gamma Crucis (the third brightest) point almost straight to the south celestial pole.

The striking Southern Cross, which has four stars brighter than the second magnitude in a cross or kite shape, takes up only 68 square degrees of the sky. The area defined by the Southern Cross has other interesting features, notably the Coalsack Nebula, which looks like a round blank spot in the sky but is actually a cloud of gas-laden dust that blocks the background starlight, and the Jewel Box cluster, designated NGC 4755, an open cluster of more than 100 stars surrounding Kappa Crucis, which is bright red in a modest telescope.

HELLO OUT THERE!

Q. In the search for extraterrestrial intelligence, or SETI, what kinds of signals would be considered evidence of transmission by intelligent life? How would scientists respond?

A. Such a transmission might take many forms, but would probably encode mathematical formulas. The reply would depend on the content; it would not be made by scientists, but would come after extensive international consultation.

As for verification, the main feature distinguishing signals produced by a transmitter from those produced by natural processes is their spectral width—that is, how much room on the radio dial they take up. As far as scientists know, any signal less than about 300 hertz wide is artificially produced.

Other telltale characteristics might be coded information, like the message beamed from the Arecibo telescope in 1974, which included data like the senders' location (third rock from the Sun, in the case of Earth). Another important test would be a confirming observation of the same signal at another radio telescope.

Once confirmed, the discovery would be announced based on a plan set up by six international space agencies. First, the scientific community would be notified through the International Astronomical Union and the United Nations. Then international authorities would draft a reply.

SITCOMS IN SPACE

Q. How far out in space could Earth's television and radio signals be detected?
A. The speed of light can seem fairly slow when you're talking about communicating across galaxies. FM

broadcasts and the earliest television programs from, say, half a century of broadcasting have reached a distance of 50 light-years, or about 294 trillion miles, from Earth.

The nearest star is about 4 light-years away, and there are on the order of several thousand stars within the 50-light-year range. So the earliest episodes of *I Love Lucy* are washing over a new star system at the rate of about one system a day.

Any civilization on the receiving end would need a very large antenna to pick up the broadcasts, about the size of Manhattan, but scientists suggest it could be done. But the chances that one star in a few thousand had some sort of civilization might be a big overestimate.

SHINE ON, HARVEST MOON

Q. Is the harvest moon brighter than other full moons?
A. Ordinarily, the mid-September harvest moon is no brighter than any other full moon, but it does provide more hours of moonlight.

In autumn, the orbital path of the Moon and its visibility in the sky combine so that it stays above the horizon for an unusually long time at the full moon and a day before and after.

The brightness of the Moon is determined by how much sunlight falls on it, which is pretty much constant; how much appears to be lit up from where we see it, from crescent to full; and how high it is in the sky. The higher the Moon is, the more light we see, because it has a shorter path through the dust and smog of the atmosphere.

In 1997, the harvest moon of September 15 was the brightest of the year, by a small margin, because it came within a few hours of perigee, the Moon's closest approach to Earth. The difference in brightness between the Moon's closest approach and farthest point amounts to 12 to 13 percent. It was also the largest full moon in angular size; its apparent diameter, normally about 30 arc-minutes, was 32 or 33 arc-minutes.

The varying Earth-Moon distance is why solar eclipses are sometimes total, when the Moon completely blocks the Sun, and sometimes annular, with a ring of light visible around the Moon.

ON THE THIN SIDE

Q. Did the Moon ever have an atmosphere?
A. It has one now, though it is a very thin and highly dispersed collection of molecules, not suitable for breathing by Earthlings.

The existence of a lunar atmosphere was reported in 1933, based on observation of the Moon using a mask that filtered out moonlight in order to study the spectrum of light emitted by sodium. Although sodium is believed to be just a trace in the Moon's atmosphere, it is studied because it is relatively easy to detect and is used as a marker for other components, such as potassium, neon, argon, and helium.

A 1993 study of lunar sodium by Boston University

scientists using improved instruments determined that the atmosphere extended at least 5,000 miles above the Moon's surface. The molecules, however, are few and far between, only an estimated 10 million per cubic centimeter near the Moon's surface; Earth's atmosphere is about a billion times as dense.

The sources of the atmosphere are believed to be the release of gases from within the Moon by moonquakes (a phenomenon called outgassing) and the loosening of molecules from the surface by the impact of molecules from the solar wind or by meteorites.

A few moons of other planets have much more impressive atmospheres, like that of Jupiter's Titan, a thick haze of nitrogen and methane, and that of Europa, a thin wisp of oxygen.

MARS COORDINATES

Q. How is zero degrees longitude, the equivalent of the Greenwich meridian, determined for Mars?
A. A small, well-defined crater named Airy-0, near the planet's equator, was designated as the starting point for the 360 degrees of Martian longitude.

The satellite Mariner 9 began photographing Mars on November 13, 1971, sending back thousands of detailed pictures of the planet's surface on which to base a map. Using the information captured by this mapping project, the scientists at the U.S. Geological Survey's Center of Astrogeology at Flagstaff, Arizona, were able to refine their calculations so that the line for the prime meridian goes through the exact center of the crater, which is about three-tenths of a mile in diameter.

The zero-degree crater was named Airy-0 in honor of George Biddell Airy, a British astronomer who lived from 1801 to 1892. He became Astronomer Royal in 1835, and among his many accomplishments was the building of the Transit Circle telescope in the Greenwich Observatory's Meridian Building in 1850. The cross-hairs in the eyepiece of the telescope define zero degrees longitude for Earth.

ROCKS FROM THE RED PLANET

Q. How do scientists determine that a rock on Earth came from Mars rather than someplace else?

A. The best idea scientists have of the geochemistry of Mars comes from the two Viking robots that landed on Mars in 1976. Findings from the robots' weeks of readings of things like the Martian atmosphere are compared with the chemical signatures of meteorites found on Earth.

The first such object confidently identified as Martian was reported in 1983. The object, a rock eight inches in diameter that weighed 17.5 pounds, had been picked up in 1979 at the Elephant Moraine near McMurdo Sound in Antarctica.

Trapped in bits of glass in the object, designated EETA 79001, were some so-called noble gases—neon, argon, krypton, and xenon—strikingly similar in abundance to those of the Martian atmosphere, as determined by the Viking missions.

There are now about two dozen meteorites thought to be from Mars.

PALE IN COMPARISON

Q. Why is Venus so much brighter in the sky than Mercury, which is closer to the Sun?
A. Venus is brighter because it is much larger, because it has a reflective atmosphere, and because it makes close approaches to Earth.

First, Mercury is about 3,100 miles in diameter, compared with about 7,700 miles for Venus.

Second, there is no atmosphere surrounding Mercury, while Venus has a thick atmosphere, composed chiefly of clouds of carbon dioxide. These clouds have a very high reflectivity, causing Venus to appear to shine with great brilliance.

Third, Venus can approach the Earth much more closely than Mercury. In fact, Venus periodically comes closer to Earth than any other known celestial body, except for the Moon, as close as 25 million miles. All of these things allow Venus to shine more brightly than not just Mercury, but than any of the other planets in our solar system.

Because Mercury and Venus are closer to the Sun than Earth is, they can show phases like those of the Moon. When Mercury shines at its brightest, it appears through a telescope as a gibbous or nearly full phase. When Venus appears to shine at its most brilliant, it appears in telescopes not as a nearly full phase, but as a crescent.

ON THE TRACK OF VENUS

Q. I have been told that the Maya made precise measurements of Venus. What did they learn?

A. It would be more accurate to say that the ancient Maya of Central America, who had no telescopes, did not measure Venus itself but kept careful records of its apparent track in the sky.

Because of the relative orbits of Earth and Venus, Venus is first invisible, then appears in the morning sky, then disappears, then reappears in the evening sky, then fades from view again.

An important part of the complex Mayan calendrical system is based on the 584 days it takes for Venus to make that complete cycle. The Venus cycle was meshed with a sacred calendar of 260 days and the 365-day solar calendar to come up with a cycle of about 2,920 days, or 8 solar years, in which the calendars came out approximately even.

COSMIC COLLISION

Q. Pluto sometimes crosses the orbit of Neptune, suggesting to me that they might collide at some point. Should I worry?

A. No. Their closest approach is not close at all—about the distance between Uranus and the Sun.

One reason they cannot pass any closer is that Neptune completes its orbit three times in the time that Pluto goes around twice. This exact relationship is called a resonance.

Another such relationship, called the Kozae resonance, provides an added protection. The orbit of Pluto is not in the same plane as Neptune's but is inclined to it at an angle of about 17 degrees. When Pluto is closest to the Sun, it is about as far away from Neptune's orbital plane as it can be, and there is close to the maximum separation when the two planets are crossing at the same distance from the Sun.

If the planets didn't have these protections, a collision would have happened long ago and we would never have known about Pluto's existence. Perhaps over hundreds of millions of years they could get out of resonance, but that is a long enough period that no one would have to worry.

Pluto is not alone in the Kozae resonance; at least fifty other objects orbiting the Sun, called Plutinos, enjoy the same protection.

The Planetary Plane

Q. Why are the orbits of the Sun's planets arranged in a more or less flat plane?

A. The planets are believed by many authorities to have coalesced from a cloud of gas early in the evolution of our solar system, beginning roughly 5 billion years ago. Since the gas cloud was disk shaped, when the planets came to be within this cloud, they all formed basically along the same plane.

There is a notable exception, the tiny planet Pluto, which has an orbit that is tipped as much as 17 degrees to the plane of the solar system. It has been hypothesized that Pluto might be everything from an escaped moon of Neptune to a special type of minor planet or asteroid.

Because of its anomalous orbit and other factors, there is great debate among astronomers as to Pluto's exact status as a member of the solar system.

RING AROUND THE SUN

Q. How does a coronagraph work? How could I build one?

A. A coronagraph is an optical device that blocks the light from the Sun's disk, making it possible to observe the corona, the very thin and hot upper level of the solar atmosphere, at the edge of the disk. A lens focuses an image of the Sun onto a masking or occulting disk that prevents the light from proceeding farther into the telescope.

A coronagraph requires very high quality optics assembled in a dust-free atmosphere. Near sea level, a coronagraph would be virtually useless, because the scattered light from the Earth's atmosphere would overwhelm light from the corona. Scientists put coronagraphs high in the mountains or launch them into space.

But any telescope can be turned into a coronagraph, simply by taking it to observe a total solar eclipse. (Just remember, for safety, never to look at the eclipse directly; project the image out through the eyepiece onto a piece of paper.) Because of the happy coincidence of the Moon's size and distance, when the Moon passes directly between the Sun and the Earth, it is usually in just the right position to make a very effective occulting disk. And during an eclipse, the Earth's atmosphere is also in the Moon's dark shadow, so light scattering is not a problem.

In fact, scientists still find a total solar eclipse to be an unexcelled opportunity to study the Sun's corona.

SPACE TRAFFIC CONTROL

Q. Is there an international agency that coordinates satellite launchings?
A. The United Nations keeps a registry and a data center at NASA assigns designations, but only communications satellites are subject to practical controls.

Every satellite must be registered to a particular country, for reasons of liability under space law. A registry has been maintained by the UN Secretariat since 1962, and another registry, established under a 1976 agreement, is kept by the agency's Committee on the Peaceful Uses of Outer Space.

Registry listings include a designation, determined by the World Data Center for Rockets and Satellites at NASA/Goddard Space Center, for each satellite. The listings include details of each object's orbit, altitude, and function.

But only the International Telecommunication Union coordinates launchings, by assigning the frequency slots for transmissions so that satellites won't interfere with one another.

STEERING THE SHUTTLE

Q. Why does the space shuttle roll after launching? How does it catch up to the space station without bumping into it?

A. Shortly after the shuttle clears the launching tower, the software of its automated guidance, navigation, and control system initiates a roll command to line it up on the desired course and heading. The roll program tells the engine nozzles how much to gimbal, or swivel, to aim the shuttle properly. It goes straight up for only a short time, then rolls to take advantage of Earth's rotation under it to get into orbit.

The shuttle goes downrange to get into orbit, actually heading downrange much faster than it goes up in altitude.

As for catching up to the space station, it is useful to consider the analogy of runners on a track. The station is in the outside lane, its orbit 240 miles above Earth, where it takes 92 minutes to go around the world at 17,500 miles an hour. The shuttle, in the inside lane at a lower altitude, takes only 90 minutes a lap. Over two days, its altitude is slowly raised until it matches that of the station. With both vessels traveling at the same orbital speed, the impact speed is about an inch per second.

SCI-FIDELITY

Q. Why is it that video from the space shuttle is usually as clear as most TV pictures, while audio is nearly as scratchy as transmissions from the sixties?

A. It has largely to do with the fidelity of the microphones, not the quality of space-to-ground communications systems. The astronauts wear wireless mikes that are as light and unobtrusive as NASA can make them. An FM signal goes from the astronaut to a communications device, then is radioed through a satellite system to the ground.

The microphones are fairly low fidelity. The better they are, the heavier they are, and on the shuttle, every ounce counts. NASA is not trying to obtain broadcast quality, and as long as the astronauts can be understood, that is enough.

Astronauts are given instruction in techniques for using a microphone, like not talking directly into it and avoiding the explosive *t*s and *b*s that are likely to make the mike pop. But they have got other things to worry about, and proper mike procedure is far down on the list.

GUNSMOKE IN ORBIT

Q. If I write a murder mystery set in space, can I have one of my characters kill another by firing a gun?

A. Yes, a gun fired in space or on a space station or rocket ship should work as well as it would on Earth or possibly even better.

The laws of physics still apply in space. The path of the bullet should be fairly straight, as gravity is greatly reduced, though not entirely absent.

There may be a reduced air supply on a spaceship, and there would certainly be one outside it, so the bullet would encounter less friction and would probably continue on its path longer.

Newton's third law, that for every action there is an equal and opposite reaction, means there would still be a recoil from the explosive expellation of the bullet.

As for the explosion that gets the bullet going, an old-fashioned six-shooter should still work very well, even in the relative absence of air. Gunpowder contains its own oxidizing agent, saltpeter, formally known as potassium nitrate, or KNO_3.

Some problems present themselves for the shooter. If he is aboard a spaceship, a bullet hole could cause the loss of his own air supply; he should probably wait for a space walk.

LOST IN SPACE

Q. Astronauts who stay in space for a long time lose muscle and bone mass. Is it permanent?
A. There is growing evidence that exercise can help astronauts recover from muscle and bone losses and limit such losses.

In the near absence of gravity, bone mass decreases in the load-bearing regions of the skeleton, and muscles shrink when not used. But Michael Foale, who was on

the Russian space station Mir for four and a half months, said that he had been able to recover most of the bone density and all of the muscle he lost on Mir through weight lifting, running, and swimming. Muscle recovery took about six months; bone rebuilding, to up to 99 percent of his preflight levels, took a year.

After earlier long flights, astronauts often had trouble recovering. On the 184-day Skylab 4 mission in 1974, astronauts lost 4.5 percent to 7 percent of their bone mass and were still down about that much 5 to 7 years later.

When both Shannon Lucid and Norman Thagard spent long periods aboard Mir, he lost up to 11.7 percent of his bone mineral and 17.5 pounds of overall muscle and weight, while she maintained her weight and lost less muscle mass and bone mineral than he did, even though she was in space 73 days longer. Dr. Lucid exercised more; she put in hundreds of hours on Mir's treadmill and stationary bicycle.

Getting Home from Mars

Q. Once people finally get to Mars, how will they ever get back?

A. The current plans involve bringing along a rocket that could be launched from Mars into a low orbit, where it would meet another craft that would return to Earth. The vehicle that returns to Earth would carry some kind of Earth-entry vehicle, like a capsule or shuttle plane.

To make the return cheaper by bringing less material from Earth, the Martian atmosphere would be used to produce much or most of the fuel to get the rocket from Mars into Mars orbit.

There are two alternative plans for providing fuel. In the first version, the travelers would carry along some fuel—methane, propane, or hydrazine—to burn with oxygen from the carbon dioxide that makes up most of the Martian atmosphere.

In the other scheme, both the carbon and the oxygen from the carbon dioxide would be used. The carbon would be combined with hydrogen carried from Earth to make methane to be burned with the oxygen.

An unmanned spacecraft might be sent to Mars to make the fuel even before humans leave Earth.

CHAPTER 2

Down to Earth

FINDING THE CENTER

Q. What is meant by the term *geographic center*? How is it determined? What is the geographic center of the United States? Is that with or without Hawaii and Alaska?

A. What the United States Census Bureau calls the geographic center of area is the point on which the surface of a geographical entity would balance if the surface were a plane of uniform weight per unit of area.

For the United States, that point has been in Butte County, South Dakota, on the state's western border, since the census of 1960, the year the bureau began including Hawaii and Alaska in its calculations. If only the forty-eight contiguous states are included, the point is in Smith County, Kansas, which is roughly in the middle of the state's northern border.

The Census Bureau also determines the population center of the United States at each census. The statistical method it uses to do this assumes that the map of the United States is flat, weightless, and rigid; the population center is the point on which this surface would balance if weights of equal value were placed on it, with each weight representing the location of one person on a particular date.

For the 2000 census the point lies in Crawford County, Missouri, about 90 miles southwest of St. Louis.

FROM NORTH TO SOUTH

Q. When Earth's magnetic field reverses, do the compasses change? Would an electrical appliance run?

A. If there were a sudden overnight flip of the Earth's magnetic field, scouts might be in trouble with their compasses, but most electrical appliances would not be affected. The compass needle is just a little magnet that lines up with the magnetic field lines of Earth; these imaginary lines converge on a spot near Greenland.

In a field reversal, these fields would change, and the "north pole" of the needle would indeed try to line up with the south pole of the terrestrial magnet.

As for appliances, the magnetic field of an electric motor such as the one in a blender or refrigerator compressor is far more powerful than that of the Earth. A motor's magnetic field is typically measured in the hundreds of gauss, the unit of magnetic induction, while the Earth's is a mere half gauss, so a shift in Earth's polarity would be of little moment to a running motor.

ROCKS THAT TELL A STORY

Q. My students tell me that rocks found on Earth show that Earth's magnetic poles have reversed. Is this true?
A. Your students are right.

In the 1960s, an Australian graduate student found rocks from an ancient aboriginal campfire, perhaps 30,000 years old, that were lying in place, magnetized in the opposite direction from the present-day orientation of the earth's magnetic field. The student suggested to his amazed professor that this was evidence of a shift in the magnetic field in such a way that a compass needle would have pointed south 30,000 years ago.

Since then, studies of successive layers of cooled volcanic lava flows and of some sedimentary rocks on the ocean floor have enabled scientists to determine approximately when several reversals of the earth's magnetic field have taken place over the eons. This field of study is called paleomagnetism.

What happens is that heating destroys a rock's original magnetism; upon cooling, it becomes magnetized in the direction of the surrounding magnetic field. This is because groups of atoms in magnetizable material organize themselves in the direction of the field when the material is hot, and are then frozen in place when it cools.

SHOCKING EVENTS

Q. How do scientists distinguish between aftershocks and new earthquakes? I understand that aftershocks can sometimes occur years after the original quake.

A. It is partly a matter of definition, based on the sequence of events and on the magnitude readings and other accumulated data about a given large seismic event. Seismologists define not only aftershocks but also foreshocks.

Foreshock and aftershock are relative terms. Foreshocks are earthquakes that precede larger earthquakes in the same location. Aftershocks are smaller earthquakes that occur in the same general area days to years after a larger event or main shock and in the span of time before the level of seismic activity returns to the normal or background range. (The general area of a shock differs from fault to fault and is defined as being one to two fault-lengths away.)

Aftershocks represent minor readjustments along the portion of a fault that slipped during the main shock. The frequency of these aftershocks decreases with time.

Historically, deep earthquakes are much less likely to be followed by aftershocks than are shallow earthquakes.

Taking the Measure of a River

Q. When rivers flood, how are things like flood stage and crest determined? How do they predict when a river will crest?

A. *Flood stage* and *crest* have fairly simple definitions. The flood stage is the height of a river above which damage begins to occur, typically because the river begins to overflow its banks. The crest is the highest level that a river reaches.

Prediction is a more complex matter, involving thousands of readings of river stages and water flows and computer models of likely outcomes. The predictive models are based on experience and must be updated with changes such as each new rainfall. The U.S. Geological Survey monitors flood conditions in cooperation with the National Weather Service.

A river's stage, whether it is flooding or not, is the height of the water surface above a predetermined reference elevation. River stages are continually monitored by the Geological Survey, typically with automatic measuring devices linked to satellite transmitters, so that the data can be obtained even in extreme weather. If the stage of the streambed is known and is subtracted from the water-surface stage, then the result is the depth of water in the stream.

Monitoring devices called stilling wells are sheltered tubes linked to the water with several inlets. They "still" the waters so that momentary surface fluctuations such as waves and surges are smoothed out. Inside, a float goes up and down with the water level, moving a pulley that drives a recording device.

Other devices, called bubblers, measure changes in water level indirectly, by bubbling gas out a tube below the water surface. Changes in the pressure on the gas reflect changes in the depth of the water over the outlet.

Measuring water volume, or discharge, involves physical measurement of the cross-sectional area of the stream and the velocity of the stream. The discharge in cubic feet per second is determined as the product of the area times the velocity.

Velocity is measured by using a current meter with a propeller that is rotated by the action of flowing water. The rotation depends on the velocity of the water passing by. With each complete rotation, an electrical circuit is completed and recorded. A stream is marked off into sections and separate measurements are taken for each segment of width, depth, and average velocity of flow. The total of these measurements is the discharge of the river.

AFTER THE DELUGE

Q. Do scientists suspect the flood described in the Bible was caused by an earthquake like the one in 1999 along the Anatolian fault line?

A. Rising sea levels worldwide following the last Ice Age are a more likely explanation for a great flood about 7,500 years ago, or 5500 B.C., that suddenly inundated areas around the Black Sea. Some scientists suggest it could have been the basis for flood stories in both the Hebrew Bible and the Babylonian epic of Gilgamesh, though others say the accounts came too long after the event to have been inspired by it.

The outlines of such a flood were reconstructed by American scientists from seismic soundings of the seafloor and sediment data gathered by a Russian research ship in 1993, tracing former shorelines. The dating of the flood was based on radiocarbon dates for the transition from freshwater to marine organisms in the cores.

Before the flood, the scientists say, the Bosporus was a narrow spillway carrying freshwater from the Black Sea to the Aegean and Mediterranean. Then there was an abrupt rise in the level of the Black Sea, perhaps a foot a day at the height of the flood, as the flow of water through the Bosporus reversed in a great torrent. In less than a year, the Black Sea became brackish and its level rose as much as 500 feet. Land around it was inundated at a rate of half a mile to a mile a day, leaving about 60,000 square miles of formerly dry land covered by water.

HOW MURKY WATER GETS THAT WAY

Q. Gazing upon the clear, aqua-colored water ringing Bermuda, I wondered why southern waters look that way while shallow waters off New Jersey, for example, are murky. What accounts for the difference?
A. Questions of pollution aside, the answer, oceanographers say, is that cold northern waters tend to teem with great concentrations of tiny plants and animals (phytoplankton and zooplankton), while southern waters are (in terms of numbers of individual organisms) empty deserts, with a few species-rich oases, such as coral reefs and waters fed nutrients by river runoff.

Phytoplankton need sunlight, nutrients, and carbon dioxide to thrive. Cold waters are richer in nutrients like oxygen and in carbon dioxide because the water molecules move more slowly than they do in warmer waters, allowing more dissolved gases to stay dissolved. The result is seasonal crops of the phytoplankton, which in turn feed the zooplankton.

This rich soup of microscopic plants and animals and decaying plants makes cold northern waters appear murky. By contrast, a tropical sea has almost nothing suspended in the water to refract light or block the view.

PUTTING THE PRESSURE ON WATER

Q. Is the freezing point of water altered by pressure? Why does deep sea water not freeze?

A. The freezing temperature of water drops about 1 degree for every 75 of the units of pressure called atmospheres, but the change is small compared with the difference even one atmosphere of pressure makes in raising the boiling point. (One atmosphere is equal to 14.69 pounds per square inch.)

Why deep sea water does not freeze depends less on pressure than on two other factors, salinity and heat. The ocean is salt water, which interferes with the freezing process and lowers the freezing point, and at depths of a mile or so, there is considerable heating from inside the earth.

At normal atmospheric pressure, water freezes at 32 degrees. But when water is compressed to about 20,000 atmospheres and cooled, other varieties of ice form, with different molecular arrangements and linkages among hydrogen and oxygen atoms.

The form called Ice II is 12 percent denser, and Ice III is 3 percent denser. The known types go up to Ice X, beyond the infamous "Ice Nine" in Kurt Vonnegut's 1963 novel *Cat's Cradle.*

Ice IX exists, but it does not have the properties Vonnegut gave it, like forming at room temperature and being able to spread quickly. It was discovered after the novel came out, so his version was based on good speculation.

THE TREELESS PLAINS

Q. If trees grow out of rocks with virtually no soil, why were there no trees to speak of on the prairies of the Great Plains?

A. One important reason is that the complex ecology of the prairie environment is formed by a cycle of fires and regrowth of a succession of fire-tolerant plants, and trees do not survive the periodic fires. The other limiting factor is a dry climate, affecting trees more than grassland plants, which hoard water.

The fires sustained the prairies by clearing dead thatch, fertilizing the soil, and destroying trees. Perennial grasses, with their extensive root systems forming an underground sponge, survived both fires and dryness.

In efforts to restore remnants of the tallgrass prairie of the Middle West, ecologists have employed controlled burning to destroy invading trees that suppressed the original vegetation. These fire-adapted species included goatgrass, rattlesnake fern, ebony spleenwort, lady's tresses, and foxtail barley.

Before European settlement, the tallgrass ecosystem covered more than 220,000 square miles, from Canada into Texas and from Nebraska to the Great Lakes. In the dry season of midsummer, most of the fires there were probably caused by lightning. In spring and fall, most were probably set by Indians. The quick new growth was grazed upon by the great herds of buffalo, who left behind dead grasses and stalks that fed the next round of fires.

BENDS IN THE RIVER

Q. Do meandering rivers meander more over time or do they straighten out?

A. There are three basic channel patterns for a river: straight, meandering, or braided. Depending on such factors as terrain, soil, and water volume, different stretches of a river may show different patterns, and channels may shift over time.

There is no fixed rule for the evolution of a river's channel, but one typical progression is from meandering to even more convoluted to straight. What happens in such a case is that the flowing water, which reaches its maximum velocity at the outside of a bend, causes the greatest amount of soil erosion there. The eroded material is deposited as what is called a point bar on the inside of the bend.

The position of the strongest current shifts from side to side, and the meanders migrate and accentuate over time. The migration can be very rapid: Some Mississippi River meanders, for example, move as much as 65 feet a year. As the looping meanders become more pronounced and migrate, getting closer and closer together, they are vulnerable to being cut off during a flood. Eventually the river bypasses a loop, and an oxbow lake is formed as the main course of the river takes the straighter path, past the cutoff lake.

BIG STONES AND SMALL

Q. Farmers often have to clear their fields of big stones. Is this because the stones keep working their way up?
A. Physicists say it is not so much that big stones work their way up as it is that smaller particles work their way down.

Physicists have long known that in a mix of large and small objects, the large ones tend to end up higher while the small ones end up lower. This holds true whether the substance is powder, cornflakes, nuts, or fieldstones, and regardless of the texture, shape, or weight of the particles.

It was not until 1987, however, that scientists at Carnegie Mellon University in Pittsburgh published the results of a simulation study that appears to explain why this happens.

The scientists created a computer model based on particles left to interact with one another completely at random. With each shake of a simulated container, the particles bounce a little, lose energy, and settle down again. As particles bounce upward, gaps open up beneath them, sometimes large gaps, sometimes small, with small gaps much more common.

As the particles fall, a small particle can move down into either a large or a small gap, while a large particle can move down only if many small particles happen to have moved out of the way. That happens, but not often. So over time the small particles tend to head downward and the large particles upward.

WHEN THE EQUINOX COMES EARLY

Q. Our sixth-grade class charted the number of daylight hours based on the times of sunrise and sunset listed in the weather report. We were surprised to find that in New York City on March 17, there were exactly twelve hours of daylight, with sunrise at 6:05 A.M. and sunset at 6:05 P.M. That was three days before March 20, the spring equinox. Shouldn't that be the day with twelve hours of daylight?

A. It would be if this were an airless world with no atmosphere. However, Earth's atmosphere acts like a lens and bends, or refracts, the Sun's light above the horizon. When you see the disk of the Sun resting on the horizon at sunset, you are looking not at the Sun but at a refracted image of the Sun, which is already below the horizon.

The image lingers about three and a half minutes after the actual sunset. For the same reason, the Sun's image appears a few minutes before sunrise.

On average, the atmosphere's lensing effect adds about six or seven minutes to the duration of daylight. Day and night again appear to be equal a few days after the autumnal equinox.

SAVING LIGHT, OR WHAT?

Q. What is the rationale behind daylight saving time? You can't really "save" daylight.

A. The chief practical reason for setting the clock an hour later for a certain period of the year, so that the Sun sets later by the clock, is not to "save" daylight, but to make daylight hours coincide more closely with the time when most people use energy.

A major effect of daylight saving time is that it leaves more hours of natural light at the end of the day, reducing the time between sunset and the typical bedtime.

Energy use and the demand for electricity for lighting homes is directly connected to when people go to bed and when they get up. Bedtime for most people is late evening throughout the year. And when people go to bed, they turn off the lights and TV.

In the average home, 25 percent of all electricity use is for lighting and small appliances, like televisions, VCRs, and stereos.

Studies done in the 1970s by the U.S. Department of Transportation found that the country's electricity usage went down by about 1 percent each day of daylight saving time.

Many people have suggested that the time shift be extended or even kept all year, as has occasionally been done during wars or energy crises. But the savings depends on having people set their bedtimes and rising times by the clock, not the Sun.

CHAPTER 3

The Weather, Rain or Shine

LAYING OUT THE ODDS

Q. When weather forecasters say there is a 50 percent chance of rain tomorrow, what does that mean? And how far ahead can a reliable forecast be made?

A. When the National Weather Service forecasters use the term *probability of precipitation,* they mean that in ten instances of weather patterns similar to the one they are looking at, it rained five times.

The service keeps cumulative records, and the probability forecast is a statistic based on what has happened. For example, if a cold front is expected in mid-July in late afternoon, and it has rained seven out of ten times in such a situation, there is a 70 percent chance of rain. The forecast covers precipitation at any time in a stated period, such as today, tonight, and tomorrow.

As to how far ahead it is practical to forecast, there's a high degree of accuracy up to about three days. But after that, for four to seven days ahead, forecasts are less reliable.

Forecasters can also give a sense of what the weather might be like up to two weeks in advance as a trend—for example, wet or dry and warmer than normal or cooler than normal, based on a pattern that favors hot and dry or a pattern that favors cool and dry.

THE COLOR OF CLOUDS

Q. What determines the color of clouds?
A. A cloud's color depends chiefly on the cloud's relationship to the light of the Sun. In some cases, it depends on the color of the surrounding sky.

If a cloud covers the whole visible area of the sky, the depth of the cloud determines the color of the cloud; the deeper it is, the darker it is. As a ray of sunlight hits

the cloud, the water in the cloud can either reflect the light back toward space or absorb it. Either effect will dilute the strength of the sunlight that gets through.

If the wavelengths of the Sun's visible light, in the familiar red to violet spectrum, are not blocked but scattered equally, the result is white light. So if the Sun is shining and the cloud is not covering the Sun, in general the cloud is white.

Sometimes particles in the atmosphere and the angle of the path the Sun's rays must travel through can result in preferential scattering of wavelengths so that a particular color, like gold, predominates in a cloud. This is the same reason the sky is predominantly blue, because the blue wavelengths are the most scattered.

At other times, when the sky is orange, for example, some of that light is reflected off a cloud, just like a colored light shining on a mirror, so the cloud appears orange.

CLOUD CAPACITY

Q. Clouds seem so light and airy that they couldn't possibly hold as much water as floods down in a storm. How large must a cloud be to hold, say, a gallon of water?
A. It would take a cloud about 60 feet by 60 feet by 60 feet to hold enough water vapor to condense into a gallon of water.

The calculations assume a liquid water content of roughly between ⅓ and 1 gram per cubic meter of water vapor. The amount varies with pressure and temperature; the higher the temperature, the higher the vapor pressure and the more water a cloud can hold. (At a higher altitude the pressure would be lower, and a given volume of cloud would contain less water.)

TRAIL OF THE JET

Q. Why do contrails form?
A. Contrails, or condensation trails, are clouds of ice crystals formed when hot, moist air from aircraft engines mixes with cold, drier air in the upper atmosphere.

Contrails are similar to cirrus clouds, naturally occurring clouds found at altitudes around 20,000 feet.

Portions of the upper atmosphere are too dry to produce condensation, so aircraft flying through them do not leave contrails.

However, significant areas are cold enough and contain enough water vapor for ice particles to grow, provided small particles are already present. It is hard to make ice form from water vapor unless solid surfaces are present, and such surfaces presented by existing ice crystals are rare in the upper atmosphere. Ice can form only if the proportion of water vapor in the cold air is particularly high. In such conditions, the addition of a small amount of water vapor from an aircraft can trigger the formation of a contrail or a cloud. A somewhat similar mechanism is at work on a cold day when your moist, warm, but cloud-free breath meets cold, cloud-free air and a miniature cloud forms.

SOWING THE SKIES

Q. Whatever happened to seeding clouds to make it rain?

A. Cloud-seeding experiments and government programs continue, but in this country at least, they are not regarded as a panacea for drought. The programs are usually subject to strict controls. Some thirty-two states have enacted laws regulating who can practice cloud seeding.

Cloud seeding dates from experiments in 1946 at the General Electric Laboratories in Schenectady, New York, and usually relies on silver iodide as a seeding agent, providing nuclei for the rapid formation of ice crystals that may eventually produce raindrops.

There are some unknowns about effectiveness and safety. For example, seeding at the wrong time and in the wrong place may actually decrease rainfall. Some skeptics worry that there is a possibility of creating severe weather such as hail or floods or of increasing the rainfall in one region at the expense of another. Other scientists say the possibilities of creating hail are remote and that seeding can be suspended if there is danger of flooding.

Cloud seeding has been used for more than twenty-five years in parts of West Texas and has been an important part of water policy in Utah, one of the driest states, since 1973. There have been recent major programs in Florida, Thailand, and Cuba.

MEASURING RAIN

Q. I recently bought a rain gauge, a cylinder with a flared upper rim and a scale in inches on the side. The diameter at the bottom is about two inches and at the top about four inches. Why is it shaped and marked that way?

A. A rain gauge shaped like a megaphone is not the standard shape meteorologists use, but it should work if it has the correct ratios between the cross-sectional area at the top and the part of the gauge that actually collects and measures the water.

If this gauge was a straight-sided cylinder that did not

narrow toward the bottom, it would be very difficult to measure small amounts of precipitation. It would require the bottom inch, for example, to be divided into 100 separate markings for hundredths of an inch, and most rainfall is much less than an inch.

Meteorologists commonly use a gauge that consists of a small straight-sided cylinder within a bigger cylinder. The rain is collected by a funnel at the top of the smaller cylinder, which is only a fraction of the diameter of the bigger cylinder. The inner tube is open at the bottom. The markings on the outer tube reflect a ratio of ten to one, so that an inch of rain would reach a mark ten inches from the bottom.

IT'S RAINING HAMBURGER BUNS

Q. Why are raindrops round? Or are they?

A. Considering the physical forces on precipitation as it falls, drops would probably be more properly described as shaped like a hamburger bun, flat on the bottom but rounded on the top. The shape of the drop as it comes down is ultimately a product of the interaction between the force of gravity acting downward and air resistance acting upward.

In addition, the size of the raindrop matters. The smaller ones tend to be more spherical, while the bigger ones are probably flatter, similar to the hamburger bun. The air resistance they meet on the way down tends to flatten them on the bottom, while they retain the rounded shape on top.

When precipitation is forming in the clouds, rain often starts as snow. Once the snowflakes melt, when they encounter air at a temperature above freezing, they initially have a more spherical appearance, and they would keep that shape if there were no air.

When they encounter air resistance, they behave the way something that is spherical but pliable, like a balloon, would act when pushed upward by the palm of the hand.

BAD TIMING

Q. Why does there seem to be a thunderstorm in the Rocky Mountains every time I try to have a summer picnic?

A. Summertime conditions in the Rockies constitute a recipe for thunderstorms. The ingredients are strong sunshine coming at a direct angle to warm the land below, sharp differences in temperature between air warmed by the mountains and cooler air over adjacent plains, and enough water in the air.

Thunderstorms owe their existence to thermals, or localized pockets of warm air that rise, and the topography of the Rockies is predis- posed to create intense thermals. The sun heats a mountain chain averaging 8,000 feet in elevation much more than it heats the low-lying plains, and the mountains in turn heat the air. The magnitude of the updraft is directly proportional to the intensity of the heating, and the summer sun is the hottest.

When the resulting warm bubble of air accelerates upward because of its pressure difference, it can cool to the point that the water vapor within it condenses, and if there is enough, precipitation occurs.

It so happens that summer airstream patterns bring in plenty of moist air from both the Gulf of Mexico and the Gulf of California; at other times of the year, there is more dry air from the continent. The outcome is a cloud, rain, and a ruined picnic.

HOT AIR, COLD PEAKS

Q. If hot air rises, why do we get snowcapped mountains?

A. Hot air undoubtedly rises, because it is less dense than the cold air next to it. However, as the air moves up, it expands and gets colder. It is the same expansion-and-cooling principle that makes a refrigerator work, because the molecules are moving away from one another and slowing down as the pressure steadily decreases.

The pressure decreases because as the hot air rises, there is less and less air above that weighs down on it. Therefore, the air at higher altitudes is almost always cold, no matter how hot it was to begin with, and by the time it gets to the top of a high mountain, it is cold enough to allow for snowcapped peaks.

BENDING SOUND

Q. Does weather, especially humidity, affect how far a train whistle carries?

A. Humidity is one of several atmospheric factors affecting the propagation of sound. Heavy, muggy air actually carries sound better. Bone-dry air greatly attenuates sound.

But humidity is not as prominent a factor in affecting low-frequency sound as the bending of sound rays (or sound waves going in the same direction) by wind and the temperature profile of the air.

A steady wind blowing toward you from the sound source increases the sound, and one blowing away from you decreases it. The rays that would otherwise go out to space are bent down toward you if the wind is toward you, up if the wind is away. With some loud sounds, like artillery fire, people very close hear the sound, then there is a dead zone, and then people farther away hear it again.

This lensing effect leads to dangerous situations at unguarded railroad crossings because the whistle of a high-speed train may not be heard until it is quite close to the road.

The other lensing effect occurs in a temperature inversion, the weather pattern that traps smog in California. In a normal atmosphere, as you go up in altitude, the temperature drops. In a temperature inversion, as you go up, the temperature rises, rather than falling, and this type of temperature profile bends rays down toward the receiver.

VOLCANOES AND EL NIÑO

Q. Is it possible that warming in the Pacific Ocean is caused by undersea volcanic action?

A. Some scientists think it is possible that volcanic activity might be at least partly responsible for the periodic weather phenomenon called El Niño. This theory was inspired in part by the discovery in 1993 of the largest known cluster of volcanoes, covering an area the size of New York State. The area in question is 600 miles northwest of Easter Island, and it was found to have 1,133 seamounts and volcanoes, far more than any other area then known on land or under the ocean.

While many researchers dismiss the theory, and even proponents concede that there is no proof of cause and effect, some scientists say the idea is plausible enough to merit more research.

When the cluster of volcanoes was discovered, scientists said they were interested in determining whether periods of extreme volcanic activity underwater, like the simultaneous eruption of a dozen or more volcanoes, could be enough to set off El Niño, which alters global weather patterns every two to seven years.

When El Niño is active, a giant high pressure system centered near Easter Island drops slightly in pressure and touches off a change in Pacific currents, bringing warmer water to certain areas and colder water to others. In 1995, scientists reported that a spate of undersea quakes and lava eruptions had preceded the onset of the El Niño cycle then in effect, leading some scientists to tentatively link the seismic activity to El Niño.

INVISIBLE ICE

Q. Is black ice really black? What is it, exactly?
A. What weather reports call black ice is not black at

all; it just looks that way because it is transparent and whatever color the road's surface is shows through.

Whether ice on the road is visible depends on how it is formed. Rime ice, which is visible, forms when droplets of freezing drizzle adhere to the roadway with air trapped inside because the drops do not splatter when they hit.

Black ice, which is not easily seen, is a coating of thin
ice that is often the result of
thawing and refreezing road-
side snowbanks. It may also
come from freezing drizzle or
rain that splatters when it
hits the road, so that no air is
trapped inside.

In daylight, black ice may look like a dull patch of road surface that is darker than the rest of the highway. It is most treacherous at night, when it is difficult or impossible to spot. Unfortunately, it is also most common at night, because that is when temperatures drop, traffic flow eases, and melted snow refreezes.

Black ice should be suspected, and driving speeds should be reduced, when temperatures are near or below freezing, especially in fall and early winter, when there is no obvious precipitation on the road.

CHAPTER 4

Food, Glorious Food

THE NATURE OF THE YEAST

Q. What is the stuff that comes in yeast packages? Why doesn't it die in the sealed package?

A. Yeasts are simple one-celled plants, members of the large Ascomycetes family of funguses. The powder or cake sold for baking is billions of cells of one of 160 or so useful funguses that are called yeast. Commercial baker's yeast is a pure, selected strain of *Saccharomyces cerevisiae.* It is a "tame" yeast, raised in factories on a solution of aerated molasses, as opposed to wild yeast strains, which are almost ubiquitous in soil and on plants.

You can catch your own wild yeast in the form of sourdough starter, leaving food like milk out in the open to capture whatever stray yeasts are wandering by (mostly *Saccharomyces exiguus*) and then saving a bit of dough from each batch of bread to start the next. Commercial yeasts are pedigreed and consistent from batch to batch.

Bread yeast ferments sugar to produce alcohol, carbon dioxide, and heat. The carbon dioxide gas bubbles make the bread rise, and the alcohol evaporates. Edible yeasts, which also make beer and wine, synthesize protein, vitamins, and enzymes, and dried yeast is highly nutritious.

In 1876, Louis Pasteur demonstrated that yeast, especially bread yeast, can shift its metabolism from fermentation to oxidation in the presence of air, a shift called the Pasteur effect; oxidation is used in the commercial production of yeast. When yeast is sealed in a package and kept cool, it shuts down most of its metabolic activity, waiting for warmth and food to multiply and raise bread.

HOLES IN THE CHEESE

Q. What makes the holes in Swiss cheese?
A. The holes are made by sizable bubbles of gas produced by a special kind of bacterium in the cheese-ripening process.

There are three basic steps in producing most kinds of cheese: making curds from milk, concentrating the curds, and ripening the curds.

First, hungry bacteria, pure cultures of streptococci and lactobacilli, feed on milk sugar, or lactose, and their digestive processes make lactic acid. The acidic environment is favorable to the action of a curdling agent like rennet, a material found in cows' stomachs. The milk separates into the familiar curds and whey.

Then the solid curds are drained of most of the liquid whey and cooked, pressed, and salted to remove the rest.

The final process, ripening, the breakdown of the curd into simpler, tastier molecules, is left to the enzymes produced by a number of microbes, including the molds that produce the veins in blue cheese.

However, it is evenly dispersed starter bacteria that finish off Swiss cheeses, which are ripened from within by the starter bacteria. An additional strain of bacterium, *Propionibacter shermanii,* is included in the starter. It lives on the lactic acid excreted by the other bacteria and gives off prodigious amounts of carbon dioxide gas, which collects in large pockets, or eyes, in the curd. The bacteria also give off propionic acid, which contributes to the flavor.

The characteristic holes fail to develop properly when the casein (the bundles of protein molecules that clump into curds) has been preheated in pasteurization. In the United States, regulations require that most cheeses that are aged less than 60 days at temperatures lower than 35 degrees Fahrenheit be made from pasteurized milk. Swiss cheese is one of the few cheeses exempt from this regulation.

FORMING A SKIN

Q. What is the skin that forms on the surface of milk when it is heated?
A. It is a complex of casein, or milk protein, and calcium, and results from evaporation of water at the sur-

face of the heated liquid and the concentration and coagulation of protein there. Skimming the skin off removes significant amounts of nutrients. Skin formation can be minimized by covering the pan or whipping up a little foam; either slows down evaporation.

BUBBLING AWAY THE BOOZE

Q. Is alcohol removed from wine or liquor when it is used for cooking?
A. Wine that is simmered for a long time in a stew would probably retain only a small fraction of its alcohol, but other dishes, like briefly flambéed crepes Grand Marnier or a soup with sherry added at the last minute, would probably still have enough to be of concern to those who want to avoid it altogether.

A study first reported in 1990 found evidence that alcoholic beverages retain from 5 percent to as much as 85 percent of alcohol after cooking.

In that study, six recipes using wine or spirits were prepared according to directions and analyzed. The study found that the amount of alcohol left behind varied by the type of heat applied (simmering, baking, or flaming), the source of the alcohol (wine or spirits), the length of cooking, and the treatment of the food after preparation and storage.

A sauce made with Burgundy accompanying pot roast retained 5 percent of its alcohol after it had simmered for two and a half hours. Another wine sauce accompanying a chicken dish retained 40 percent of its alcohol. It simmered only ten minutes after the wine was added.

Forty-five percent of the alcohol in sherry used to make scalloped oysters remained after baking for twenty-five minutes. Brandy that was heated and quickly flamed before being served over cherries jubilee retained 75 percent of its alcohol. Two tablespoons of a Grand Marnier sauce, cooked slightly, retained 85 percent of the alcohol. The liqueur was added to a hot liquid sauce after it had been removed from the heat.

A slice of brandy alexander pie, made with brandy and crème de cacao, was not heated. After it sat uncovered for sixteen hours in a refrigerator, the researchers found, it had lost 25 percent of its alcohol, probably through evaporation.

In other words, there can be enough alcohol left in food to be of particular concern to recovering alcoholics, pregnant women, and children old enough to eat the table food served to the rest of the family.

However, as food writers pointed out when the study was first reported in 1990, it seems likely that further heating of the cherries jubilee and cooking of the Grand Marnier sauce would have further reduced the alcohol content.

GAUGING A PEPPER'S HEAT

Q. How is the heat of hot peppers measured?
A. The best-known method relies on the amount of a pepper extract mixed with water that a panel of tasters need to sense the heat. Invented in 1912 by Wilbur L. Scoville, a pharmacologist, the rating is given in Scoville units.

The sample is dried and mixed with alcohol; then

sugar water is added. The tasters are given shot glasses holding increasingly more dilute versions of the concoction and are asked to determine the dilution at which the pepper no longer burns the mouth.

A mild salsa might rate a puny 400 units on the scale; a jalapeño pepper might be 1,500 to 4,500, while a much hotter habanero pepper could hit 150,000.

The method relies on the subjective human palate, and scientists have increasingly turned instead to measuring the amount of capsaicin in the pepper. Capsaicin, a substance that gives the sensation of heat when it hits nerve receptors, is analyzed in terms of parts per million using computerized devices.

Substances other than capsaicin may be involved in heating up the mouth, and both ratings can vary widely from crop to crop and even from sample to sample from the same crop.

If eating a highly rated pepper causes distress, drink milk or eat yogurt; casein will help neutralize the capsaicin, while water usually does not provide relief.

PERFECT BANANAS

Q. How does temperature affect ripening bananas?

A. Temperature changes can either delay or hasten the ripening of bananas. The banana is a tropical fruit, adapted to ripen most quickly at a certain stage of its development and at a particular temperature and humidity. Bananas continue to ripen after they are harvested, with more and more of their starches converted into sugars by the action of enzymes. When harvested, bananas contain about 20 percent starch and only 1 percent sugar. By the time the fruit is ripe, the proportions are reversed.

Bananas also release comparatively large quantities of ethylene gas to help themselves ripen; the gas will even ripen other fruit put in a bag with a ripening banana.

Bananas are usually harvested while still green, cutting off the supply of nutrients at the stem, and then shipped at a temperature low enough to slow the action of the enzymes of ripening. Later, the bananas are brought back up to a temperature and humidity that let the enzymes become active again. Too high a temperature destroys enzymes, and too low a temperature can break down the cell walls of the fruit so the contents mix and the fruit oxidizes, browns, and softens abnormally.

The optimum temperature and humidity conditions for ripening are 62 to 68 degrees Fahrenheit and 90 to 95 percent relative humidity. Storage temperatures should be 53 to 56 degrees Fahrenheit.

THE TELLTALE FISH

Q. Why does fish start smelling awful in the garbage pail so much sooner than meat does?

A. Fish contains quite a bit of a substance that gives rise to two chemicals that make the rotten-fish smell, while red meat has hardly any. The chemicals are trimethylamine and dimethylamine, both derived from trimethylamine oxide, which is particularly common in the flesh of fin fish, especially cold-water, surface-dwelling ocean fish like the cod. Ocean fish start to smell faster than, say, catfish.

When the fish is killed and exposed to the action of air, its own enzymes, and bacteria, the trimethylamine oxide undergoes a chemical process called carboxylation. The products are amines, which are volatile and quite odoriferous.

Fish dealers test for the amount of amines to determine how fresh fish is. A consumer's nose knows, too, but those who do not eat fish find it more objectionable than others.

A TOMATO OF A DIFFERENT COLOR

Q. I see yellow tomatoes, among other exotic types, at vegetable stores. Do they differ in nutritional value from red tomatoes?
A. Like all vegetables and fruits, tomatoes differ somewhat in nutritional value from variety to variety, and even from season to season. For example, the U.S. Department of Agriculture lists different average nutrient contents for tomatoes harvested from November to May and for those from June to October.

Many food values are comparable for red and yellow tomatoes, or are a trade-off. For example, the amino acids are found in similar smidgens. The precursor of vitamin A called beta-carotene is found in valuable amounts in red and yellow tomatoes.

Both colors have vitamin C, though a red tomato has about three times as much. Minerals are similar, though a yellow tomato is higher in sodium. Yellow tomatoes have more niacin and folate; red tomatoes have more vitamin B_6 and pantothenic acid, and so on.

GINSENG PEDIGREES

Q. What is the difference between American ginseng and Asiatic ginseng? What about Siberian ginseng?
A. Asiatic ginseng, *Panax schinseng,* and the American wild ginseng, *Panax quinquefolius,* are closely related and similar in both appearance and effects. Siberian ginseng includes species of a different family, the Eleutherococcus family, which is not real ginseng.

There is not a big medicinal difference between the two "real" ginsengs. Each has a slightly different composition of ginsenosides, active ingredients that can be either stimulants or the opposite; American ginseng is slightly less stimulating than Asiatic ginseng.

The principal use of ginseng is to make people feel better, and there is evidence that it works, especially in older people. Its reputation in ancient Chinese medicine as an aphrodisiac is not scientifically proven.

Prepared ginseng root should be bought from a reputable source. Side effects can result from adulterants used to extend an expensive product. Makers offer different concentrations, from about 4 to 7 percent, so follow the dosage on the label.

ANATOMY OF A BAGEL

Q. How many calories are in a plain, sesame, or poppy seed bagel from a New York coffee shop? What are the ingredients and nutritional value?

A. Let us assume that you get the biggest plain, enriched bagel analyzed by the U.S. Department of Agriculture, 4½ inches in diameter, weighing 110 grams, about 3.8 ounces.

The ingredients—flour, water, salt, yeast, and malt, but no sugar, if it is a classic bagel—are boiled and then baked. They add up to 302.5 calories, the USDA says.

On a standard nutrition facts label, the bagel would boast 1.76 grams of fat, no cholesterol, 587.4 milligrams of sodium, 111.1 milligrams of potassium, 58.74 grams of carbohydrate, and 11.55 grams of protein. Vitamins and minerals include a significant amount of folate, 96.8 micrograms, from the enriched flour, but most others are present in trace amounts. A bagel preserved with calcium propionate has more calcium than one without it: 81.4 milligrams, compared with 19.8 milligrams.

Oddly, the USDA does not differentiate among plain, onion, poppy seed, and sesame bagels. Poppy seed, which the department considers a spice, not a food, would probably not add enough calories to make a weight watcher feel guilty. There are only about 15 calories in a teaspoonful, fewer calories than would be in a spoon of sugar. Sesame seeds have perhaps 26 calories in a teaspoonful, figured at a sixth of an ounce, by volume.

THE PHYSICS OF NOODLES

Q. How are "instant" cereals, rice, and other foods processed to diminish cooking time?
A. It is really a physics problem involving the interaction of water with a carbohydrate, and the process differs from food to food.

When you have a solid food that you want to be able to cook faster, such as rice, you hydrate it, then dehydrate it under controlled conditions, adjusting the chemistry and physics of the particle to maximize its ability to rehydrate. Then when you rehydrate it to cook it, it cooks much faster.

For many foods, the processing involves increasing overall surface area, so the water does not take so long to migrate through the food. For tea and coffee, it involves agglomerization, building up the particle size so the surface area increases dramatically, which makes it easier for water to be absorbed.

For some products, sugar or another hydrophilic (water-loving) additive is mixed in to speed absorption. For noodles or dried vegetables for instant soup, the process may involve quick drying in a vacuum, which puffs up the food so it will rehydrate more quickly.

CHAPTER 5

Flora! Flora! Flora!

Staying Vertical

Q. How do trees on a hillside sense the vertical so they can grow straight up?

A. Trees grow vertically because of two things: gravity and light.

Geotropism, in which microscopic particles in plant cells react to gravity, tends to make the roots grow straight down, which means that the stems grow straight up.

Phototropism tends to make plants grow vertically as well, following the direction from which light comes. Phototropism was originally called heliotropism, or bending toward the sun, until scientists found out that plants would bend toward light in general, not just sunlight. The phenomenon was studied by Charles Darwin and his son Francis, who recognized that the bending started just below the tip. But they did not discover the mechanism that caused the bending.

Subsequent researchers found that a class of plant hormone called auxins can regulate the growth of plant cells, interacting with other plant substances to direct and control the plant's final shape, both above and below the ground.

In a growing tree, auxins, produced at the growth tip, promote the elongation of plant cells. Auxins are present in greater concentrations on the darker side of the plant shaft, so those cells grow longer than the cells exposed to light. Thus, the tree bends toward the light.

IT'S EASY BEING EVERGREEN

Q. Why do evergreens keep their leaves?
A. Evergreen trees do not keep their leaves indefinitely, but rather may grow new ones before the old ones fall, or keep some and drop others over a period of time.

As any southern gardener can tell you, some broadleaf evergreens, like *Magnolia grandiflora*, drop their heavy leaves in a staggered cycle over the course of the year. Some, like the live oak, may show a heavy leaf loss in early spring, but retain a few old leaves while the new ones develop.

There is also seasonal needle loss with evergreen species of conifers, like pine, spruce, and fir trees. The leaf drop is a normal process, not a disease. The older, inner needles senesce, or grow old, turning yellow or brown, and drop from the tree after one to several years, depending on the species. By November of most years, for example, white pines may have only a year's worth of needles attached to the tree.

Austrian and Scotch pines usually retain their needles for three years. Spruce and fir needles also yellow and drop with age, but these trees retain their needles for several years, so needle drop is often not noticeable. Arborvitae and some cedar needles usually turn brown rather than yellow with age.

These general patterns of needle drop may vary from tree to tree and year to year; adverse conditions in the summer and fall may lead to a more pronounced needle drop.

Unable to Let Go

Q. Why do some trees hold on to their leaves longer than others?

A. The timing of leaf loss varies with species, site, and season. Day length and temperature are the two triggers for color change and leaf loss. The timing is usually species specific but is also related to site conditions.

For example, a fairly dry midsummer to fall in the Northeast can mean that some trees drop leaves early, before they turn, in a reaction to drought stress; leaves may also die on the tree but hang on until much later.

Species variations are also important. Norway maples normally have green and fully functional leaves that keep on photosynthesizing until two or three weeks after leaves of sugar maples have turned. If both are on a cramped site, Norway maples, with extra weeks of energy storage, may outgrow and outlive sugar maples.

Oaks keep their leaves much longer than many other species because a layer of cells that forms where the leaf stem is attached, called the abscission layer, does not form a complete barrier. In beech trees, which are in the same family, an incomplete layer is seen in younger trees, but mature beeches, twenty-five to thirty years old, form a complete layer.

There are also sex differences; for example, leaves of female ginkgo trees usually color and drop earlier than those of males. And trees near streetlights may be affected by the longer light exposure and keep their leaves longer.

TREES' PARTNERS

Q. I heard there was a fungus that helps trees absorb water. What is it?

A. What you heard about is mycorrhizae, complexes formed by beneficial fungi and plant roots. There are many different ones, and particular plant species form relationships with particular species of fungi.

There are three basic types, depending on where the complex is formed: endomycorrhizae, inside the root hair; ectomycorrhizae, outside the root hair, and endo-ectomycorrhizae, both inside and outside.

The fungus and the plant have a symbiotic relationship, meaning they help each other to thrive. Fungal cells take in some nutrients and water from the soil more easily than plant cells can, while the plant gives the fungus other resources.

Mycorrhizae have been known for many years, but only recently have plant scientists been able to isolate the strains for certain plants and reproduce them en masse for application.

Commercial mycorrhizae preparations are available for many conifers and broad-leaved trees and for certain annuals and turf. The association forms only in the fall, and the fungus normally needs to be injected into the soil.

DOOMED BAMBOO

Q. Is it true that all bamboo in the world dies off at the same time every hundred years or so?

A. No, but certain species among the hundreds or thousands of known bamboos die off all at once after their single episode of flowering. That can create problems for gardeners who cultivate a particular ornamental type.

More seriously, a mass die-off of a bamboo species in the phenomenon called gregarious flowering can endanger a species, like the giant panda, that finds its usual food source, *Gelidocalamus fangianus*, gone from a wide area.

However, flowering bamboos (and not all species are known to flower) vary widely in their cycles; the fixed periods range from a year to a few years or even more than a century. Not all species are so weakened by flowering that they die.

Gregarious flowering usually occurs when all plants from what bamboo enthusiasts call a clone (that is, offspring from a single parent, which has been repeatedly divided and distributed) flower at about the same time.

There has been extensive research on how to keep a stand of bamboo that starts to flower from dying because bamboo grown from seed may differ significantly from the parent plant. Techniques include cutting back flowering culms (or canes), fertilizing generously, and propagating by planting a section of a culm with several nodes or joints.

LOVE THAT SALT

Q. Are there plants that can survive if watered with salt water?

A. Yes, there are such plants, called halophytes. Some are natural species that grow well when the water they get has a high salt content. Others are species that scientists are tailoring for the purpose by selective breeding or crossbreeding for salt-tolerance genes.

Halophytes include grasses, shrubs, and trees. Some are edible crops suitable for areas with salty soil or irrigation water, and others are ground-cover varieties that are useful in wetland restoration.

One edible halophyte is salicornia, which produces an oil high in polyunsaturates. Another crop plant is atriplex, which yields animal feed similar to alfalfa. Still another is tecticornia, which grows in coastal mudflats and has seeds that the Australian aborigines grind into a flour.

Seawater contains 35,000 to 38,000 parts of salt per million, and researchers believe most conventional crops could not be bred to tolerate levels that high.

However, brackish water with salt levels of 5,000 to 7,000 parts per million has been successfully used in drip irrigation for some crops. Drip irrigation provides a constant trickle directly to root areas, keeping them moist but adding a small total amount of salt to the soil.

FROM SILK TO KERNEL

Q. Is it true that each strand of silk on an ear of corn represents a kernel of corn?
A. Yes, but only if pollen falls on the silk. Otherwise, a kernel does not develop. A corn plant produces corn silk surrounding each ear about two months after the plant emerges from the ground. The plant matures after about four months.

Tassels, the male part of the plant, emerge at its apex and shed pollen for a week or two, fertilizing the individual silk strands below. The silk strands grow a little more than an inch every day and continue to grow until they are fertilized.

Pollination occurs when the falling or wind-borne pollen grains are caught by these new moist silk strands. A captured pollen grain takes about twenty-four hours to move down the silk to the ovule, where fertilization occurs. The ovule then develops into a kernel.

Generally, two to three days are required for all silk strands on an ear to be exposed and pollinated. Ovules that are not fertilized will not produce kernels and will eventually degenerate. Stressful conditions, including lack of moisture, tend to dry the silk strands and pollen grains, usually resulting in a nubbin, or an ear with a barren tip.

WAITING FOR ROSES

Q. Can I grow a rose from seed? How long would it take?

A. With patience, a rose can be grown from a seed, and indeed all the Peace roses of today are descended from a plant grown in 1939 from a single seed nurtured by Francis Meilland, the hybridizer. But a random seed from a Peace rose or any hybrid would be unlikely to produce a plant like the one it came from.

As for the time it would take, a wild, unhybridized rose like *Rosa rugosa* would be relatively quick and easy to grow from seed, with little preparation; in the early fall, remove the seeds from the ripe rose hips, the fruit of the rose, and plant them.

For many other roses, however, the seeds must be refrigerated for about four weeks at about 40 degrees,

 for what gardeners call stratification, a cold period, and again for about four months, at a somewhat higher temperature, for germination, with a light on in the refrigerator. They can be nurtured in moist peat moss.

Before sprouting, seeds

can be tested for viability by seeing if they float in water. Floaters are hollow and unlikely to germinate.

The sprouts from the refrigerated seeds can be planted, preferably in sterile soil, perhaps with a cutoff plastic bottle as a greenhouse. If they survive, they may produce miniature roses in just a couple of months, previews of the color of mature roses, but not their shape. The plants and their roses should reach full size in about three years.

THE DREADED RHUBARB

Q. Are rhubarb leaves toxic?
A. While not poisonous, large quantities of rhubarb, stems or leaves, offer possible risks, and the stems may be as bad as the leaves for susceptible people. To complicate things, some rhubarb chemicals can have positive or negative effects.

In cell cultures using an extract of the entire plant, studies found some antimutagenic effects, depending on whether water or organic solvents were used.

Rhubarb also contains some chemicals called sennosides that are used as laxatives. Very large quantities can cause severe dehydration. The laxative effect may be where the idea of a poison arose, but the laxatives are in the stems, too.

When one sennoside, called emodin, is metabolized by the liver, one of the products, under alkaline conditions, has weak mutagenic effects, but in tests, emodin halted cancer cell growth in the test tube.

Rhubarb also contains oxalic acid, which is somewhat toxic. If there is a difference in the concentration in leaves and other parts, it is less significant than the fact that rhubarb has a high oxalic acid content overall. Oxalic acid scavenges calcium and magnesium, and a buildup may be risky for people genetically predisposed to kidney stones.

PLANTS AS INSECT REPELLENTS

Q. Can you use the Osage orange to repel insects?
A. It may be that the rich orange smell of the fruit, which folklore has long rumored to be an insect repellent, scares them off, or it may be that the latex-rich leaves gum up the mouth parts of insects, eventually discouraging others. You could try leaving the fruit around your house, or experiment with planting it or some of the other fragrant plants that have been reported to keep insects away.

The Osage orange, *Maclura pomifera*, a spiny shrub commonly used as a living fence in the American Southwest, is just one of the plants containing chemicals that may (or may not) help repel some or all insects. There is a wealth of lore about them, and many anecdotal reports of success, though relatively little hard data. Like the Osage orange, many of these plants are also sources of perfume fragrances.

Depending on climate and space, backyard experimenters could include some of the following candidates: marigolds, chrysanthemums, basil (for mosquitoes), rosemary (for moths), patchouli, vetiver, citronella, peppermint, spearmint, and pennyroyal. The tree spices cinnamon and cloves are also reputed to be moth repellents.

Gaining a Toehold

Q. How does mistletoe nourish itself on oak trees?

A. Members of the Loranthaceae family like the American mistletoe, *Phoradendron flavescens,* take food from the sap of woody plants through special roots called haustoria. Mistletoe also grows on other deciduous trees, including the sweet gum and red maple.

Man-Eating Plants

Q. Are there any carnivorous plants that are harmful to humans?

A. No, because even the largest carnivorous plants are only big enough to digest something the size of a frog, and the digestive enzymes they secrete are comparatively weak.

Very rarely, a rat or bird has been found drowned in the liquid contained in the bottlelike appendages that hang from the vines of *Nepenthes rajah,* a pitcher plant from the tropical highlands of Borneo. The bottles can be up to 14 inches long, with mouths as big as 7 inches.

However, frogs are more typical Nepenthes prey, and birds or rodents that get caught are probably sick animals too weak to fight their way out of the trap. Most carnivorous plants are completely harmless to something larger than a small insect.

Botanists say that the many kinds of carnivorous plants evolved to get nutrients, especially nitrogen, that are lacking in the soil or water where they grow. Some live with their traps submerged in water, eating very small prey up to the size of mosquito larvae and fish fry.

Some land-dwelling carnivores consume gnats, flies, and moths; others eat ants and other crawling insects. The most familiar carnivorous plants, Venus flytraps, will capture and digest any insect or spider that happens their way.

CHAPTER 6

All Bugs Great and Small

BUGS ON THE WINDSHIELD

Q. When I was a child, clouds of bugs used to hit the windshield on vacation drives. What were they?

A. Depending on the part of the country, time of year, and time of day, they could have been anything from flies to moths to dragonflies. Especially in the South, the most likely culprit is flies, and fly populations are highly cyclical.

In coastal Florida, Alabama, Mississippi, and Louisiana, lovebugs—the bibionid fly species *Plecia nearctica*—form clouds twice a year during their spring and fall mating seasons. The problem comes and goes, with some years being much worse than others.

Lovebugs form linked pairs during their nuptial flights. The windshield smashing may occur in mating season.

In Florida, it was discovered that part of the problem

was that the flies were breeding and feeding in decaying grass clippings along the highways, left there by state mowing projects. The state changed the mowing schedule.

A Backyard Census

Q. How many insects and other arthropods might you find in a northeastern backyard?

A. The number of individuals and species would depend on many variables, like soil condition and chemical use, but if the first few inches of soil were included, the totals might be impressive.

One survey of backyard insects in the 1930s collected 1,402 species, including 467 butterflies and moths, 258 flies, 259 beetles, and 167 wasps, bees, and ants, from a 75-by-200-foot garden in a northeastern New Jersey suburb. The survey did not include arachnids like spiders and mites.

A suburban lawn is a monoculture, a single-crop field, and since, in general, biodiversity increases with complexity, the number of large, easily visible arthropod species on the surface of the soil or in the grass itself would be fairly low. One estimate is 25 to 50, with the number greatly reduced if pesticides had been used.

However, if the fauna of the litter layer and the top few inches of the soil is included, a survey could find huge numbers of individuals of springtails and mites, as many as tens of thousands per square yard. Up to 50 species of springtails per square yard have been found in woodland soil.

THE SWARMS OF THE ANNOYING

Q. Why do gnats and mosquitoes and other annoying insects get together in swarms?

A. Many insect species swarm, both the beneficent (like honeybees) and the irritating (like mosquitoes). In many cases, springtime swarms consist of groups of males all looking for suitable mates. Pheromone signals probably keep the group together. As insect mating, egg laying, and hatching tend to take place in synchronized waves, it is not surprising that a generation emerges with one goal.

Formation of mosquito swarms, which vary from species to species, can depend on variables like available space, lighting conditions, and winds. Mosquito swarms often focus on a defined point like a bush or hedge, where the air is undisturbed, and there are even reports of swarms that form over the head of a person and follow him around as he slowly walks.

Other large insect groups, all moving in the same general direction, may be migratory insects, like monarch butterflies, or social insects setting up new colonies.

The next time a cloud of mosquitoes buzzes around your head, count yourself lucky. The desert locust, *Schistocerca gregaria*, can blacken the sky for miles around. A swarm in Kenya in 1954 was estimated to cover more than 77 square miles.

Aphid Husbandry

Q. Do aphids milk ants or vice versa? In any event, how can I rid my houseplants of the aphids?

A. Several ant species "herd" the small pear-shaped insects called aphids and "milk" them for a sweet fluid that they excrete after feeding on sap from roots or leaves. They are sometimes called dairying ants. Ants that "milk" root-eating aphids often dig them chambers to serve as "barns."

The ants protect their aphids, carry them from plant to plant, and gently stroke them with their antennae to get them to release droplets of the liquid, called honeydew. Some species of yellow ants called Acanthomyops feed almost exclusively on honeydew harvested from roots by aphids.

Aphids harm houseplants and some crops by sapping them of their fluid and sometimes by coating the leaves with so much honeydew that mold grows, inhibiting photosynthesis.

Agricultural extension agents recommend some steps to counter aphids on houseplants without using commercial insecticides. First, isolate new plants until it is obvious that they are not infested, or remove the infested leaves. If an infestation is advanced, try swabbing or spraying the leaves with rubbing alcohol or soapy water, repeating at intervals of a few days to get rid of eggs and new hatchlings; rinse off the soap. Or buy ladybugs, which feed on mites, not plants.

Lines of Communication

Q. Watching ants traveling in a line, I noticed they meet head-on for a moment, then continue on their way. Is this some type of communication?

A. If there was any foreleg contact or waving about of antennae by the ants, some communication may have been involved. But the wide range of communication methods among ants is weighted heavily toward chemical signals, and visual signals have not been solidly documented.

Ant communication, which has been extensively but not exhaustively studied, includes tappings, chirplike grating noises, strokings, graspings, nudgings, tastings, and streakings of chemicals, as well as activities like the exchange of special eggs and anal secretions.

In a typical worker ant, more than ten organs have been implicated in producing just one class of chemical signal. However, a typical ant colony operates with only about ten to twenty signals, most of them chemical.

If a fire ant is laying a food trail using such signals and meets another worker, the homeward-bound worker may turn to face her, rushing into her before continuing on or even pausing briefly to shake her, but researchers think this behavior may serve only to enhance the effects of the chemical being used.

Calling In Reinforcements

Q. Are there really caterpillars that scream to protect themselves? If so, what types? Can we hear the sound they make?

A. While they do not exactly scream, some caterpillars have noise-making organs, and the sound they produce is used to call in troops of ants to protect them from predatory wasps. The noise has an average frequency of 1,877 hertz, which would be audible to human ears if it were not so very faint.

Some noisy butterfly larvae species belong to the Riodinid family and live in the tropical rain forests of the New World. Members of the Lycinid family, which has a worldwide range, also make sounds, for similar purposes.

The caterpillars' sound-producing organs and their relationship with ants were first reported by Dr. Philip J. DeVries in research published in 1990. There are actually two sets of organs: just behind the head is a pair of grooved rods, and rows of projections resembling guitar picks protrude from the top of the head. Dr. DeVries described the noise as being like the sound of a comb running over the edge of a table. The caterpillars reward the ants with amino acid secretions that the ants feed on.

Butterflies over Broadway

Q. In mid-September, I saw many monarch butterflies headed south in midtown Manhattan. Is this unusual? Do they congregate around New York City somewhere?

A. That is the right time of year for the eastern monarchs' migration, and they do congregate in Cape May, New Jersey, by the thousands.

The monarchs seen in and around New York City are flying through on the way to their wintering sites in the mountains of central Mexico. The butterflies seek out microclimates congenial to an overnight rest and are off again in the morning.

The migration happens every year, but is much more noticeable in some years because insect populations are highly variable. Factors such as wind patterns may influence the exact route. However, each year there are reports of sightings in Manhattan, even of big groups flying by office windows thirty floors up.

The eastern population of monarchs overwinters in the Transvolcanic Range in Mexico, on the border of the states of Michoacán and Mexico. The site, 10,000 feet above sea level, was discovered in 1975. The western population winters on the coast of California.

Fat for the Flight

Q. With its small body mass, how does a monarch butterfly obtain enough energy to migrate 1,800 miles?
A. The energy is gathered from nectar, and the butterflies that make the trip, those born in the early fall, are able to convert nectar into fat.

Those born in September know to fill up on nectar. Their abdomens get really large. Unlike the other generations, these monarchs have a little area of fatty tissue where the sugar of the nectar is converted into fat. They can live off this cushion in winter and need only water to rehydrate their bodies.

Monarchs born in September or late August live seven, eight, or sometimes nine months. Their children, grandchildren, and great-grandchildren live just a month. By the time you get to the great-great-grandchildren, you're back at September.

DRAGONFLY DIPPING

Q. I have seen dragonflies that appear to be dipping their abdomens, not their mouth parts, into the water. What are they doing?

A. You may have observed female dragonflies depositing their fertilized eggs into the water, where they will hatch into larvae. The eggs are sometimes inserted into underwater plant stems and sometimes smeared onto the surface of the water.

More than three hundred eggs may be laid at one time. Sometimes several hundred females lay their eggs in the same spot, producing large egg masses up to two feet across.

HIGH FLIES

Q. How high can a housefly fly? Are some insects better adapted than others to high flight?

A. How high an insect can fly depends on air temperature. Generally speaking, most insects can fly as long as they stay in air above 50 degrees Fahrenheit. If the air temperature at ground level is 90 degrees, the 50-degree border is around 6,000 feet; if ground temperatures are in the 70s, the ceiling is around 3,600 feet.

Insects have the ability to adjust their altitude, looking for the temperature they want to fly in. When it gets too cold, they tend to fold their wings and drop.

A number of insect species are adapted for long-range migration. Some of these species have large bodies and wings, but some that have very small ones, like leafhoppers, also migrate long distances. All seem to sense approaching storm fronts and ride the fast-moving winds ahead of them. They use energy to get up into the fast-moving air, then glide as the storm front moves them along.

The fast-moving air begins at the planetary boundary layer, about two and a half times the height of the largest surface obstruction around. So if there are 80-foot trees, it would begin at roughly 200 feet.

Bites in the Sunlight

Q. Since I seldom see mosquitoes in daylight, can I avoid bites by going out only in the sunshine?
A. Unfortunately, no. There are many species of mosquitoes, perhaps 3,000 worldwide and 150 in the United States. The females, which seek a blood meal to produce eggs, have many different kinds of feeding habits.

While many of the mosquitoes that carry disease are

most active at dawn and dusk, even they may be roused to bite if their resting places are invaded in the bright daytime. Others may feed all day.

For example, the Asian tiger mosquito, *Aedes albopictus*, which is associated with the transmission of dengue, eastern equine encephalitis, and dog heartworm, is a very aggressive daytime biter, with peaks in early morning and late afternoon.

The dark ricefield mosquito, *Psorophora columbiae*, which in large numbers has been reported to kill livestock, has females that are furious biters, day or night. Luckily they prefer the blood of cattle to that of humans.

Aedes trivittatus, while not a major disease carrier, is a severe nuisance, because it attacks in swarms. Its bite is more irritating to humans than that of many other mosquitoes, and it does not hesitate to bite in bright sunlight when its haunts are invaded.

MORE OF A STING

Q. Is the toxicity of a scorpion's sting related to its size?

A. Scorpion experts have found that scorpion species with smaller and more slender claws typically have more toxic venom. But just as with bee stings, any scorpion's sting can be fatal to a person who is severely allergic to it.

The toxicity of the venom also varies by species and prey. A species' particular cocktail may contain many chemicals, some aimed at insects and some toxic only to mammals.

The different chemicals cause many different kinds of damage and symptoms. Some merely produce pain and swelling and are believed to be protective. Some, used for killing prey, cause severe neurological damage by blocking chemical channels in nerve cells. Some cause direct damage to the heart muscle. In humans, the toxic effects can lead to respiratory paralysis, extremely high body temperatures, dangerously low or high blood pressure, a rapid heartbeat, and other conditions.

The stings of most American scorpion species are not usually fatal; for example, the Arizona Poison and Drug Information Center says that only one of the thirty species in the state is regarded as life-threatening. But stings are much more perilous for children.

Long Live the Spider

Q. How long do spiders live?
A. With some exceptions, spiders in temperate regions have one-year life spans, with the females outliving the males by weeks or months.

Perhaps the most interesting exceptions belong to the family Lycosidae, or wolf spiders. Some members of this family live in elaborate silk-lined underground burrows. The females protect their eggs in sacs that they carry everywhere and care for assiduously. In burrowing species, the female may even carry the sac to the surface to be warmed by the sun.

After hatching, the spiderlings may spend the winter in the home burrow and may not reach full maturity until the second year, eventually moving out to build their own burrows.

The life span of a black widow spider depends on when it is hatched. Those hatched in late spring or early summer reach maturity in about four months, before cold weather, but may delay egg laying until spring and then die a few days later.

Those that emerge later may find their development severely retarded by the cold and the shortage of food. Only when warm weather arrives again do they mature. They may live a year and a half before reproducing. In the laboratory, some have lived through two or three summers.

THE CHIRPING THERMOMETER

Q. Do crickets chirp more slowly as the temperature drops in the fall?

A. In some species of cricket, the number of chirps per minute used by the male to attract females rises and falls along with the outside temperature, and can in fact be used as a rough thermometer.

Since insects are small (with a high surface-to-volume ratio) and cold-blooded, with relatively slow metabolisms unless they are exerting themselves, their temperatures reflect the outside temperature. Muscular activities

such as chirping tend to vary with that temperature.

The formulas for determining the surrounding temperature depend on counting the chirps in a certain number of seconds, usually 13 to 15, and adding a constant number, usually from 37 to

40. The most carefully studied species for this purpose is the widely distributed snowy tree cricket, *Oecanthus fultoni Walker*. Scientists have determined that by counting how often it chirps in 15 seconds and adding 40, a consistent approximation of the temperature in degrees Fahrenheit can be obtained.

Each species makes a different sound, and the chirping speed varies between species as well. There are silent crickets among the 3,000 or so known species (they use scent to attract mates) and even a few katydids that chirp faster to warm themselves up.

SOURCE OF THE FLIES

Q. When I bring fruit into my insect-free home, fruit flies seem to materialize. Are they drawn to the fruit or do they come in with it?

A. It is hard to be sure, but depending on when the flies show up, you can make an educated guess.

Flies have a particular amount of time to spend as egg, larva, and pupa before they climb out of the pupa. In the common fruit fly, this takes about eight to perhaps ten or twelve days. So if you buy a banana and bring it into your warm home and flies appear immediately or in two or three days, more than likely they came out of the banana skin. If the fruit sits around for ten days or so before flies appear, more than likely it drew flies that came in from outside.

The buyer would not see pupae embedded in the fruit's skin because they are only 2 to 4 millimeters (about 0.08 to 0.16 inches) long.

MIGHTY MITES

Q. What are dust mites? What can be done about them?

A. Dust mites are often referred to as tiny insects, but they are not. Instead, they are arachnids, part of the large group of eight-legged creatures that includes spiders and ticks. Several species of dust mite belong to the genus Dermatophagoides, a name that describes in Latin their way of life: They live mostly by devouring the skin cells that human beings shed.

Dust mites are very small; about 7,000 could fit on a dime. They set off allergic reactions when their feces and jettisoned external skeletons are inhaled. The proteins that cause the reaction are now being isolated in the hope of finding ways to fight allergies and asthma.

Dust mites thrive in human clothing, decorative fabrics, upholstery, and especially bedding. Warm, moist sleeping bodies provide them with an ideal environment.

Fighting mites involves cutting off their sources of warmth, food, and water, especially in the bedroom. Vacuum regularly, but wear a mask to avoid breathing in the dust you stir up; try an air filter. Remove rugs, curtains, upholstered chairs, and other fabric items. Keep mattresses and pillows in mite-proof plastic covers, and use synthetic pillows that can be washed rather than feather pillows. Launder clothes and bedclothes frequently, preferably in hot water.

Keep temperatures and humidity low, if possible, because dust mites prefer high humidity and temperatures above 68 degrees Fahrenheit.

CHAPTER 7

It's a Zoo Out There

How the Fittest Stay That Way

Q. How come zoo animals such as lions, not to mention my pet cat, seem to lie around all day and yet stay fit?

A. It is partly a matter of appearances, with zoo animals less active at peak visiting hours, and partly a matter of normal rhythms of carnivore life. Lions in the wild are normally inactive for twenty to twenty-two hours a day because they need to conserve their energy for hunting, never being quite sure where their next meal is coming from.

As for the house cat, although it does know when the next can will be opened, the basic behavior pattern is the same. Even a cat that has never seen real prey will stalk a butterfly through the window. Young animals can afford to do that, but from an evolutionary point of view, old lions especially must conserve their energy for the business of surviving. At some point in life, when the metabolism does begin to slow down, a sedentary cat may become overweight.

Of zoo animals, many are from hot climates and are most active in early morning and late afternoon, zookeepers say. They sensibly lie low from eleven to three on hot days.

Zoo animals have the benefit of a nutritional staff that prepares diets as close to natural as possible. Modern zookeepers also make sure that animals mimic natural behavior, living in groups, with plenty of space, and foraging and competing for food. Some do tend to get chunky, like the dominant animal in a group that always gets its fill, but most stay lean.

GETTING THE MOST FROM GRASS

Q. People are told to eat a well-balanced diet, but if cows eat only grasses, how do they obtain all the nutrients their cells need?

A. All animals need various nutrients—things like amino acids and vitamins—to build and maintain their cells and to provide energy for bodily processes.

Carnivorous animals get many of these nutrients ready-made from the other animals they eat. Vegetarian animals get the nutrients not just by chemically changing plant material through enzymatic processes but also from the action of beneficial fermentation microbes in their guts and from the bodies of the microbes themselves.

Omnivorous animals, like humans and pigs, can obtain their nutrition from both animal and plant food, or from either one.

In the cow, for one vegetarian example, there is a multi-stomach system. In the large, multi-compartmental forestomach, microorganisms ferment plant cellulose and release volatile fatty acids; the acids come into contact with cells with a large surface area that absorb them to provide much of the energy supply.

Later on in the digestive process, chewed and rechewed food enters a true stomach and intestines, more like those of humans, where it is mixed with more digestive juices that change the chemistry of the food. There, amino acids and other nutrients are absorbed and the bodies of the microorganisms from the forestomach are also digested.

THE MIGHTY WOLVERINE

Q. A nature TV program showed a wolverine driving three much larger wolves away from its kill. How is this possible?

A. Pound for pound, a 40-pound wolverine, formally *Gulo gulo,* is simply stronger than many of its adversaries and is capable of killing animals much larger than itself. Wolves are probably aware of this.

For example, a wolverine's jaws are so strong that it can completely crush a frozen caribou's large bones, part of its adaptation to life in a wintry climate. It can also use its relatively large flat feet like snowshoes in the efficient pursuit of hooved animals over soft, deep snow. Its main food in winter is reindeer or caribou, which it may kill or scavenge. It also devours smaller rodents and occasionally berries.

The wolverine is the largest member of the weasel, or Mustelidae, family, weighing up to 55 pounds. In Alaska, it averages about 33 pounds for males and 22 for females. It is widely distributed in the arctic and subarctic tundra.

Because of its ferocious and wily nature, it has been comparatively poorly studied, and the status of the wolverine throughout its range is largely unknown, according to the Wolverine Foundation, with headquarters in Kuna, Idaho. The foundation was started in 1996 to promote interest in the wolverine's status and ecological role.

To Sleep, Perchance to Hibernate

Q. Help settle a family dispute: Do bears hibernate or not?

A. Bears do hibernate, though not as deeply as some other hibernating animals.

Deep hibernators spend most of the winter with drastically lowered body temperatures. Bears lower their body temperatures only slightly and continue to burn about 4,000 calories a day, resulting in a Zen-like state of watchful rest. They can quickly rouse themselves in response to intruders and can even nurse their young during hibernation.

But bears' state of hibernation, which is also called denning, can outlast that of deeper hibernators, like the ground squirrel. Ground squirrels do not sleep straight through the winter but rouse themselves every couple of weeks to urinate or defecate, presumably with complex metabolic triggers. Bears can spend up to five months without eating, drinking, defecating, or urinating.

Scientists now suggest that recycling is what permits bears to engage in what seems like a physiological impossibility and emerge healthy. They seem to be able to use products of bone degradation to build new bone and to use urinary wastes to make protein.

BEAR PAIRS

Q. Can the polar bear mate with the brown bear to produce fertile offspring? Is the polar bear *Ursus maritimus* or *Thalarctos maritimus?*

A. The polar bear can breed with the brown bear, and the offspring would probably be fertile. But it would never happen in the wild. The ranges of polar and brown bears do not overlap, and even if two met, they would see each other as competitors, not mates.

Such interbreeding has occurred in captivity, but not in more than two decades. In the early 1980s, an Asiatic black bear and a spectacled bear interbred, but the male offspring was sterile. Modern-day zoo management frowns on these things.

The polar bear has been formally called both *Ursus maritimus* and *Thalarctos maritimus*. *Ursus maritimus,* meaning sea bear, was originated in 1774 by Commander C. J. Phipps, a British naval officer and author of *A Voyage Towards the North Pole.* The more recent designation *Thalarctos maritimus* combines the Greek *thalasso,* or sea, and *arctos,* or bear of the north. *Arctic* itself means "Country of the Great Bear," but the name comes from a bear in the night sky, the Great Bear constellation, or Arktos.

ASLEEP ON THEIR FEET

Q. Why do horses sleep standing up?

A. Horses can doze standing up and spend more time upright than other animals, but get their deepest rest, the so-called REM sleep, only when lying down. In total relaxation, which rapid eye movement or dream sleep involves, the system of tendons and ligaments that keeps horses' legs extended does not work. If a horse goes into REM sleep while it is standing, it tends to fall on its knees.

Wild horses lie down less, a fact that some researchers attribute to the need to be ready to flee predators. But others suggest they lie down less because during certain

times of the year, notably winter, they eat day and night because less feed is available.

In summer, wild horses lie down a fair amount. When they do lie down, one usually remains standing as a sort of guard.

REINDEERS' CLOSE RELATIONS

Q. Are caribou the same as reindeer?

A. They are very closely related, so closely that they are now usually considered different races of the same species, *Rangifer tarandus*. Even the somewhat smaller domesticated reindeer are part of the same group.

Caribou coloration varies widely, from nearly black to brown to gray to almost white, and some populations migrate hundreds of miles, with some preferring the arctic tundra for summer and the edges of woodlands for winter. Their coats may vary from mostly brown in summer to gray in winter.

Caribou or reindeer range from Scandinavia, European Russia, and Siberia to Greenland, Alaska, and Canada. They have even been introduced into the island of South Georgia in the South Atlantic.

There are nine races or subspecies of caribou or reindeer; many of the European races are domesticated.

Reindeer are the only deer in which both sexes have antlers, which they shed at different times of the year. It has been suggested that the females' antlers help them compete for food in the unusual herds that reindeers form, which are both large, with up to forty females per male, and coed, though adult males are often solitary until it comes time to gather a harem.

VIRTUOSO BUILDERS

Q. Why do beavers build dams?

A. Beavers make their complex domestic arrangements to improve security from predators and to move and store a reliable food supply. Dam building is only one of their construction activities, along with canal building and lodge building.

The dammed-up ponds make an important contribution to the beavers' well-being by creating storage at the right depth to stash a winter's supply of bark, twigs, roots, and leaves at temperatures above freezing, but cool enough to keep their nutrient value intact. The ponds also improve security and must be deep enough for a family of beavers to swim under winter ice from their lodge to the hidden food.

The dams are constructed by moving mud, stones, sticks, and branches across a shallow stream. Beavers use their forepaws to move mud and small stones from the stream bottom to the dam site. Large sticks and branches are towed to the site with the beavers' large incisors and are used to support the dam and keep the other components in place.

The females are the most active in dam building, though all adults and yearlings may take part. Most construction takes place at night.

CHATTY CHIPMUNKS

Q. Why do chipmunks sometimes chirp loudly and continuously for fifteen to twenty minutes at a time? It doesn't seem to have anything to do with food, as the ones in our backyard do this even when well fed.

A. As you suspect, the noise probably has less to do with foraging, as the familiar fat-cheeked eastern chipmunk (*Tamias striatus*) can easily collect and store a lifetime supply of food in a single season, than with protecting territory and warning off interlopers.

Chipmunks have a variety of vocal sounds, not all of them translated by scientists, but the one you describe, which has also been rendered "chip-chip-chip" or "chuck-chuck-chuck" or "chipp-R-R-R," is often associated with driving away an intruder perceived as threatening the burrow. The high-pitched sound is repeated every few seconds and may be echoed by a chorus of concerned neighbors.

The scolding is probably being delivered by females, as they are apparently even more territorial than the males. But neither sex is particularly gregarious, except for the period around mating, when the couple may play and vocalize together for some time. Shortly afterward, the male is vociferously driven off. The female can have two litters a year, and the young are, in turn, loudly urged to leave home in six to eight weeks.

CALLING A SNAKE A SNAKE

Q. Do the terms *snake*, *viper*, and *serpent* have scientific differences?

A. The subject is a confusing one because of the rather inexact use of terms in most post-Roman cultures. Especially large or poisonous snakes are commonly called serpents, and biblical tradition calls the shape

Satan assumed to tempt Eve a serpent. But technically speaking, all snakes can be called serpents, from the Latin *serpere*, meaning to creep.

However, scientists use the word *snake* to mean any member of the taxon Serpentes, generally considered a suborder of the order Squamata, although Serpentes actually sits closest to monitor lizards in the evolutionary tree of lizards. (Snakes, then, are really just one legless subset of lizards.)

While the word *serpent* may be used as a synonym for any snake, a viper is any member of the solenoglyph snakes, including rattlesnakes, adders, water moccasins, and copperheads.

Generally, systematic herpetologists place vipers in two families. They are the Viperidae, or Old World vipers (adders, puff adders, etc.), which lack heat sensory pits on the face, and the Crotalidae (pit vipers), found in southeastern Asia and the Americas, which do have sensory pits on the face, including the rattlesnakes, bushmasters, fer-de-lance, cottonmouths, and tree vipers.

A MEAL IN ONE GULP

Q. How can a snake swallow prey that is bigger in diameter than it is, such as a whole rabbit?

A. Most snakes have specialized body structures that let them swallow things that are larger than their heads or necks. First, a snake's skin is very elastic. Even more important is the fact that the snake's jaws are made up of four elements, not two, and they are only loosely attached with ligaments that can stretch during feeding.

The two sides of the upper jaw are independent, and

at the back of the bottom jaw, where there is a single hingelike joint in other animals, a snake has an extra bone that drops down so the two parts of the jaw can open to allow prey to pass into the neck.

A snake's ribs are also flexible, not fused to a sternum as they are in human beings, so they, too, can spread and allow food to pass down into the stomach. Finally, the whole process is pushed along by a complex group of strong muscles.

Some large snakes that are 12 to 15 feet long have no trouble handling a 15-pound rabbit. About 98 percent of snakes can do similar tricks with prey appropriate to their size, but a few underground snakes that feed on insects and soft-bodied invertebrates have lost the ability.

Up a Creek with No Legs

Q. Can rattlesnakes swim? I need to know before I take a dip in a lake bordering on Rattlesnake Hill.

A. Rattlesnakes are good swimmers, though they are not in a class with species that spend all or most of their lives in water or even with the familiar garter snake. From anecdotal accounts, we know that rattlesnakes will swim readily enough when their travels in search of food, mates, or refuge require them to cross water.

Rattlesnakes are buoyant and float well, and they propel themselves fairly fast in water with a sinuous motion. They may hold their rattles above water when resting or floating, but they use their tails for propulsion, with their rattles below the surface.

Although rattlesnakes can bite when in or under water, they cannot strike efficiently because they lack a solid base. You'd have to be pretty careless to get close enough to a swimming rattler to be within striking range and then get it mad enough to bite.

CHAMELEON COLORS

Q. How and why does a chameleon change its colors?
A. There are two groups of lizards commonly called chameleons, and they change colors in different ways.

True chameleons belong to an Old World family called Chamaeleontidae, with two genuses and about eight-five species. They have a variety of colorations, which they can change, to a greater or lesser extent, by concentrating or spreading out the pigmentation in skin cells, called melanophores.

The process is under the control of the autonomic nervous system, and the change is not just a matter of color matching. Rather, it is a complex response to a variety of conditions, including light and temperature, but also "emotional" factors such as fear or triumph in battle with another chameleon.

The strength of the light is apparently the most important factor, and for certain species, this sometimes results in camouflage. For example, the flap-necked chameleon, *Chamaeleo dilepis,* an African species, turns green when among leaves and yellow or reddish-brown when on bark. However, in response to a threat, it turns blackish-green, with yellow and white spots.

Members of the other group sometimes called chameleons, anoles (which are New World relatives of the iguana in the genus Anolis), have a limited color-change system under the control of hormones rather than nerves.

THE FERTILE TURTLE

Q. How do turtles reproduce?

A.   *The turtle lives 'twixt plated decks*
     Which practically conceal its sex.
     I think it clever of the turtle
     In such a fix to be so fertile.

The poet Ogden Nash was right about the turtle's external ambiguity and fertility. Turtles are not only enthusiastic breeders, they also have external sexual characteristics that often make it hard for creatures other than turtles to determine which is which.

The male is sometimes distinguishable by an indentation or curvature in its plastron, or lower shell, which fits over the back of the female; females have a flat or convex plastron. To fertilize the female's eggs, the male turtle conceals a sexual organ inside the cloaca, or waste removal chamber. The male positions itself over the female and often grasps the upper shell, or carapace, with its claws, then curves its tail until the vent contacts the female's vent; the penis emerges for fertilization. The often dozens of eggs develop internally and are then usually laid and buried in sandy soil.

Fertilization is sometimes preceded by elaborate courtship rituals, with hours of demonstration followed by a few minutes of copulation. The female can store sperm to fertilize its eggs, sometimes years later.

FROGS' FLYPAPER TONGUES

Q. What is the sticky stuff on a frog's tongue, and how does it work to let frogs catch prey?

A. There is no special name for the sticky substance, but scientists do know it is secreted by mucous glands at the moment the frog's tongue hits the prey. Otherwise it would stick the frog's mouth together.

The tongue of a frog, which is hinged at the front of the mouth, not the back, can be envisioned as working like a human arm with the fist folded up to the shoulder.

When the "arm" is flipped out straight, the part of the tongue that hits the prey corresponds to the back of the hand, not the palm. Where it touches the prey, muscles in the tip contract so that it instantly exudes a sticky substance. Then, like an arm folding back up to the shoulder, it carries the prey back into the mouth.

The tongue moves in and out as fast as the blink of an eye. Then the eyes are depressed by a further set of muscles, which forces the food backward into the mouth. Once it is in the throat, hairlike projections called cilia move it toward the gut.

Some aquatic frogs have evolved with no tongues. They never come out of the water and move food into their mouths using their limbs.

FLIGHT OF THE FISH

Q. Why do flying fish fly?

A. The several species of oceanic flying fish seem to take flight either when they are alarmed or when they are attracted by a light shining in the night.

Most flying fishes belong to the family Exocoetidae and live in the surface waters of all tropical oceans. They are able to leap out of the water and glide above it because they have overdeveloped pectoral fins and in some cases pelvic fins as well.

The flying fish that have two pairs of "wings" build up swimming speed much as an airplane taxis before takeoff; they gather speed at the surface by sweeping the tail fin rapidly from side to side, vibrating it like an outboard motor. Having reached speeds that sometimes exceed 35 miles an hour, they finally launch themselves into the air. Flights last from about ten seconds to as long as thirty seconds and may carry the fish 650 feet or more.

Flying fish species range from about 5½ inches to 20 inches in length. They are often good eating, and one technique of fishing for them relies on their attraction to light. A fisherman may simply anchor a canoe with a foot or two of water in it and a lantern hanging over it. The next morning, the boat may be full of fresh fish trapped in water too shallow for them to make a take-off.

AMBIGUOUS FISH

Q. Is it true that some fish are both male and female?

A. Yes, some fish are simultaneously hermaphroditic, possessing the reproductive equipment of both sexes at one time; a few can fertilize their own eggs. In some species, called sequential hermaphrodites, an individual can change from male to female, from female to male, or back and forth. Some fish species are entirely female and reproduce by cloning their own DNA, though the process is triggered by sperm from males of closely related species.

Conversion from male to female is called protandry; conversion from female to male is called protogyny.

Sex changes in fish were once thought to be extremely rare. It is now known that changes from female to male occur in at least fourteen families and changes from male to female in at least eight.

In a study of a reef fish called the bluehead wrasse, reported in 1984, sexual identity and behavior were found to vary with the density of the population and the size of the reef. For example, sometimes a large dominant male fertilized the eggs of many females, and sometimes fish took turns releasing eggs to be fertilized by sperm of other fish, which in turn released eggs for fertilization.

In another wrasse species, a solitary male fertilized the eggs of several females; if the male died, one of the harem became male.

In some hermaphroditic species, the adaptation is thought to help ensure reproductive success when other members of the species are few and far between.

Changes in the sex of the fish are presumed to be influenced by hormones, but the mechanism is not fully understood.

TELLING THE DOLPHINS FROM THE PORPOISES

Q. What is the difference between a porpoise and a dolphin?

A. They are cousins but belong to different families. All are members of the cetacean order, which includes whales, and all belong to the suborder odontoceti, literally meaning toothed whales.

The thirty-two species of seagoing dolphins (members of the family Delphinadae) are perhaps most easily distinguished from the six species of porpoises (members of the family Phocoenidae) by the fact that most dolphins have a well-developed beak and a bulbous forehead. Dolphin bodies also tend to be more slender and streamlined than the whalelike porpoises. River dolphins in the family Platanistidae, which inhabit muddy rivers, have even longer, more slender beaks, prominent forehead pads, and small, weak eyes.

The bulging forehead of the dolphin houses a pad of fat called the melon, which is thought to help focus the high-frequency sonar beams with which dolphins navigate and find their food.

Orca, the killer whale of motion picture fame, *Orcinus orca*, is actually a kind of dolphin, but one that lacks a pronounced snout. Performing dolphins are Atlantic bottle-nosed dolphins, *Tursiops truncatus*.

FACTS OF LIFE FOR WHALES

Q. Is a third whale involved in positioning whales for mating?

A. In some whale species, a third whale may have a role in courtship, but it is now thought to involve competition, not assistance.

The California gray whale, *Eschrichtius robustus,* has many more males than females. During courting, two

males will often follow one female, and the trio will stay together right up to the moment of copulation. The female slows down, signaling a willingness to mate, and the males use their flippers to slow her down even more. The males swim upside down beside her, each trying to mate. When one succeeds in rotating his underside alongside that of the female, copulation occurs.

There was some speculation that an extra male, or males, held the mating pair together to brace them for mating. However, this idea is now mostly dismissed as a misinterpretation of what is going on in a process that is difficult to study.

As for getting into position to mate, the female usually floats right side up and the male comes up from below. What you do see in mating whales is a lot of rolling around.

Sex and the Single Fossil

Q. How can scientists tell what sex a fossil is, or was, when they have only one example?

A. Although it can be difficult to know with certainty, there are clues in the shape and size of bony landmarks on the skull. You usually can't sex other bones reliably, except for the pelvis.

With the skull, what scientists look for is the difference between what is called robust morphology, meaning typically heavier, larger shapes and sizes, and gracile morphology, meaning smaller and more "graceful" shapes. Males tend to be more robust in the browridge, the mastoid process behind the ear and the lower jaw.

But with only one fossil example, researchers must rely on what they know of the species and make an educated guess. Often it can be unclear whether researchers are looking at a species that has a marked difference in size between the sexes, called sexual dimorphism, or an entirely different species.

The Species Census

Q. How many living species are there? What is the breakdown of plants, vertebrates, etc.?

A. One recent estimate is 10 million to 13 million living species. A 1988 study said only about 1.5 million species then had scientific names, though far more certainly exist. The study pointed out that "total" figures are not actual counts, but theoretical reckonings based on things like the number of species that make up typical food chains in different climates. Some groups, like mammals, have been intensively studied, and others, like mites, are little known. A big problem is defining a species: some biologists discern two hundred kinds of British blackberry, for example; others might list twenty, or two or three.

Two kingdoms, the prokaryotic monerans and the eukaryotic protists (two kinds of microscopic unicellular organisms), make up about 5 percent of recorded living species; the kingdoms of funguses and plants make up about 22 percent; the rest are animals.

In one estimate of the animal kingdom, well over half the total species are insects; mammals make up 0.388 percent of the total, and other chordates (animals with at last a precursor of a spinal cord) are just over 3.7 percent.

CHAPTER 8

Secrets of Cats and Dogs

ITCHY ANIMALS

Q. You hear all the time about people who are allergic to cats and dogs. Do cats and dogs ever develop allergies?

A. Yes, allergies are common in cats and dogs. They arise by similar mechanisms and can cause similar symptoms, though skin eruptions are more common in cats and dogs than sneezing or digestive distress. Treatments may be similar, too.

In an allergy, the animal's immune system is hypersensitive to some substances it encounters, called allergens. For example, it is very common for pets to be hypersensitive to certain proteins in the saliva of fleas.

Pets, like people, can be allergic to substances that are airborne and inhaled, like pollen, mold, and dust; to substances that they come into contact with, like wool or flea collars; and to foods, like corn, wheat, soy, beef, or dairy products. The allergic tendency can be inherited or develop after repeated exposure.

It would be very unlikely for a cat to become allergic to its owner, since humans do not ordinarily lick themselves clean the way cats do, spreading some allergy-causing protein in their saliva onto fur and dander that is then blown about in the air.

Treating a pet's allergy may involve protecting the animal from re-exposure to the allergen, desensitization therapy, shampoos and rinses to remove an irritant from the skin, and the use of antihistamines and steroids.

A CAT'S MAD DASH

Q. Why do cats periodically run around madly as if they were chasing a fire engine?
A. It is probably more evolutionary than it is anything physiological, and is possibly related to hunting techniques. It is not usually seen in farm cats, who have to work for a living. Their predatory behavior involves sitting beside a mouse hole for hours, then pouncing.

Instead, the mad dash is often seen among well-fed,

secure, happy house cats. Cats are crepuscular animals that hunt at dawn and dusk, and the running around often coincides with the time they would ordinarily be hunting.

It may also be a form of play. Cats often seem to be stimulating themselves, similar to a child on a swing. If all the dashing around is a problem, veterinarians suggest trying interactive play with a pouncing toy. That might reduce the fire-engine behavior.

FELINE ANTENNAE

Q. What are cats' whiskers for?

A. Whiskers give cats important sensory information and also have a role in communication between cats. They are far more important to a cat than a dog's whiskers are to a dog, and they should never be trimmed, as they tell a cat whether it can squeeze through a narrow passage, for example.

Technically called vibrissae, whiskers or tactile hairs are clustered in three major groups on the sides of the cheeks, above the eyes, and farther back on the cheeks. There are also a few on the chin and shorter ones on the back of the front legs.

Stiffer and at least twice as thick as ordinary hairs, vibrissae have roots that go three times as deep in the skin and are surrounded by nerves and blood vessels. The slightest motion of a hair, even from a breath of air, triggers a sensation.

Vibrissae are helpful to a cat maneuvering in dark areas, especially when hunting, and when a cat has prey in its cupped paws, ready to move it toward the mouth, the hairs give signals of the next meal's exact position.

As for communication between cats, whiskers pushed forward may indicate friendliness or inquisitiveness, but when they are pulled back flat against the cheeks, they can signal either aggressive or defensive hostility.

SHOCKING BEHAVIOR

Q. How can I avoid shocking my cat with static electricity when I pet her in cold, dry weather?

A. There are two approaches. One is avoiding the buildup of the charge; the other is discharging it so you cannot shock the cat or yourself. (The cat also builds up a charge, but because of its smaller size, most of the flow is from you to the cat.)

In friction between any two materials with different affinities for electrons, one winds up negatively charged, with a surplus of electrons, and one positively charged, with a deficit. The more different the affinities, the greater the charge. Either a surplus or a deficit can make a spark.

One simple way to discharge a human buildup from walking across a rug with rubber-soled shoes, for example, is to touch a water pipe, faucet, or other grounding device just before touching the cat. To prevent a strong shock to yourself, touch the keys from your pocket to the pipe. You will still feel something, but the sharpest part of the spark is at the point of the key. The discharge tends to occur at the minimum radius of curvature.

There are also antistatic sprays, some for preventing static cling in garments by insulating the fibers and some for use around computers that spread the charge around and allow the discharge of electrons to leak out over a wide area.

In either case, be sure to spray your pant legs and carpet, not the cat.

A KIDNEY FOR THE CAT

Q. Can cats have organ transplants?

A. Yes, in some cases. Kidney transplants were pioneered by the School of Veterinary Medicine at the University of California at Davis and are now performed at some other veterinary colleges around the country. They can cost $3,000 or more.

There are no other transplant programs for dogs or cats, though there was initial research on partial liver transplants.

Because there is no organ procurement program for animals, veterinarians have to use live donors that can survive donation of one of two kidneys. At Davis and other schools that have transplant programs, the school maintains a colony of donor cats, and the owner of a cat that receives a kidney has to agree to adopt the donor.

No need has been found for tissue matching in cats, and rejection of a transplanted kidney can easily be suppressed with cyclosporine. Without the drug, rejection occurs in about twenty-one days. The school at Davis also has a dialysis unit. Cats with acute kidney failure, caused by things like poisoning, usually need three to four weeks of dialysis, costing $3,000 to $6,000. In cats with chronic kidney failure, a few weeks of dialysis before a transplant makes success more likely.

Sensing a Storm

Q. Why can my dog sense when a storm is coming an hour before it arrives?

A. "Sense" in its physical meaning is the key word. Many case reports cite instances of animals' behaving in strange ways before natural phenomena, but there is little scientific data.

Domestic animals, dogs and cats in particular, have hearing and other sensory capacities that are greater than those of people. Their hearing is more sensitive and covers a wider frequency range, so it wouldn't be surprising if they could hear the sounds of an approaching storm.

Dogs and cats also have a much better sense of smell. Meteorologists say that storm winds may carry smells from other areas and temperature and humidity differences that are detectable far in advance of any actual precipitation. Even people sometimes say they can smell when snow is coming. That is especially true of certain kinds of heavy snowstorms accompanied by winds from the south.

Fido's Brain

Q. If a Chihuahua and a mastiff have such different head sizes, does their brain size vary that widely, too, and does it affect their comparative intelligence?

A. Brain size is not generally seen as a reflection of intelligence in dogs or in other species. That is evident if you compare other species with different brain sizes — for example, elephants and people: People are far more intelligent despite the huge disparity in physical size.

Intelligence has more to do with the development of different areas of the brain over the course of evolution and the devotion of different areas to specific functions. The potential development of the brain is equal among the various breeds.

However, not all animals develop equally regarding genetics and environmental influences. There could be marked differences in intelligence between dogs of nearly identical breeding, even littermates. And as any Chihuahua owner could tell you, some of the smallest dogs can be some of the craftiest.

Dogs were selectively bred over millennia for different kinds of intelligence and behavior. People who have tested dogs with obstacle courses and other measures of talent have found that some breeds excel in particular areas, such as herding or retrieving. Some, like the border collie, German shepherd, and poodle, seem to excel in many fields.

GARRULOUS PARROTS

Q. Do parrots and other birds that talk have any special physical equipment in the larynx or tongue that helps them speak?

A. There is no special equipment, just a highly developed ability to imitate. The ability to imitate a species' own song is present in all songbirds.

Some birds, like woodpeckers or chickens, do not actually learn songs. But of the birds that do, some learn a little and some learn a lot.

Among the star imitators are parrots, mockingbirds, mynahs, and starlings. If these birds spend a lot of time with a person, they will learn a lot from the person, although it is not certain what brain structures are involved in the ability to imitate human speech.

The brain structures by which birds learn songs, however, have been largely mapped. Other research found that the series of structures informally called the song system is larger and more complex in birds that learn more complex songs than it is in those that can learn only simpler songs.

GUINEA PIG IDENTITY CRISIS

Q. Are guinea pigs rodents?
A. Probably, based on structural features and fossil evidence, though some scientists studying DNA evidence suspect otherwise.

There are studies, primarily of mitochondrial genes, suggesting that guinea pigs might not be rodents, but might belong to their own separate order. (Mitochondrial DNA is carried by the structures in cells that act as cellular power plants. It is inherited in a manner different from ordinary DNA.)

However, most of these studies were based on a limited sample of genes in a limited number of orders. More gene sequences should be studied for more mammals before we can be sure of the answer.

Another recent analysis showed that by using the same data as some of these studies, but employing another commonly accepted model of gene evolution, guinea pigs can be placed in the rodent group.

Finally, the traditional kind of evidence in mammal evolution is very strong that guinea pigs belong in the order Rodentia, both from morphology (structural features such as the head and the development of the gnawing teeth) and from paleontology (fossils from Central Asia).

CHAPTER 9

Animal Aviators

BEYOND LUNGS

Q. How do birds breathe? Is it more like mammals or like fish?

A. Like mammals, birds take in air and extract oxygen from it to supply body tissues, while fish respiration depends on getting the oxygen dissolved in water through organs called gills.

But bird respiration is significantly different from that

of mammals. In the very efficient avian system, the lungs are small, taking up just 2 percent of body volume.

The external respiration system uses the lungs and a much larger series of air sacs distributed throughout the body so that the oxygen supply communicates directly with body parts. Oxygen is taken in and exchanged for carbon dioxide waste in the blood, then the carbon dioxide is moved out; so far, much like mammals.

But in birds, the air flow is one way, through tubes and chambers, rather than two ways, in and out of the lungs, as it is in mammals. And when a bird inhales, air actually leaves its lungs; fresh air enters the lungs as it exhales.

First, a constant stream of air enters through the back of the mouth and goes into the larynx and trachea. It is channeled in a pair of tubes straight through the lungs and into the system of air sacs and hollow bones. Gases from the air sacs are sent forward through the lungs again, then through more air sacs into the trachea, and then finally expelled from the body.

SENSING SOMETHING IN THE AIR

Q. Do birds have a sense of smell?

A. Yes, and though it is highly variable from species to species, research is leading to a higher estimation of birds' smelling abilities.

Sensitivity to odors varies among orders of birds with the size of the olfactory bulb in the brain relative to that of the cerebrum. The bulb tends to be small, but it is well developed in some birds, especially those that fly and hunt by night, and research has found that some birds with relatively small olfactory bulbs can smell well enough to detect certain odors.

Scientists now suspect that most birds can use the sense of smell in daily activities, and individual species have been found to have high sensitivities adapted to needs like mating (finding a female in season by detecting gland secretions), feeding (smelling carrion or worms), or even finding their nesting burrows.

Some birds can smell just a trace of a substance that might lead them to food. For example, bacon fat poured on the surface of the ocean has been known to attract black-footed albatrosses from more than 18 miles away. Turkey vultures have been used to find leaks in a 42-mile-long oil pipeline; when ethyl mercaptan, which smells like rotting meat, was pumped through, the birds gathered at the leaks.

INVASION OF THE CROWS

Q. How can we get rid of the crows that have invaded the big garden in our city apartment complex, where we used to get songbirds?

A. Short of exterminating all the crows in town, there is not much chance of getting rid of them. Driving out one family simply opens a place for another young male to move in.

One possible way is to make things less attractive, but what attracts crows is the same thing that makes gardens attractive to humans. Crows like open green space, and a big lawn with a few trees is ideal. The lawn provides food like earthworms, mole crickets, and June beetle larvae.

If you don't want to cut the trees down and pave the lawn, another possibility is scaring the crows, who tend to be a bit more wary than other birds. A few disposable aluminum pie plates on a string might just change things enough so that the crows don't want to come into a particular yard.

Crows have moved into urban areas around the country in the last thirty years, becoming urban rather than rural birds. Family groups average three birds but range up to fifteen or twenty, many of them young males waiting for the opportunity to breed. Males usually breed first at the age of 5, females at 3½ to 4.

As for the songbirds that disappeared, the crows probably did not play a direct role, and the cardinals and others are probably still around.

HIGH-SPEED DIVE

Q. What bird flies the fastest?

A. The winner, wings down, is the peregrine falcon, *Falco peregrinus*, which may also be the fastest animal of any kind on earth. Estimates of its top speed when diving start around 200 miles per hour, and some authorities put it considerably higher, perhaps 275 m.p.h. Its top horizontal speed is 60 m.p.h. or more.

The high speeds are essential to the normal feeding habits of the peregrine falcon, which overtakes and kills other birds or bats in midair. The bird cruises for hours, then plunges in a move known as a stoop. The prey is often killed by violent impact with the peregrine's snatching talons.

The peregrine falcon is about 15 to 21 inches long,

and its wingspan is about 36 to 44 inches. The population of peregrine falcons has made a well-publicized recovery since the pesticide DDT was banned in 1972. The residue of the poison in the peregrines' prey built up in the fatty tissue in the parents, and the female falcons laid eggs that were deficient in calcium and too weak to withstand the incubation of thirty-two days or longer under a mother who weighs about three pounds.

STAYING IN THE PINK

Q. Is it true that flamingos are pink only because they eat pink shellfish?
A. The pinkness of flamingos is determined by food, but not by pink shellfish. The factors in the flamingo diet that ensure pinkness are carotenoid pigments, which are found in plankton, diatoms, and blue-green algae that the birds strain out of the muck in which they feed. The birds process yellow carotene into a red compound, canthaxanthin, which is stored in their legs and feathers.

If flamingos do not get enough of the right pigment, they lose their color when they molt. The color is important, because flamingos do not seem to breed successfully without it. In captivity, they were once fed ground-up carrots and red pepper to keep them pink, but now zookeepers try to reproduce their natural diet or give them synthetic canthaxanthin.

Flamingos are not the only birds that change color with diet. "Red" canaries may be fed special nutrients to keep them red, though bird shows may frown on this color feeding. Cardinals also fade noticeably in winter, when they do not have access to their normal wide variety of foods.

Flamingos have very unusual feeding equipment. They eat with their heads upside down. The lower jaw contains a thick, fleshy tongue that moves back and forth to create powerful suction. Both upper and lower jaws contain rows of projections called lamellae that meet to create a strainer to filter out edibles as water is pumped past them by the tongue. The projections range in size from large hooks to a Velcro-like fringe.

The greater flamingo, with larger lamellae, strains out and swallows small invertebrates, while the lesser flamingo, with a finer sieve, captures blue-green algae. The two species can feed side by side and eat different foods.

SOARING INTO OLD AGE

Q. If I had a pet bald eagle, which I could never have, of course, how long could I expect it to live?

A. Smaller eagles have occasionally been "domesticated" by falconers and were traditionally reserved for the hunting pleasure of medieval kings.

The American bald eagle, which has a wingspan of up to 7½ feet and would therefore require a very large falconer, has been reliably reported to have lived for 30 years and 5 months in captivity at the National Zoo in Washington. One banded bird in the wild in Mexico lived 10 years and 5 months and might have lived much longer but was shot.

A bald eagle, formally *Haliaeetus leucocephalus*, does not even develop its distinctive white-feathered helmet until its fourth year. Before that, it goes through a series of immature plumages, which are wholly or partly replaced by a series of molts, or feather losses.

While the bald eagle's head is not bald, but fully feathered, the legs are unfeathered, and the bare-legged look helps bird-watchers distinguish between immature bald eagles and immature golden eagles.

TURNING ON THE FLY

Q. How do birds turn in flight?
A. The assumption that a bird's tail functions only as a horizontal surface is erroneous. A bird also can twist its tail from left to right and downward, so it acts almost as a braking system that allows it to bank into turns.

Some birds are better at this than others. Some hawks in the group known as accipiters, which spend most of the time in forested settings, use their tails as rudders so they can rapidly weave their way through trees without striking them.

There are other turning mechanisms as well. The large webbed feet of waterfowl are used to steer during landing by creating wind resistance.

Birds also steer by changing their wing configuration. They can change the angle at which the wing intersects the stream of air, known as the angle of attack. A greater angle of attack creates more wind resistance, and applying this differentially on each wing allows the bird to turn.

THE BIRDS AND THE BEES AND BIRDS

Q. How do birds have sexual intercourse?

A. Parents have supposedly explained human reproduction to children in terms of the birds and the bees; if birds were really used to make this explanation, it would be widely believed that fertilization occurs after the briefest period of proximity of the waste elimination organs.

Most birds do not have external sex organs. The transfer of sperm from male to female usually takes place while the male bird is standing or treading on the female's back. The male twists his tail under that of the female so that the opening of the male bird's cloaca, or waste storage chamber, is close to that of the female's.

Sperm transfer takes place when both cloacae open outward. Tiny projections called papillae protrude from the back walls of the male's sperm sacs into his cloaca. These are brought into contact with the opening of the female's oviduct, or egg tube (most female birds have only one that works), and the sperm is released to fertilize the eggs.

Ornithologists usually describe the contact as a "cloacal kiss." It commonly lasts one or two seconds.

BIRD BOMBS AWAY

Q. Why are bird droppings whitish or spotted with white?

A. Bird droppings combine the whitish waste products processed by the liver and kidneys with the darker wastes that come from the digestive tract. In birds, the nitrogen-rich wastes are turned into a white-colored paste that is composed mostly of urates. The urates often form a separate white blob, as anyone who has worn a new hat outdoors at the wrong time has probably noticed.

The excretory system of birds is different from that of mammals because it takes up a minimum of space and requires a minimum of water for processing.

In mammals, nitrogen waste is turned into urea, a toxic substance that requires large amounts of water to flush it safely from the system and a urinary bladder as a holding tank for all the liquid. The urates excreted by birds, on the other hand, are concentrated but not toxic, and most birds do not have bladders to hold liquid to flush it out.

WHERE THE GULLS ARE

Q. I have observed gulls perched on all sorts of structures, but never on a tree. Why?

A. Most gulls do not have feet that are adapted to perching in trees and clinging to tree branches. Most have slightly webbed feet that help them move about in the water, so when they are on land, they do better walking on rocks or soft surfaces like sand.

Pure probability also puts gulls on the structures of civilization. Birds like gulls and crows have done quite well adapting to human-created environments, and the nice flat surfaces associated with human habitation — pilings, piers, and lighthouses, to name just a few — are ideal places to perch.

Gulls that can nest in trees, like mew gulls, have feet that are not fully webbed. Mew gulls make their nests fairly low, in spruce trees, not deciduous trees, where there is more surface area to cling to.

Many forest birds, in contrast with gulls, have feet with tendons that keep their toes automatically wrapped around branches. For these birds, it takes an effort to unclench.

HARD-HEADS

Q. Why don't woodpeckers damage their brains?
A. Woodpeckers like the acorn woodpecker of California, which hits the wood with its bill at speeds of 12 to 15 miles an hour, manage to keep their wits because their brains are held firmly in a case, which acts as a shock absorber. The bird's body also moves in a single plane like a metronome, avoiding the rotational forces that would twist and tear its brain loose from its moorings.

The human brain does not enjoy this kind of protection. Instead, it is encased in a sac of fluid. Thus when a cyclist hits the pavement, for example, the impact can make the brain bounce around in its sac, hitting first one side of the skull and then the other. That motion can tear nerve fibers and cause permanent damage.

CHAPTER 10

How Humans Get That Way

THERE MUST BE A REASON

Q. Is there an evolutionary reason for morning sickness?

A. Evolutionary biologists have suggested that morning sickness is a mechanism to help women avoid noxious substances that might harm the fetus at an early stage of development.

Formerly, scientists had assumed that the sickness early in pregnancy was related to a sharp rise in the hormone estrogen. But as some scientists point out, the sickness almost always occurs in the first three months of pregnancy, when organs are in a formative stage and therefore most vulnerable to trace poisons in the diet. Nausea would help a woman temporarily avoid foods that contain substances that are harmless to adults but that might cause birth defects or miscarriage. Studies have found that there is a higher rate of miscarriage among women who have little or no morning sickness.

A Bath for the Fetus

Q. What is amniotic fluid made of?

A. Fetal urine is the main component of the amniotic fluid that bathes the developing fetus. It is excreted into the fetal sac inside the womb as the fetus develops. Normally, the fetus "breathes" this fluid into its lungs, and it is essential for the normal development of the lungs.

The fluid contains some fetal cells, which can be drawn out in the process called amniocentesis and analyzed to find out whether the fetus has some genetic diseases.

Younger and Taller

Q. Has any statistical relationship been found between birth order and height?

A. Many studies have found a relationship between birth order and birth weight, with the later-born children in a family tending to be larger, and birth weight has some correlation with eventual height.

For example, a 1988 study at the Children's Hospital of the University of Kiel, Germany, investigated adult height in families with three or more adult children. The researchers found that the first-born siblings had a statistically significant deficit in average height as compared with the average of all the siblings, but the gap amounted to only a fraction of an inch.

That study also found that men tended to increase in height with increasing birth order, while women did not, beyond the second born. The researchers concluded that birth order is a factor that contributes significantly to the variance of adult height among siblings.

The reasons for the tendency of younger siblings to be born larger are not clear. In an Israeli study that adjusted for a number of factors—like maternal age, education, marital status, religion, smoking, height and prepregnant weight, gestational age, and sex—birth weight increased with increasing birth order both in a large cross section of newborns and in a group of large families, where many of the possible variables would presumably be constant.

When $X/Y > 1$

Q. If genetically the ratio of human males to human females should be 1 to 1, why are there more females than males?

A. In fact, each year more males are born than females. The normal slight excess of male births is usually attributed to the slightly greater motility of sperm carrying the male, or Y, chromosome.

It was recently discovered that in the average ejaculation, there are slightly more sperm carrying the X chromosome, necessary for conception of a female, than there are sperm with the Y chromosome. But emerging studies of embryos that have been conceived through in vitro fertilization indicate that more males are actually conceived.

Scientists suggest that the Y-bearing sperm are so much better at fertilizing eggs than the X-bearing ones that even though there are fewer of them to begin with, they end up penetrating more than half of all eggs.

What happens to the sex ratio after conception is another story. For example, in societies where women are not valued as much as men, they may be purposely aborted, neglected, or actually killed. In others, where men are subjected to greater stress or risk (from wars, for example), more women survive longer.

The ratio of males to females can vary from time to time and from population to population, whether it is animals or people, and there are numerous suggested reasons. For example, it has been reported that women in lower socioeconomic groups, presumably under greater stress, bear slightly more girls than boys.

THE ADVANTAGES OF BEING FEMALE

Q. I recently read that infant girls usually have lower infant mortality than boys because of "biological advantages." What might these be?
A. The advantages for girls begin even before birth, and like so many other differences between the sexes may be tied to hormones. For example, significantly more male fetuses are spontaneously aborted or stillborn.

The reasons need more investigation, but they seem to

include sex differences in chromosomal structures and possibly a slower maturing of boys' lungs because of the effects of testosterone. In most societies this pattern of excess male mortality continues for the first six months.

An inborn biological advantage may persist at least until menopause because premenopausal hormones like estrogen offer some protection from heart disease caused by damage that narrows blood vessels.

The advantages may also include differences in susceptibilities and immunities to some disease-causing organisms. Still, some diseases are more likely to sicken and kill women.

BOY TWINS, GIRL TWINS

Q. Are twins more likely to be one sex or the other? What about conjoined or Siamese twins?

A. Slightly more than half of all twins born are male. In conjoined or Siamese twins, the picture is complicated both by their extreme rarity and by their very low overall survival rate, which is variously given at 5 percent to 25 percent.

Conjoined twins are always identical, because they always come from a single fertilized egg and so are always the same sex. The developing embryo splits within two weeks of conception, but is only partly separated and continues to mature into two infants that are connected to a greater or lesser degree. Many die at birth and many have severe birth defects. About 35 percent survive just one day. However, historical studies of about 600 sets of conjoined twins over five centuries list more than 70 percent of the surviving pairs as female.

In the United States there has been a sharp rise in multiple births overall, associated with the two overlapping and related trends—older age at childbearing and increased used of fertility-enhancing therapies, many of which have multiple pregnancies as a side effect.

THE LONGEST DIGIT

Q. Why might the middle finger have evolved to be the longest?
A. There is no definitive answer, but its structure suggests a key role in the strong grip for hanging and power grasping.

The middle finger's length is one aspect of hand evolution that people have in common with apes. For many primates, the middle finger is the functional axis of the hand and the longest finger. All the muscles of the hand are arranged around an axis through the middle finger, so it is in position to exert the greatest amount of force, and the middle finger bones are the longest and most robust of any finger. All this suggests that this part of the hand blueprint came from apelike ancestors 5 million to 6 million years ago. Apes all have a powerful grasp, with well-developed fingers and a tiny thumb, unlike the long and very maneuverable human thumb.

The middle finger's bony anatomy suggests it is important in power grasping, while the thumb and index finger are for precision grasping, like holding a needle or stone tool. The third finger would be more devoted to the hook grip, used in hanging from a branch or, for modern humans, holding a heavy suitcase.

LIMITS TO GROWTH

Q. Will I grow up to be short like my mother or tall like my father?
A. Your adult height will probably be somewhere in between.

Some rough estimates can be made based on the growth patterns of many children. These methods assume that there is no disease or hormonal problem to hinder your genetic potential.

Because height at the age of 3 is about 60 percent of adult height for girls and 55 percent of adult height for boys, two times your height as a 2-year-old will be roughly your adult height.

Another rule of thumb uses your parents' heights. Add them, divide by two, then add three inches for a boy or subtract three inches for a girl. The result is said to be correct within two inches about 95 percent of the time.

Most often, however, doctors refer to standard growth charts. Your current height and age give an indication of where you fall relative to the average for children of your age and sex. Because you tend to stay in those same rankings as you grow, you can estimate your eventual height.

X rays of the gaps, or epiphyses, between the ends of

your bones do not predict eventual height but could determine if there is a condition that would prevent further growth. As you grow, the gaps shrink. When you complete puberty, the bones are fused, and no more growth takes place.

STROLLER POTATOES

Q. I see children old enough to walk being pushed around in strollers. Can this stunt development?

A. Experts suspect that the problem is not that tired parents are using strollers while shopping, but rather that they may be preventing their children from moving enough the rest of the time.

Child development specialists think that freely crawling, cruising, and toddling are a normal progression in a child's physical and cognitive development. But as soon as babies can move independently, they tend to be confined much of the time to strollers, infant seats, high chairs, playpens, and walkers. Young muscles can languish.

In 1997, research at Case Western Reserve University found that walkers, in which children can "walk" without seeing their feet, are likely to impair motor and mental development, apparently because movement is limited and children cannot freely explore their environment.

Many experts recommend more activity for very young

children, not necessarily with formal exercise but by allowing normal walking, running, and climbing — within the limits of safety — and playing games as simple as catch, tag, and chase.

THE PAINS OF CHILDHOOD

Q. My 4-year-old occasionally complains of excruciating but ill-defined nighttime pains in his calves and shins. Friends say they recall similar pains, which used to be called growing pains. What are they? What helps?
A. The description fits what doctors still call growing pains, or benign limb pains of childhood. The suffering is real, though the source is still not understood.

Most pediatricians do not believe growing pains are actually related to the child's growth. For one thing, the location is ill defined, not specifically at the limbs' growth plates, and for another, the pains occur mostly in the age group from 4 to 12, while the periods of most rapid growth are usually earlier or later.

About 20 percent of healthy children get growing pains, usually at night and usually in the legs. They are somewhat more common in girls than in boys. Once other possible causes, like injury or inflammatory disease, have been ruled out, such pains are diagnosed as growing pains.

Usually, the use of gentle massage, warm towels, and perhaps acetaminophen or ibuprofen is all that is needed to let the child go back to sleep. The pains have no lasting consequences, and the next morning some children do not even remember being awakened by the pains.

STRAIGHTENING THE SPINE

Q. I got a brace when I was 7 to correct idiopathic scoliosis. Is this still the standard practice? Is it true that
this problem is disproportionately common in girls?

A. Idiopathic scoliosis, a sideways curve of the spine of
unknown cause in adolescence, is now believed to
require active treatment in only about 10 percent of
cases. When treatment is called for, a cast or a device
called a Milwaukee brace is widely used.

At least 60 percent to perhaps 80 percent of the cases
are in girls, and girls tend to have worse curves and
greater progression.

A review of studies on scoliosis and its treatment found
that the Milwaukee brace,
which has been in wide use
since the late 1940s, has been
the subject of few long-term
studies to evaluate its results.
Of the studies, most did not
keep track of the progression

of the curvature, making it uncertain whether patients
with braces would have gotten worse without it.

Bracing tends to stop the curve's progression in 85 to
90 percent of patients, but there is wide variation in
response. Most common is a moderate correction while
the brace is worn with slow, steady progression back to
the original curve after its use is tapered off.

Wake Up, You Sleepyhead

Q. Why do so many teenagers have trouble waking up in the morning? Is there any way to train yourself to make getting up at 7 A.M. easier?

A. Morning sleepiness in teenagers (or in anyone else) may have a cause as simple as lack of sleep, perhaps because of too much homework after a part-time job, followed by television. In that case the cure may be to sleep more, cut down on some sleep-robbing activities, and gradually change bedtime and waking time in fifteen-minute increments until the person wakes refreshed at a desirable time.

However, some researchers suggest that there may be physiological causes for drowsiness in teenagers, not just in the morning but in afternoon classes, and some even say that teenagers have a natural sleep pattern that would make them go to bed at 2 A.M. and stay in bed until noon. They base these suggestions on studies of changing levels of the hormone melatonin, which is involved in sleep regulation, and on comparisons of the academic performance of teenagers with early and late school starting times. In one study, some students in an early starting group built up a sleep debt and suffered ten-second micronaps of drowsiness and lapsed attention in the afternoon.

CHAPTER 11

Our Bodies, Our Aches and Pains

MIX AND MISMATCH

Q. Why is your blood type—A, B, AB, or O—so important? I have never understood exactly what would happen if you got a transfusion of an incompatible type.

A. The most basic classification of the hundreds of ways to type human blood, the ABO system, is important because incompatible types of blood react with each other to form sticky globs of red blood cells that can cause serious and sometimes fatal blockages.

The classification was developed in 1901 by Karl Landsteiner, a Viennese-born pathologist and immunologist. For the first time, it explained why certain blood transfusions were beneficial while others caused severe problems.

The red blood cells of people with type A blood have a protein called the A antigen on their surface; people with type B blood have the B antigen. In type O, the cells have neither A nor B antigens; in type AB, there are both antigens.

In one example of incompatibility, type A red blood cells (erythrocytes) have the A antigen, and the liquid part of the blood (the serum) contains antibodies against the type B cells; type B blood has the opposite configuration. So if the two types are mixed, the antibodies from the serum react to the "foreign" types, making the cells clump together.

MANUFACTURING BLOOD

Q. Will it ever be possible to synthesize blood the way insulin is made?

A. Artificial blood will not be available any time soon, and the need for donations will remain acute for the foreseeable future.

Synthesizing blood is much more complex than synthesizing insulin. Blood includes many different kinds of cells, while insulin is a protein.

There are ways to make hemoglobin, the protein in blood that carries oxygen, and most of the blood alternatives or substitutes that are being worked on are hemoglobin molecules aggregated together. They will serve as a bridge for people who need transfusions. However, the products that are being worked on would not be substitutes for transfused blood, except in emergencies or acute blood loss. Artificial blood cells are way off in the future, a decade or more.

Pigs' blood, with minor modification of the surface of its cells, would be compatible in humans, but its use raises other issues, like disease transmission, that would have to be worked out.

Many products have been available for some time that serve many, but not all, of the functions of plasma, the liquid that carries the cells and proteins of blood. These products can be used in certain situations.

THOSE ICY FINGERS

Q. When my fingers feel cold as ice indoors, how cold are they? What causes it?
A. What seems like frozen fingers is very subjective and could cover a wide range of temperatures.

Having fingers that are icy cold is a real sensation and can be very distressing, but it is usually not reflective of something dangerous. What is more dangerous is where one finger is cold or has changed color, or where feeling is absent, as it is in frostbite.

Skin temperature is controlled by the sympathetic nerves and the adrenal gland, part of the system for conserving or losing body heat. If it is cold outside, the system keeps heat inside the body by cutting skin circulation, reducing heat loss from the surface. If the nerves are overactive, the small blood vessels in deeper layers of the skin will contract, so the skin of the fingers may be cold while the body may not be.

Diseases that cause cold fingers are easily identified. They include Raynaud's syndrome; vasculitis, an inflammatory disease of the small blood vessels of the skin; and some arthritic diseases, such as rheumatoid arthritis. Smoking or caffeine can cause a problem if the sympathetic nerves are sensitive.

MEN, WOMEN, AND TEMPERATURE

Q. It seems that women are more sensitive to temperature changes than men. Is this true?

A. Sensitivity to temperature is much more complicated than a simple gender split, physiologists say. The reaction depends on many factors, such as exercise, previous conditioning, diseases, and any other tinkering with the complex system of signals to and from the hypothalamus that sets the body's temperature controls.

Some doctors suspect psychological factors make a difference, but it is difficult to separate psychological reactions based on a strong aversion to heat or cold from physiological responses. It is also possible that women do not dress as warmly.

But some male-female physiological differences may be significant in this area. Women tend to have more subcutaneous body fat than men, making them more likely to have a hard time dissipating body heat when temperatures rise. But women may do better than men as a room cools, because fat holds heat.

Larger animals have a smaller surface area relative to their volume than smaller animals, so they can stand colder temperatures with less heat loss. Men as a group are larger than women, although the size difference may not be enough to cause different reactions to temperature changes.

Some conditions, including an overactive thyroid, which is more common in women, can also cause hypersensitivity to heat.

THE BIG CHILL

Q. If a body temperature of 107 degrees Fahrenheit is nearly always fatal, what low body temperature is generally fatal?
A. Medical literature contains few if any cases in which people have recovered after their inner, or core, temperatures dropped below 55 degrees Fahrenheit.

Core body temperature is usually measured by electronic sensors inserted into the digestive tract. It cannot be measured with an ordinary oral thermometer. Hypothermia is considered to exist whenever the core temperature is below 95 degrees.

Hypothermia occurs when the body loses heat faster than it can burn fuel to replace it. How severe a person's reactions to low temperatures will be depends on age and overall physical condition, with the very old and the very young the most vulnerable; about 80 percent of hypothermia deaths occur in those older than 65.

Age increases the risk for several reasons. The ability to generate body heat declines because the heart rate is slower, blood vessels do not contract as well, and the elderly often lose muscle tone (which generates heat) and body fat (which conserves heat and supplies body fuel).

Exposed skin, cold air, cold water, cold wet clothing, and sitting on a cold surface that conducts heat away from the body all greatly increase the rate of heat loss. Dehydration also adds to the risks.

The rates of chemical activity in the body are slowed by very low temperatures. Eventually the heartbeat and breathing may stop, but even a very slow heartbeat and rate of respiration may maintain vital body functions.

Immediate treatment for hypothermia victims involves stopping further loss of heat by wrapping the person in warm, dry blankets. Gentle handling is essential because jolts can cause fatally irregular heart rhythms.

LIVER SPOTS

Q. What causes liver spots and how can they be removed?

A. Liver spots, also called age spots or lentigines, are the result of hyperpigmentation, or the buildup of excess pigment in patches of the skin.

Liver spots have nothing to do with the liver and most often result from a lifetime of exposure to sunlight. Other possible causes include surgery, pregnancy, and some medications.

Liver spots are usually flat and brown, with rounded edges, and are most often found on the face, hands, back

and feet. If the spots have irregular borders, a dermatologist should look at them to make sure they are not melanoma, an invasive skin cancer.

As with so many other results of photoaging, age spots can be prevented or minimized by keeping out of tanning booths and direct sunlight at midday, routinely using sunscreen, covering arms and legs, and wearing a hat with a four-inch brim.

Treatment may involve bleaching or fading creams, which can take weeks or months; chemical peels; prescription drug treatments like tretinoin, a derivative of vitamin A, used with sunscreens; related over-the-counter products containing retinols; and surgical resurfacing, often with lasers, to remove the pigmented cells.

THOSE ACHING FEET

Q. Why do my feet get more tired and sore when I am standing still than when I am walking?

A. If we leave aside the possible presence of diseases like arthritis or diabetes, several mechanical factors could make standing still more tiring than walking. First, the action of the muscles in walking keeps the circulation of both blood and lymph going, preventing the pooling of fluids in feet and ankles.

For another thing, when a person stands still, each foot is supporting about half the body's weight all by itself all the time. But in walking, there is a momentary respite for each foot as the other makes contact with the ground. When the unburdened foot swings forward, it is free of weight-bearing duty for the time it takes to complete that stride.

Experts in easing the fatigue of those who must work standing up for long periods often suggest making a conscious effort to shift weight from one foot to the other and elevating the feet alternately on a footrest.

Another fatigue factor in standing still is that the surface underfoot remains the same. Studies of store employees and shoppers have found that there is less perceived fatigue even in walking if the flooring changes periodically, perhaps from wood to carpet. A resilient surface also helps.

Also, someone who plans to take a walk may have chosen more supportive and comfortable shoes than the person who unexpectedly encounters a long line at the bank.

THOSE ACHING EYES

Q. Why do eyes burn, itch, and often turn red and feel swollen after a night with too little sleep? Why the relief from a good night's sleep?

A. Such a condition is probably an inflammatory response to the irritation of having the eyes open and exposed to the drying air. The effect is common knowledge and a clear symptom of sleeplessness but has not been completely studied.

Eye lubricants and tears dry in the air and may form scratchy particles. The skin around the eyes is pretty loose, and it can gather fluid fairly easily, so the swelling can be a sign of irritation. Redness, a result of capillary dilation, is another sign of irritation.

In some cases, the condition might also be a manifestation of an allergy, especially one to mattress mites, microscopic arachnids that infest many people's bedding. In such cases, a water bed might help.

A night of sleep helps cure the condition by protecting the eyeball. Even if you can't sleep, keeping the eyes shut will help.

PROTECTING THE EAR

Q. What is the function of ear wax? Where does it come from?

A. Ear wax, known to scientists as cerumen (pronounced suh-ROO-mun), traps dust and dirt particles to keep them from going down the ear canal to the eardrum. Besides protecting against dirt and water and lubricating the canal, ear wax is slightly acidic, so some experts say it has mild antibacterial properties and helps fight the growth of fungus or bacteria that can cause the outer ear inflammation called swimmer's ear.

Ear wax is formed by small glands under the skin of the outer part of the ear canal. It builds up in different amounts in different people. It may get thicker and drier in old age. Normally, the ear is self-cleaning; the wax gradually dries up, flakes, and either falls out or can be gently wiped away.

If too much wax accumulates, the traditional warning never to use cotton swabs or other objects to remove it still holds true, because a small instrument can push the wax deeper into the ear canal, against the eardrum, where it can block hearing or injure the drum.

Your doctor can remove the wax or suggest commercial or homemade drops to soften it. In some cases, stronger prescription softeners can be called for. Softeners or even water should never be used without medical advice if a perforated eardrum is suspected, because an infection may result.

Not Just an Appendix

Q. Does the appendix have any use in the human body?
A. The vermiform (Latin for worm-shaped) appendix, a dead-end branch of the intestines, plays at least a minimal role in the immune system and is also sometimes regarded as a potential spare part for replacing things like a diseased urinary bladder.

Along with the adenoids, tonsils, and spleen, the appendix is classified as part of the mucosal immune system, a secondary set of immune organs along the mucus-lined membranes of the body. This system is also called the mucosal-associated lymphoid tissue, or MALT.

Like the rest of the gut, the appendix contains nodules called Peyer's patches where certain types of immune cells mature and "learn" whether or not to react to foreign substances by calling in cellular troops to attack the invaders. This function of the appendix is most pronounced in the first few decades of life and declines thereafter.

However, the appendix is not a specialized immune organ and is not essential to health. It is a vestigial part of the gut that was important in animals whose diets were composed of more fiber than humans consume.

It is not normally full of immune cells called lymphocytes, except when it becomes infected, and since it is a pouch, this occurs with some frequency. Then lymphocytes and macrophages, which clean up microbial invaders, infiltrate in order to deal with the infection.

WRINKLING OVER TIME

Q. Why do we wrinkle as we age? What can be done about it?

A. Skin changes that cause wrinkles do accompany aging, as the deeper layer of skin, the dermis, gets thinner. But it happens more quickly in sun-exposed areas and in people who smoke. The breakdown of two kinds of molecules, collagen and elastin, is at fault.

Collagen type 1 is the molecule that makes up the bulk of the skin. Loss of this type of collagen, the same type found in bones, affects the elderly, and smoking can make it worse.

At least five studies have found that smoking is associated with "smoker's face," one that is prematurely aged by fine wrinkles that can accentuate the coarser wrinkles that occur along the lines of expression.

As for elastin, the stretchy molecules that help support the skin, ultraviolet rays cause direct damage, breaking the molecules down.

To help avoid wrinkles as you age, avoid smoking, stay out of the sun, routinely use hats and sunscreens, and use a good moisturizer, which holds water in the dermis and plumps it up.

LOSING COLOR

Q. Is there any treatment for vitiligo, the loss of skin pigment that leaves white patches on the body? And what causes it?

A. There are treatments for vitiligo that are at least partly effective in many cases, but its cause is still under study.

A prominent theory is that an autoimmune reaction is involved. The condition may also be associated with certain ailments, including thyroid disorders, and may flare up after injury, stress, or severe sunburn.

Patches occur in all races when pigment cells in the skin, called melanocytes, are destroyed and can no longer produce the pigment melanin. The most common treatment involves a drug called psoralen, taken orally. When followed by exposure to natural sunlight or ultraviolet light, the drug seems to make pigment cells migrate from hair follicles to white areas.

In some patients, steroids stop the spread of pigment loss. In others, such as the singer Michael Jackson, doctors use chemicals to lighten unaffected skin areas so they blend in with those where pigment has been lost.

Medical authorities also recommend avoiding excessive exposure to the sun. Tanning darkens normal areas, which makes the light patches more prominent because they do not tan.

SOAKING UP THE SUN

Q. How do people get a tan?

A. Exposure to the sun's ultraviolet radiation darkens granules of the pigment melanin in the surface layers of the skin. Part of the radiation also stimulates pigment-producing cells, called melanocytes, in deeper layers of the skin, causing a delayed-reaction tan, about three days after exposure.

When the top layers of skin wear off, so does the tan.

All adults have about 60,000 melanocytes per square inch of skin. Skin color is determined by how much pigment the cells make and what color it is; it ranges from black to light tan. Other factors that stimulate melanin production include X rays, heat, certain chemicals, hormones, and drugs (usually in combination with sun exposure), and inflammatory skin diseases.

Dermatologists warn that tanning goes hand in hand with skin aging and a higher risk of skin cancer. Ultraviolet B, or UVB, radiation, the so-called burning rays, is the kind most sun products protect against. They usually offer little protection against the ultraviolet A, or UVA rays, the so-called tanning rays. These are the rays that affect deeper layers of the skin, causing the breakdown of supporting tissue, resulting in premature aging, wrinkling, and a leathery appearance.

Some newer sunblocks protect against both kinds of radiation, but nothing works as well as avoiding midday sun exposure altogether and wearing a hat and long sleeves.

DAMAGING THE DNA

Q. How does ultraviolet radiation cause skin cancer?

A. The prevailing theory involves damage to the DNA of skin cells. It is the shorter UVB rays, which penetrate only the top layers of the skin, that are suspect, while the longer and more deeply penetrating UVA rays cause wrinkles and aging.

In tissue cultures, UV damages the DNA of cells, but humans have an enzyme that repairs it. Due to a genetic defect, some people lack the repair enzyme. The hypothesis is that in the body such DNA damage occurs all the time and is constantly repaired, but some cells do not get repaired, or get repaired improperly, and this is how skin cancer begins.

Researchers found a specific kind of DNA damage in a gene called CQ that occurs in this way. In the error, two DNA units of the type designated as thymine are side by side, instead of two units of the cytosine type. The error is called a thymine dimer. It is presumed that the brakes on cell multiplication come off because of it, leading to uncontrolled proliferation of cells into a tumor.

Ultraviolet radiation is implicated in the vast majority of nonmelanoma skin cancers, like basal cell carcinoma and squamous cell carcinoma. It is also linked to melanoma, though less clearly.

PUTTING THE PINCH ON A NERVE

Q. What is a pinched nerve, and what is it pinched between?

A. A pinched, compressed, or entrapped nerve can be surrounded by swollen tissues or impinged upon by bony processes in many areas of the body. The cause can be injury, disease, or even pregnancy. The result is pain, numbness, tingling, and weakness in the part of the body to which the nerve normally carries impulses.

One kind of nerve entrapment, carpal tunnel syndrome, is produced in the wrist because of repetitive stress from movements like typing; the resulting swollen tissues compress the median nerve, which runs through a bony tunnel in the wrist called the carpal tunnel.

Similar problems can affect the ulnar nerve, which runs through the elbow, and another nerve in the arm, the radial nerve.

The pain of sciatica results from compression of the sciatic nerve, which runs down through the buttocks to the back of the leg. The cause is often a herniated spinal disk; normally, this gelatinous cushion with a tougher outer ring separates the vertebrae, but injury can squeeze out the soft core so it puts pressure on a nerve.

A pinched tarsal nerve or plantar nerve can cause numbness in the foot. Some other commonly compressed nerves include the femoral nerve, which extends from pelvis to knee, and the peroneal nerve, along the side of the leg.

RUNAWAY SCARS

Q. What is a keloid and how do you get one?
A. A keloid is a scar that does not know when to stop forming, becoming large, shiny, smooth, and often pink and dome-shaped. It is not known why some people get overgrown scars after injuries, surgery, or acne, but

keloids are more common among people of black and Asian descent, so a genetic factor is suspected.

In normal scarring, after the inflammation that follows an injury subsides, scar tissue begins to form, along with tiny new blood vessels. Cells in the skin around the injury, called fibroblasts, produce collagen, a fibrous connective tissue. As more and more of the fibers link up, the scar becomes harder.

In a keloid, the process continues long after the wound is covered over, and the scar can become quite large. Keloids are not dangerous but can be disfiguring, tender, and sometimes itchy.

Removal of a keloid by surgery or the use of lasers, followed by corticosteroid injections at the site, is sometimes but not always successful, and can cause even worse scarring.

Someone with a tendency to form keloids may want to avoid plastic surgery, though doctors can sometimes use hidden incisions in facial surgery or avoid making cuts in the periphery of the face, where keloids are more likely to form.

TOO MUCH OF A GOOD THING

Q. Can a human breathe pure oxygen?
A. Yes, but it is not a good idea except under very special circumstances, because too high a concentration of oxygen or oxygen at too high a pressure can be toxic. For example, when a diver gets too much oxygen at high pressure, oxygen toxicity can cause lung damage and even convulsions.

However, pure oxygen in the form of O_2 is sometimes administered in an entirely closed chamber at greater than the normal air pressure at sea level; this is called hyperbaric oxygen therapy. Hyperbaric oxygen may be called for in cases of carbon monoxide poisoning, decompression sickness in divers who ascend too quickly, gas gangrene, smoke inhalation, some burns and infections, skin grafts that are about to fail, and some other conditions. In such cases, the extra oxygen may be lifesaving, but even then, it is usually used in repeated spurts.

Another well-known adverse effect of too much oxygen is the blindness in premature infants that is called retinopathy of prematurity, or retrolental fibroplasia. The blood vessels that supply the retina of a prematurely born baby are not fully developed, and in the presence of high concentrations of oxygen in an incubator, they may continue to grow in an abnormal pattern, destroying vision. Too much oxygen can also cause lung damage in infants.

OLDIES BUT GOODIES

Q. As a reasonably healthy 68-year-old, I have wondered, Is there an age limit for usable donations of organs like the heart or liver?
A. Organs may come from newborns on up, with no specific age limit. There was more of an age limit in the past, but now it is decided on a case-by-case basis.

The oldest known donor of a liver was 92, in Canada, and there was one who was at least 85 in the United States.

At the time of a donor's death, medical professionals determine whether organs are usable. Needed organs include the heart, kidneys, pancreas, lungs, liver, and intestines.

There is a general age limit of 70 for donation of tissue, including the eyes, skin, bone, heart valves, and tendons.

An important factor in donation acceptance is prompt recovery. Telling family members now, not in a will or letter, that you want to be an organ and tissue donor is the best way to make sure that your wishes are carried out.

Death by Air Bubble

Q. Is it true that air is released from a hypodermic syringe because an injected bubble could kill you?

A. Crime novels to the contrary, it is hard to dispatch someone with a needle unless you are expertly trying.

It is standard practice to make sure air is cleared from a syringe before pushing the plunger, but the chances of death occurring because of the air a fine needle might carry in a normal injection into muscle or skin are rather low; a small bubble would normally be dispersed in the tissue.

A bubble of air in the circulatory system, called an air embolism, can potentially be fatal, but usually only if the air is introduced into a fairly large vessel. If an arterial bubble cuts off oxygenated blood going to the heart muscle or a key part of the brain, for example, it could cause a heart attack or stroke. An air embolism in a large vein can also cause a dangerous air lock in the heart.

The main risk, however, lies in procedures like intravenous drips or in surgery. The rule in open heart surgery is "no air, anywhere," and heart-lung machines have filters for bubbles. There are also detectors for intravenous procedures.

FINAL CHANGES

Q. How long does it take for rigor mortis to set in? Is it a good indicator of the time of death?

A. Rigor mortis is gradual, usually noticeable about three to four hours after death, and the timing varies with several factors, including the person's activity just before death and the temperature of the body's surroundings. How long it takes the muscle stiffness to subside also varies, with rigidity usually reaching a peak after twelve hours and nearly disappearing in twenty-four to thirty-six hours.

Rigor is not a good indicator of the time of death. Coroners use the body's stiffness only in combination with other factors in estimating when a death probably took place.

Rigor mortis, literally the stiffness of death, comes about because of chemical processes within muscles. Their normal operation, in which filaments slide past each other in contraction or relaxation, depends on energy from molecules of adenosine triphosphate, or

ATP. As the supply of ATP is depleted after death, two important muscle proteins, actin and myosin, become chemically locked. Eventually, decay begins and the muscles soften.

Two other postmortem changes used in estimating time of death are algor mortis, or cooling, which proceeds at about 1.5 degrees Fahrenheit an hour under normal conditions, and livor mortis, the pooling and settling of the blood, which starts immediately after death and becomes fixed in about twelve hours.

CHAPTER 12

Things You've Always
Wanted to Know

An Icy Stare

Q. Why don't your eyes freeze when you are skiing or walking the dog in subzero temperatures?
A. The eyes have a very efficient radiator as well as a surface deicing system, at least in theory. The eye has a system of blood vessels that provides a constant irrigation of warm blood through and around the eyeball to keep it warm. This makes freezing very unlikely.

As for the surface of the eye, tears have a high salt concentration, which keep them from freezing at 32 degrees, as plain water would, and the eye is constantly coated with tears.

It is not impossible to freeze the eye, but it requires very low temperatures. For example, a freezing procedure called retinal cryotherapy, using a probe with liquid nitrogen, has been used to destroy certain parts of the retina, and the same procedure is also used to kill the cells of certain cancerous growths.

In the procedure, part of the eye is frozen for several seconds, and a visible ice ball forms, but the eye immediately defrosts when the probe is removed.

SNEEZING AFTER HOURS

Q. Why don't you sneeze when you are asleep?

A. Nobody has specifically studied this aspect of sneezing, but there are logical reasons that would explain why people do not sneeze overnight.

The reason people sneeze is that the inside of the nose swells up, much like blowing up a balloon. When a windblown particle of anything, an allergen or a particle of dust, hits the swollen lining, a sneeze results. When the wind blows or a door opens or a strong odor wafts in, a sneeze is likely to be set off.

In most bedrooms, there is no airflow at night, not even anyone walking around stirring up dust, so no particles blast the nose. Many people complain of sneezing attacks when they first wake up, throw off the covers, open closets, and stir up particles that settled overnight.

The nose lining actually tends to be even more swollen when people are lying down, but the lack of a breeze protects against a sneeze. Even with air-conditioning there is generally a filter, so particles get stirred up only if the unit is turned off for a while in a dusty room. In that case, the first blast of air may throw particles at the nose.

An allergic person by a window in pollen season will sneeze all night. But in that case, the person would probably not be asleep.

Dangerous Hiccups

Q. Can hiccups kill you?
A. Ordinary hiccups, resulting from things like overeating and stress, are usually benign. But hiccups can indicate a serious problem, and a prolonged, uncontrollable bout may lead to debilitating consequences like fatigue, weight loss, depression, problems with heart rhythm, esophageal reflux, and possibly exhaustion and death in a weakened patient.

In a famous case, Pope Pius XII had long periods of hiccups, associated with gastritis, though he eventually died of a stroke.

A hiccup is a spasm of the diaphragm, the sheet of muscle that controls breathing, accompanied by a sudden intake of breath and the closing of the epiglottis, the bit of tissue at the back of the throat that can close the airway.

The underlying cause of troublesome hiccups should be investigated. For example, the complicated nervous pathways involved in hiccups can be affected by diseases like multiple sclerosis; in such cases, and for other serious hiccups, muscle relaxants are often prescribed.

Other causes include gastrointestinal problems such as obstruction or inflammation, complications of AIDS or side effects of its treatment, nervous system tumors, encephalitis and meningitis, alcoholism, and problems with many medications.

PLEASURE AND PAIN

Q. Why does eating something really cold, like ice cream, sometimes give me a headache?

A. You are not alone, because about 30 percent of the population seems to have the same problem. The classic ice cream headache is a stabbing pain that usually peaks after thirty to sixty seconds, though it can last up to five minutes.

A doctor who gets such headaches, Dr. Robert Smith, founder of the Cincinnati Headache Center at the

University of Cincinnati College of Medicine, experimented with crushed ice applied to different parts of his mouth to see what set off the pains. The culprit, his research indicates, is at the back of the palate, from which a mass of nerves called the sphenopalatine ganglion stretches into the head. The nerves control the dilation and contraction of blood vessels, and dilated blood vessels in the head are known to cause several kinds of headaches.

Dr. Smith also found that he was able to induce such headaches only on warm days, though the internal mouth temperature remains constant. Other researchers have suggested that this is because in hot weather, a person tends to gulp cold drinks or wolf down lemonade so that the cold stuff is more likely to hit the palate hard. Ways to avoid the pangs might be to let the ice cream warm up in the front of the mouth before swallowing or to swallow it in such a way that it does not linger on the palate.

TELEVISION VISION

Q. My mother says sitting too close to the TV will ruin my eyes. Is she right?
A. Not according to experts. In fact, children can focus up close without eyestrain better than adults. That is because the lens, which changes its focus for nearby and faraway viewing, tends to lose some of its flexibility as people grow older.

Usually, sitting very close to the television set is a habit that children grow out of. However, sitting close to the screen to get a clearer image may be a symptom of uncorrected nearsightedness, and children who persist in doing it should be tested for myopia.

A lot of the traditional parental warnings about ruining your sight are only partly valid, according to ophthalmologists. For example, reading in dim light may tire your eyes, but it will not damage them.

Eye fatigue is a risk when reading in dim light and when using a computer screen for long periods, but it is reversible and preventable with commonsense measures such as accurately ground corrective lenses designed for the distance at which they will be used and sufficient blinking to lubricate dry eyes. Regular breaks to look up or across the room are strongly recommended, because looking at objects farther away usually relieves the strain on eyes.

If vision blurs or eyes tire very easily, it is time to get an eye examination from an ophthalmologist.

TICKLISH SUBJECT

Q. Why can't you tickle yourself?
A. The brain can tell which tickling sensations are caused by one's own actions and gives them low priority, so that it can be more receptive to sensations from outside sources that may be more urgent. One study suggests how brain areas may interact to do this.

In the study, a magnetic resonance imaging device scanned brain activity while volunteers had a palm tickled either by themselves or by the experimenters, using a tickling machine, a box with a pivoting rod. A piece of soft foam at the end of the rod could be moved by either the subject or an unseen experimenter.

The researchers found that the areas of the brain that process touch information, the somatosensory cortex, were more active when subjects were tickled by someone else than when they tickled themselves. The cerebellum was less active when the subject was making a movement that resulted in a touch sensation than when the movement did not produce a sensation.

This suggests that the cerebellum anticipates the sensation caused by the movement made by subjects tickling themselves and sends a message to the somatosensory cortex telling it to decrease its activity, so that the sensation is dulled.

A Pain in the Side

Q. What is a stitch in your side? What can you do to relieve the pain?

A. Many of the explanations offered for the sharp pain runners feel during hard breathing, usually on the right side, involve muscle stress or spasms in or near the diaphragm.

Because the muscle stress is probably caused by a rhythmic, repetitive activity, the solution is to develop techniques to break up that stressful rhythm. Runners could try changing their breathing patterns by breathing slower and deeper and forcefully exhaling through pursed lips. Other suggestions involve changing running position by leaning forward, backward, or sideways, stretching before running, having the stomach as empty as possible before running, and changing the foot one lands on when exhaling.

A more direct explanation is that the rhythm of running causes bouncing of the liver, stretching the ligaments that link liver and diaphragm. In this case, the suggestion is to stop running and use a hand to press the liver up against the diaphragm until the pain ends.

Catching Up on Sleep

Q. Can you "pay back" a sleep debt?

A. Yes, eventually, but it is not a simple matter of sleeping longer on a weekend after being denied adequate sleep for some days. In extreme cases, experts say, you may need six weeks of adequate sleep to repay a long-term sleep deficit.

Several studies have found that the amount of recovery sleep required to restore performance (though not mood) increases the longer someone has been awake. It might take two hours of sleep after one sleepless night, five hours after two nights.

Daytime napping can also help repay a sleep debt, and some experts even suggest that a two-hour "prophylactic nap" early in a long, planned period of sleep deprivation can help maintain productivity.

What "adequate sleep" means varies from individual to individual, and many do not even realize they are in debt. One test is to see how long you sleep before waking up naturally, feeling refreshed, with no alarm.

Sleep requirements hinge on many factors, including how efficient the sleeper is in getting the right kind of brain waves at the right time during sleep; scientists do not fully understand the function of the different kinds, but slow-wave sleep seems to be the most restorative after a sleep deficit. Most scientists seem to think that about half your normal sleep is needed to function the next day and that most people can get by on five hours, but as the debt grows, they may find themselves drowsy in meetings—or behind the wheel.

WHAT'S THAT?

Q. What does that little thing hanging at the back of our throat do? My science teacher said it does nothing.
A. The small piece of soft tissue dangling over the tongue is the uvula. It is variously described as U-shaped or tear-shaped, or classically speaking, grape-shaped; its name comes from the Latin word for grape, *uva*.

While some anatomy experts think it is only a vestigial organ, not all would agree with your teacher that it has no function. Some might say that it helps keep grapes (or anything else) from going down your breathing passage when you swallow, and that is the action that many standard anatomy texts describe.

The uvula has its own little muscle, the musculus uvulae, to help it stiffen and change shape, so it helps fill in the space at the back of the throat.

Singers credit the uvula with letting them produce a vibrato, or wavy up-and-down sound, and the jazz star Anita O'Day says that her vibrato-less vocal style, using many separate notes instead, arose because she lost her uvula in a tonsillectomy.

The uvula is one of the soft-tissue structures that is often implicated in snoring and sleep apnea, or interrupted breathing during slumber. Some treatments for these conditions involve removing excess flesh from the uvula and surrounding areas. The surgery, called uvulopalatopharyngoplasty, tightens up flabby tissues to enlarge the air passages.

LUMP IN THE THROAT

Q. What causes you to get a lump in your throat?

A. If the lump is stress related and does not involve serious difficulty in swallowing, it is probably just an exaggerated awareness of the epiglottis or spasms of muscles surrounding the throat.

After ruling out physical ailments that can cause the feeling of a lump in the throat, like throat cancer or esophageal reflux, in which some stomach contents are released upward, doctors call the condition globus hystericus.

Globus hystericus can be a small component of a larger set of symptoms that psychiatrists call generalized anxiety disorder, which may require psychiatric treatment or anti-anxiety drugs. But for such a diagnosis, the sufferer would have multiple, long-lasting symptoms from several of these groups: motor tension (jumpiness, shakiness); hyperactivity of the autonomic nervous system (sweating, pounding heart, clammy hands, dry mouth, the lump in the throat); apprehensive expectation (fear, rumination, anticipation of misfortune) and vigilance and scanning, with results like distractibility or insomnia.

If you can identify the stress that leads to the lump, and it is something as simple as a sad movie or a glimpse of an old boyfriend or girlfriend, you can probably avoid the sensation by avoiding the source of the stress or finding a better way to deal with stress, like meditation, breathing exercises, or yoga.

NERVES AND TEETH

Q. Having recently had a root canal procedure, I've been wondering: Why do teeth contain nerves?
A. Like other important organs, teeth have nerves for sensation and protection.

The diseased "nerve" removed in a root canal procedure is the common term for the combination of nerves and blood vessels that form pulp, the soft interior of the tooth. There is also a bundle of nerve fibers in the ligament that attaches the tooth to the bone. Together, these nerves let the teeth integrate with muscles, the brain, and the temporomandibular joint, responsible for the up-and-down motion of the jaw, in the complex activity of chewing.

The ability to know where the teeth are at all times is called proprioception, and nerve sensation is necessary to guide the teeth. If your bite is not quite right after dental work, or if your teeth shift, you can sense it immediately.

The nerves also let the teeth perceive heat, cold, and pain and protect them from harm. These sensations can warn of decay. Often, if there is a large cavity, the tooth becomes sensitive to sweets, as part of the body's defense mechanism.

NO STOMACH

Q. Can a person live without a stomach?
A. The stomach is not essential for human survival. Many people have survived and adjusted to total or partial surgical removal of the stomach because of diseases like stomach cancer.

The stomach is essentially a reservoir that allows people to eat the quantity of food they want, emulsify it, and pass it gradually into the small intestine. Without a stomach, one cannot consume the quantity of food one was able to before and usually must have more frequent and smaller meals.

There is an initial uncomfortable transition period after the loss of the stomach that may last months before the person can adjust to the loss.

The operation to remove a stomach is called a gastrectomy. It can be either partial or total. Doctors often place an external feeding tube directly into the small intestine, a procedure called a jejunostomy, to provide consistent nutrition during recovery and acclimatization.

If a person without a stomach eats too much, it is very quickly apparent because of an uncomfortable feeling of being very full. Other possible problems include diarrhea, a condition called dumping syndrome, in which nutrients are moved too rapidly into the small bowel, and upward reflux of bowel contents.

BRAIN FOLDS

Q. What do brain wrinkles have to do with how smart you are?

A. Brain wrinkles seem to have more to do with what makes humans smarter than lower animals than with what might have made Einstein smarter than you. In normal human brains, large grooves called fissures, small ones called sulci, and outward folds called gyri follow a standard plan from person to person.

Lower animals have smoother brains, apparently for evolutionary reasons. Cognitive brain activity takes place in cells in the thin surface layers of the cerebral cortex, and skull size did not increase as fast as brain complexity did as the species evolved. Convoluted human brains pack a larger surface area into a small container.

Human intelligence appears to be related to the branching of brain cells and the formation of complex links between them, not the shape of the platform where the links take place.

Only in a rare disease called lissencephaly ("smooth brain") is a lack of complex brain folding linked to mental deficiency. The condition is caused by the failure of developing nerve cells to migrate normally.

As for Einstein, recent studies of his preserved brain suggest that his intelligence may actually have been related in part to the absence of a fissure in a brain area involved in mathematical thinking, the inferior parietal lobe. The theory is that more links can be established between its cells because the groove is missing.

PERFECT PITCH

Q. What is perfect pitch, and why do some people have it?

A. Perfect pitch, which is also called absolute pitch, is the ability to name any note (such as A, B flat, C sharp) just from hearing the tone, without reference to other notes in a scale. Relative pitch, which is far more common, is the ability to tell what note is being played by judging the interval between its pitch and that of a reference note.

Each note in the scales used in most music is a sound resulting from a particular number of vibrations per second; for example, most modern pianos are tuned so that the A above middle C sounds at 440 vibrations a second.

How perfect pitch is developed or why some are born with it has been the subject of much study recently, and strong evidence points to both genetics and early musical training.

In a 1998 study of 600 musicians by researchers at the University of California at San Francisco, nearly all of those who had perfect pitch said they had started their training by age 6. The younger the musicians were when they started lessons, the more likely they were to have perfect pitch. Those with perfect pitch were also far more likely to have family members with the same ability.

Brain activity in response to music is now being closely studied by techniques including PET scans, and researchers have found that the area of the brain involved in processing sounds, the auditory cortex, develops clusters of specialized brain cells that are more active in response to piano tones in skilled musicians than in others.

While that study found no difference in brain activity in those with perfect pitch, other studies have found a sound-processing region in the left brain, part of the planum temporale, that is relatively larger than the same area in the right brain in those with perfect pitch and is active when they try to name a note.

This difference was found, the researchers said, even though most music processing is done in the right-hand side of the brain. One theory is that the overall contour and melodic functions of music may be handled by the brain's right side, while the task of naming notes and identifying their pitch could be concentrated on the left.

RING AROUND THE COLLAR

Q. Why does sweat leave a yellowish stain?

A. The most likely culprits for yellow clothing stains are body secretions called apocrine sweat and sebum, the oily secretion of the sebaceous glands. Deodorants and antiperspirants may also play a role.

The sebaceous glands are usually associated with hair follicles. Cells filled with fatty droplets die and burst, providing lubrication for the skin and hair. When the oils are exposed to air, they oxidize, turning yellowish, and if not quickly removed by thorough laundering, they can permanently yellow clothing. Sebaceous glands at the back of the neck cause "ring around the collar."

The underarms and groin are rich in apocrine sweat glands, which produce secretions that are milky and usually odorless until acted on by bacteria. Apocrine sweat contains many chemicals, including the acidic substances that produce the characteristic underarm odor.

The most copious human sweat, the kind produced by

widely distributed sweat glands called eccrine glands, is probably not a big stain producer unless the skin or clothing is already soiled. This kind of sweat is the body's chief means of temperature regulation, providing for cooling by evaporation. It is about 99 percent water, with only about 1 percent of it consisting of salt, urea, ammonia, and uric acid.

CHAPTER 13

Eat, Drink, and Be Healthy

ALL PIZZA, ALL THE TIME

Q. Can a person survive by eating only slices of New York City pizza?

A. Yes, if it is a real cheese pizza with real tomato sauce.

For a complete diet, first you need to consume a sufficient quantity of food to get enough calories. Then you need a good source of protein and a supply of certain essential nutrients, like vitamins B_{12} and C, found only in certain kinds of foods. Other vitamins, minerals, and useful nutrients like antioxidants should also be present in some amount.

Pizza mixes a lot of ingredients and can potentially meet all these requirements, as long as you eat enough slices.

First, pizza has plenty of calories, as dieters know. Protein is found in both the wheat crust and the cheese. Vitamin B_{12}, which is found only in animal products, is supplied by the cheese, a dairy product. (Beware of imitations; real pizza cheese is stringy when hot.) Vitamin C is found only in vegetables, the fresher the better, but canned tomatoes or tomato sauce will do. It would be preferable to include some slices of fresh tomato. A few greens on top, like parsley or broccoli or spinach, wouldn't hurt.

Vitamin E is found in the olive oil that good pizzas are made with. Vitamin A comes from the tomatoes, vitamin D can come from the sun, and vitamin K you make yourself. To top it off, tomato sauce is a good source of nutrients like lycopenes, with their rich antioxidant potential.

All pizza is not a perfect diet, but potentially you could survive for quite a long time.

PEANUT: FRIEND OR FOE?

Q. Is peanut butter good for you or bad for you?
A. It can be either very healthful or very noxious, or both. A study by scientists at the U.S. Department of Agriculture, done with money from the Peanut Institute, suggests that peanuts may contain enough resveratrol, the compound in red wine associated with a low rate of heart disease, to be helpful to human health.

The levels per ounce the scientists found were only about half those in wine, and the average serving of peanuts is only an ounce, not a whole wineglass.

And as George Washington Carver found, the peanut is very nourishing, perhaps too nourishing for weight watchers. It is rich in proteins, carbohydrates, minerals, and some vitamins. It contains no cholesterol, being a plant food, not an animal food, but it is full of oily calories; just a tablespoon of crunchy peanut butter has about 94 calories.

Another problem with peanut butter is that people who are allergic to peanuts tend to be severely allergic, subject to anaphylactic shock, which can stop breathing and cause death, if they eat even a trace. An undetectable amount of peanut butter used as a thickener in a prize chili recipe killed a Rhode Island student in 1986, leading to warnings about peanut butter hidden in unexpected dishes. A peanut allergy may be accompanied by severe allergies to other legumes.

THE TROUBLE WITH MOLD

Q. How risky is aflatoxin, a toxic carcinogen that can grow on peanuts, for American consumers?
A. The short answer is that aflatoxin is of very little concern. Aflatoxin is produced by the fungus *Aspergillus flavus*, and most people don't eat moldy food, because it tastes bad. Documented human aflatoxin problems usually occur in tropical countries, where the wet climate is conducive to mold growth, or in extremely poor ones, where people are forced to eat any food they can get.

Second, humans are much less affected by aflatoxin than animals, especially some birds. Even someone who tried to commit suicide with aflatoxin, a lab worker, did not die or suffer much long-term harm. It causes liver cancer in animals, but a big study of diet in China found no link between it and human liver cancer, except in those who had had hepatitis B.

Third, the U.S. Department of Agriculture works

with all big farmers to monitor all crops, such as grains and peanuts, that are susceptible to mold. The USDA designed a machine that kicks out suspicious peanuts, and even if you get a moldy one, chances are it is a different kind of mold. As for peanut butter, big producers test both raw materials and finished batches for aflatoxin.

TEENAGERS AND CHOCOLATE

Q. Does eating chocolate cause acne or make it worse?
A. Repeated studies have failed to find any link between eating chocolate (or anything else) and teenage breakouts. As long ago as 1950, a study by a dermatologist compared the results of giving teenagers with acne candy bars that just tasted like chocolate and those made with real chocolate. Photographs showed no difference in new breakouts.

In another study, 65 acne sufferers ate large amounts of chocolate daily; 46 showed no change in their acne, 10 got better, and 9 got worse. When the same patients received look-alike candy containing no chocolate, 53 showed no change, 5 got better, and 7 got worse.

In still another study, of Navy midshipmen with acne, four weeks of eating at least three bars of chocolate daily had no effect on skin lesions.

Some doctors suggest that an individual who observes breakouts after eating certain foods should avoid those foods, but allergists say chocolate is rarely if ever a factor in food allergies.

Some people fear the caffeine content of chocolate will keep them awake, but it is minimal, chocolate makers say. An ounce of milk chocolate has 5 milligrams of caffeine, an ounce of bittersweet chocolate has 5 to 10 milligrams and a 6-ounce cup of cocoa has about 10 milligrams, as against 100 to 150 milligrams in a cup of brewed coffee.

FEEDING THE NAILS

Q. Does eating gelatin really make your nails stronger?
A. Not any more than eating enough of any other protein. If someone is severely protein deficient, high quality protein like that in gelatin might make a difference, but the average person gets plenty of protein.

It's the same with calcium. It would help your nails if you were totally deficient, but if your bones are falling apart, you don't care about your nails.

To make a real difference in nail strength, treat your nails the way you treat your skin. If you moisturize your hands after you wash the dishes, for example, rub the product into the nails as well. Keep your nails out of harsh chemicals. Wear gloves to do housework.

Someone whose nails are really brittle might even wear latex gloves when washing his or her hair. Avoid nail polish and other drying nail-care products. Polish covers nail abnormality but actually makes it worse. Polish remover, even the kind without acetone, is very drying and hard on nails.

What if your nails split rather than break? Longitudinal splitting is something that occurs with age. Ridges and valleys develop, and splitting occurs along fracture lines, because the nails are drying.

Again, help for this problem lies in moisturizing. Wet the nails and cover them with Vaseline or even alpha hydroxy acid. It is not a quick fix, but must be done until the nail grows out entirely, which takes six to eight months.

The other kind of splitting, called onychoschizia, which occurs in layers at the tip of the nail, is something seen most often in chronic polishers or people who use fingernails as tools.

JUST ADD WATER

Q. I'm confused by what health authorities say when they recommend drinking eight glasses of water a day. How big is a glass?

A. They are usually talking about six to eight glasses of 8 ounces each, for a total of 64 ounces a day.

It does not hurt to drink more, especially if you are exerting yourself. You might weigh yourself before and after a workout and drink 16 ounces of water for every pound you lose.

With a loss of just about 2½ quarts, you start to have serious problems, like skin shrinkage, muscle weakness and fatigue, irritability, dizziness, and headaches.

Another time to drink extra water is when you are

on a diet to lose weight, to help the kidneys flush out the waste products from the extra flesh you burn, and to prevent constipation. Try drinking a glass before and a glass during each meal to control food intake. And at high altitudes, drink up to twenty glasses a day.

What nutritional authorities are talking about is not coffee, soda, or beer, but hydrating liquid, preferably plain water. Other beverages may contain diuretics (especially alcohol and caffeine) that make you lose water, on balance.

And don't count on your thirst to remind you when it is time to drink. The body can easily lose a quart or more of water before your thirst may signal you, and when you do take a drink, the feeling of thirst goes away long before you have actually replenished your water supply.

CALCIUM WITHOUT COWS

Q. I read that quinoa, a grain from the Andes, is very high in calcium. How high? What are some other nondairy sources of calcium?

A. Quinoa is a significant source of calcium, but you would have to eat a large amount of it to get a full daily supply. The National Academy of Sciences recommends 1,000 milligrams of calcium a day for most people, more for those over 50, and according to the United States Department of Agriculture, a cup (eight ounces) of cooked *Chenopodium quinoa* provides about 102 milligrams. That is more than some other grains, but a cup of cow's milk has about 300 milligrams.

There are other nondairy sources of calcium that are richer in calcium. Just two corn tortillas would provide about 120 milligrams, for example. Many greens are especially rich in calcium, and a cup of cooked turnip greens might offer 450 milligrams. Canned sardines and salmon with the bones in are good sources, too, as are some beans, peas, and seeds.

However, quinoa is a generally nutritious food, rich in protein, and it has several vitamins and minerals in it, including folate (49 micrograms a cup), a vitamin associated with a greatly reduced risk of birth defects when eaten by pregnant women.

ACID UPON ACID

Q. Is taking aspirin with orange juice a no-no? What about alcohol?

A. The *Physicians' Desk Reference for Nonprescription Drugs* (PDR) does not advise against taking normal doses of aspirin in addition to acidic foods or alcohol, itself a powerful drug, but there may be deleterious interactions for some people.

That is because aspirin is an acid, acetylsalicylic acid, and when aspirin is taken with acidic foods and drinks, like citrus fruits, tomatoes, fruit juices and drinks, colas, wine, pickles, vinegar, or drinks with caffeine or alcohol, the acids' irritating effects on the stomach are intensified.

For most adults, the doses listed on the label of the aspirin bottle are safe. But the PDR says that people who are allergic to aspirin or who have asthma, stomach problems that persist or recur, gastric ulcers, or bleeding problems should not take aspirin unless directed to do so by a doctor.

As for aspirin plus alcohol, the Food and Drug

Administration has recommended that anyone who regularly has three alcoholic drinks a day should check with a doctor before taking aspirin or any other over-the-counter painkiller. The FDA decided that alcohol plus aspirin was risky mostly because they both irritate the stomach lining in the same way. And a small 1990 study found that aspirin significantly lowered the body's ability to break down alcohol in the stomach, resulting in blood alcohol levels that were 30 percent higher than those in people who drank alcohol alone.

HIGH ON COFFEE

Q. Why is caffeine a stimulant?

A. Caffeine is not a direct stimulant; instead, it blocks the action of another chemical, naturally present in the human body, that has a calming effect on the activity of cells, especially those in the brain and spinal cord.

Caffeine, found in tea, coffee, and cocoa, is one of a class of chemicals called methylxanthines that temporarily occupy the same cell receptors as adenosine, a chemical produced by the body's energy metabolism. Adenosine is a neuromodulator, a substance that normally acts as a brake on nerve cell activity by keeping cells from staying excited too long. When adenosine's action is blocked by caffeine, nerve cells are more active.

Caffeine enters the brain very rapidly and stays active for several hours, but its effects drop off more quickly than those of some other stimulants. The time needed for caffeine concentrations in the bloodstream to drop by half is about three to six hours in a healthy adult, compared with about ten hours for methamphetamine.

Navy scientists have studied caffeine's short-term stimulation for possible use in military campaigns to counteract the effects of fatigue. The Operational Clinical Research Center of the Naval Aerospace Medical Research Laboratory reviewed the literature on the known effects of caffeine and concluded that "there is consistent and convincing scientific data that indicates the effectiveness of caffeine in counteracting the increased sleepiness and decreased alertness associated with sleep loss."

PRIMING THE HEAT PUMP

Q. Why does drinking alcohol give the illusion of warmth without keeping you warm in cold weather?

A. The assumptions of the question are not totally true. It's not just drinking, but where you drink and what kind of clothes you have on that determine whether the body ends up warmer or colder.

What happens is that alcohol causes the blood vessels in the skin to dilate, so that more blood passes through, and more blood means more heat going through the skin. So if you drink and are sitting in the living room

with a sweater on, for example, that heat due to vasodilation will be retained, and you will feel warm.

But if you go outside without enough clothing, all that heat will dissipate. Such heat loss poses a serious risk of death from hypothermia for people drinking outside in cold weather. Excessive drinking also impairs sensation and the judgment that would ordinarily tell a person that it is time to come in from the cold.

CALCIUM WITHOUT COMPLAINT

Q. What form of calcium supplement is most easily digested? And why do the supplements sometimes cause indigestion?
A. Calcium citrate, the type found in calcium-enriched orange juice, is less likely to cause stomach upset than other forms. Calcium carbonate and calcium gluconate are the two forms that are most common in supplements; they both tend to be adequately absorbed. Calcium citrate is a good alternative, because it is very well absorbed and also enhances iron absorption, which may be inhibited by some other forms.

For all kinds of calcium supplements, it has been found that vitamin D, either in foods or supplements or manufactured by the body in the presence of sunlight, increases absorption of calcium.

The 1994 National Institutes of Health Consensus Development Conference statement on calcium says that gastrointestinal side effects of calcium supplements are usually observed at relatively high dosages. Calcium ions stimulate gastrin secretion and gastric acid secretion, which can produce a rebound hyperacidity when calcium carbonate is used as an antacid. These side effects should not be major problems with a modest increase in calcium intake, the statement said.

As with other nutrients, the conference emphasized:

"The preferred approach to attaining optimal calcium intake is through dietary sources."

Tea for Therapy

Q. I bought some milk thistle tea, *Silybum marianum,* at the health food store. It's supposed to be good for the liver. Is it helpful or harmful?

A. Milk thistle does contain chemicals called flavones that appear to benefit the liver, but these compounds are not very soluble in water, and the tea has only about one-tenth the strength of the original plant material.

In fact, the chemicals are poorly absorbed through the gastrointestinal tract and would probably be medically effective only if concentrated and injected.

Toxic effects have apparently not been reported from consumption of milk thistle. As with many herbal remedies, the concentration of active ingredients varies as much as fourfold from sample to sample, so dosage would be hard to control.

Milk thistle is a Mediterranean plant, a tall herb with prickly leaves and a milky sap. It has become naturalized in California and the eastern United States. It has small, hard fruits resembling seeds. While it was long used for liver complaints, it was virtually ignored in the first half of this century.

A few decades ago, however, German scientists isolated a crude mixture of chemicals from the fruits that appeared to have liver-protectant properties and called the extract silymarin. Silymarin was subsequently found to contain a large number of flavones, some of which protect against a variety of toxins, even the poison of the death cap mushroom. There have even been human trials for conditions like hepatitis and cirrhosis, with some encouraging results. Silymarin not only protects intact liver cells by blocking the entry of toxic substances, it also appears to stimulate protein synthesis and thus accelerate regeneration of liver cells.

COLONIZING THE GUT

Q. If I eat a lot of yogurt, will the bacteria in it make me sick?

A. There is no evidence of human health problems from yogurt with live bacteria, and there is some evidence the bacteria may be beneficial.

It is controversial whether yogurt bacteria survive in the gastrointestinal tract, and conclusions must await completion of research, but there is better-than-anecdotal evidence that bacteria can help colonize the tract and keep out bad bacteria. The theory is supported by studies of young chicks sprayed with bacteria present in adult chickens. The chicks take up these microbes and are not colonized by harmful salmonella, an effect called competitive exclusion.

There is no reason to eat only yogurt without live cultures for fear of danger from the bacteria that ferment milk into yogurt. The most commonly used culture is *Lactobacillus delbrueckii bulgaricus* in combination with *Streptococcus thermophilus*. Both are harmless in the gut, if they survive.

TEMPEST IN A TUNA CAN

Q. If large fish, like tuna, can have traces of mercury, should I cut out tuna fish sandwiches?

A. There is both concern and controversy over mercury in fish, but an occasional tuna fish sandwich for an adult who is not going to become pregnant is not the main worry.

The biggest concern is the risk to a fetus. Mercury builds up in muscle cells of fish and in those who ingest it, and can remain to damage the nervous system of a fetus even months after ingestion, but what levels are dangerous has been debated. Recently, after an eighteen-month study, the National Academy of Sciences put the boundary of concern at levels only one-fifth as high as other proposed standards: 0.1 micrograms per kilogram of body weight a day. Translated to consumption of fish, to be on the safe side, a potentially pregnant woman might want to eat no more than one tuna fish sandwich a week. But the safe limit for other adults is probably much higher.

The riskiest fish are sharks and swordfish. Just behind them are the large species of tuna. But canned tuna uses much smaller species, with a smaller range of mercury accumulation, and so canned tuna is safer than tuna steaks.

CHALK MAKES ITS MARK

Q. What is kaolin, and where does it come from? Is the kaolin in diarrhea medication the same as the clay in china?

A. Kaolin, also called China clay, is a chalky rock composed chiefly of kaolinite, together with quartz and mica. It is formed by the weathering of aluminum-rich silicate rocks, especially feldspar. Over the ages, the crystals wash into large sedimentary deposits.

Purified kaolin in a suspension with pectin from apples has long been used to fight diarrhea. It is a gastrointestinal adsorbent, believed to attract and hold microbes that may be causing the diarrhea. The action of pectin is not known.

Kaolin is said to derive its name from an area of China with extensive deposits of the mineral. It is found in many other places famous for china, like Meissen, Germany; Limoges, France; and parts of England.

There are also kaolin deposits in the United States, including a great chalk mark across the state of Georgia. The China Clay Producers Association says the Georgia deposit dates from 50 million to 100 million years ago, when the Atlantic Ocean covered much of Georgia south of a line drawn from Columbus to Augusta. Above this line, known as the Fall Line, crystalline rocks from the Piedmont Plateau began to break down, and streams carried the tiny crystals seaward. The deposits were later covered with heavy layers of earth.

SEEKING A SIESTA

Q. Why am I so sleepy and drowsy after lunch? It makes it hard to concentrate.

A. There are three likely explanations, based on recent research.

First, what do you eat and drink? A lunch high in carbohydrates, especially if no protein is eaten along with bread and milk, is likely to produce calm to the point of sleepiness, because of the complex role of carbohydrates in shifting the balance of neurotransmitters in the brain. Conversely, some protein contributes to alertness. A three-martini lunch also induces sleepiness.

Second, as siesta-loving societies have long recognized, sleep researchers have found that there is an inborn readiness in human beings to take a midafternoon nap. Volunteers isolated from all evidence of day and night and left to set their own sleep patterns tended to settle into one long sleep session and a session of 1 or 2 hours about 12 hours after the middle of the main period.

Third, you may be sleep deprived. While the average adult needs 8 to 9 hours of sleep a night, most get only 7, and many get 6 or less during the workweek. People permitted to sleep as much as they choose sleep 10.3 hours out of every 24, just as monkeys and apes do.

An afternoon nap may be just what nature ordered to restore alertness.

CHAPTER 14

Battleground: The Body

WHERE DANGER LURKS

Q. How long can germs live on an object? Does the surface have to be moist? Sometimes when I get recurring colds or flu, I wonder if I am reinfecting myself.

A. Some disease-causing organisms, or pathogens, can thrive and multiply for some time on an object like a phone receiver spattered by the saliva of an infected person. But most bacteria and viruses quickly die when moisture disappears, usually after one or two hours for the saliva spray.

Different pathogens have different survival times, ranging from a few minutes or hours to days or even months, and some might lurk for weeks or months on an object like a door handle in the house of someone with hepatitis A. In such cases, infectious disease specialists recommend frequent hand washing and avoiding touching your eyes or mouth; such measures would cut your infection risk to a very low level.

Using the damp toothbrush of someone with some infectious diseases would be a very likely way to get sick yourself, but cold viruses are usually spread by hand-to-eye or hand-to-mouth contact.

A Germ's Germ

Q. Do germs have germs?
A. There are viruses that infect disease-causing bacteria, as well as many other bacteria. Called bacteriophages, meaning bacteria eaters, they were discovered during World War I and named in 1917.

Much smaller than the bacteria they attack, bacteriophages cannot grow and multiply on their own. Instead, like other viruses, they attach themselves to the surface of the target and insert their own genetic material, taking over the cellular machinery and using the bacteria's

chemical energy to build and assemble the parts of new bacteriophages.

The resulting material soon reaches a volume that weakens, then bursts, the walls of target bacteria; this process is called lysis.

Bacteriophages, which are very common, are highly specific in their targets, with each kind attacking only certain species of bacteria.

Bacteriophages have been investigated as possible alternatives to antibiotics. The ones that attack the useful microbes *Lactobacillus acidophilus* and *Lactobacillus caseii,* used as starter cultures in fermented milk products, have also been studied by researchers who want to foil the attack.

PINK AND PURPLE BACTERIA

Q. What do doctors mean when they talk about gram-negative bacteria?

A. They are referring to how the germs react to one of the basic tests in bacteriology, the Gram stain or Gram's stain, which distinguishes between two major classes of bacteria by how they take up certain dyes.

On a microscope slide, heat-treated gram-positive bacteria take up a purple dye (originally gentian violet), which is then fixed with an iodine solution, and they hold on to the color even after the slide is washed with a solvent. Gram-negative bacteria, which have thinner but more complex and less permeable cell walls, do not retain the purple dye, but take up a counterstain, safranine, and end up a dark pink.

Gram-negative bacteria are of concern because they tend to be more resistant to antibiotics. Many cause serious diseases, including the plague, Legionnaire's disease, and many bowel-related diseases, including cholera and salmonella.

Opportunistic infections from gram-negative bacteria are also a major danger in hospitals. When some of them escape from the gut and enter a patient's bloodstream through medical procedures, they can cause septic shock, which is often fatal.

The test was named for Dr. Hans Christian Joachim

Gram, a Danish doctor who developed it while working at the University of Berlin in 1884. He was trying to distinguish between two kinds of organisms that cause pneumonia: pneumococci and *Klebsiella pneumoniae.*

MASKING A COLD

Q. When Asian people wear face masks, is it to keep from getting a cold or other infection, or is it to keep from spreading one? Does it work?

A. Polite East Asian people with a cold may wear a mask with the aim of preventing its spread; this is especially common in Japan. In China, the idea may be to cut down infection or it may be a reaction to high levels of visible pollution; in some of China's industrial areas, masks are worn simply in the hope of keeping coal dust out of the respiratory tract.

However, there is little hope of cutting down on the transmission of colds by wearing a mask. Medical authorities believe that most colds spread from nose to hand and then from hand to nose, rather than through the air, so a considerate cold victim should instead wash his or her hands frequently.

The influenza virus does travel easily through the air as a passenger on water droplets, so a mask may head off its transmission.

WASH YOUR TROUBLES AWAY

Q. Is there any way to keep from getting a cold?

A. There are no guarantees, but there are some ways to cut your risks. The most important are avoiding crowds, especially during the peak cold seasons of September, late January, and April; avoiding people who obviously have colds; avoiding shaking hands with people who might have them; avoiding rubbing the nose and eyes; and washing your hands, washing your hands, washing your hands.

These precautions may help because of the way colds are often spread: not just through infected droplets in the air but through particles carried by hand to eye and nose membranes.

The greatest share of colds are caused by rhinoviruses (about a third) and coronaviruses (about 10 percent). Rhinoviruses seem to spread best in droplets from a runny nose, though they may also be sprayed by coughs and sneezes.

Once virus particles land on a surface or someone's hands, they may remain active for several hours. Then the virus can go from hand to face to eye and nose membranes.

Someone with a cold can be contagious even before signs of illness appear and for a couple of days after it is obvious, so one cannot entirely prevent colds by avoiding people with symptoms, but it helps. Other useful measures are eating a balanced diet, which is associated with a lower suscepti- bility, and staying away from children, who get five to eight cold infections a year. Those younger than 2 have the most.

Persistent Pathogens

Q. Can you reinfect yourself with an infectious disease from which you are recovering, perhaps through exposure to residual germs on your hands?

A. There is no simple answer, but in general, this is very unlikely. In theory such reinfection is conceivable, but there are no documented cases of it.

The possibility would depend on the organism and how the person's immune system responded to it. If a pathogen is on the skin a long time, the person has probably developed immunity to it. The same holds true for an infection from which a person is recovering, so it is difficult to "reinfect" yourself unless it is a totally different organism.

Even if a person has two cases of flu in the same winter, the second case would probably involve an unrelated flu virus that was present at the same time. The same patterns of disease would appear, so it would be impossible for the patient to distinguish between the two infections.

Long-Lasting Immunity

Q. Why does immunization have long-lasting effects?

A. Immunity is long-lasting because some of the many kinds of cells that make up the normal human immune system are naturally able to retain a "memory" of the defense efforts aroused by certain infections or vaccines.

There are many kinds of immune cells, including T cells and different types of white cells. Their interaction with disease is complex and involves long chains of interactions and responses.

A vaccine fools the body into thinking it is being infected and creating a defense against that organism that it keeps in its immune memory. Later, if exposed to the infection, the body fights it quickly.

For example, after an actual infection with a disease like measles, which people rarely get more than once, immune memory is created, and certain cells are ready to fight again upon reexposure. The memory remains for years.

For some vaccines, protection may last a long time, even a lifetime. But for others, vaccines may protect for only a short time.

PUTTING VIRUSES TO WORK

Q. Unlike bacteria, which can be useful in many ways, there don't seem to be any "good" viruses. Do any play a positive role?

A. From the human point of view, some viruses can be useful, potentially useful, or at least interesting.

Under the "interesting" heading would fall the mosaic virus, which produced the fantastically variegated tulips of the tulipomania investing craze in seventeenth-century Holland. The rare infected bulbs were treated almost like a currency with a constantly multiplying value until the market crashed in 1637. It was discovered that the infection weakened the plants, and now hybridizers work to create the same colorful effects by breeding rather than infection.

Unquestionably useful in the field of public health is the vaccinia virus. It was discovered that milkmaids infected with relatively mild cowpox were immune to virulent smallpox, and the knowledge eventually led to widespread vaccination, eradicating smallpox as a disease. Later, the related vaccinia virus was used for this purpose.

In genetic medicine experiments, harmless viruses are used to carry desirable genes into cells. For example, scientists have tried treating a genetic disease called familial hypercholesterolemia by letting a virus insert a crucial gene into liver cells that makes them produce a chemical sponge for harmful cholesterol.

THE SICKNESS SEASON

Q. Why is flu season in winter? Why in general are more people ill in winter?
A. It is not cold feet and wet heads that are the problem, infectious disease experts say, but the fact that human beings are warmth-loving social animals. At least in cold climates, widespread outbreaks of diseases like colds and influenza tend to start in winter months, when people spend more time together indoors in close quarters with the windows shut. The cold months also bring children, those well-known vectors of bacteria and viruses, together in the classroom and day-care center, where they can pick up infections and take them home to the rest of the family.

In the Northern Hemisphere, early winter also includes major holidays with their attendant crowds and socializing. And even air-kissing under the mistletoe and

New Year's handshakes may help transfer germs, some of which travel in airborne respiratory particles while some are spread from hand to hand.

ALTITUDE ADJUSTMENT

Q. I am physically fit, but I almost always suffer altitude sickness on skiing weekends. What can I do?

A. Try a longer vacation. Altitude sickness is not linked to a person's general condition but to specific adaptations to high altitudes; even puny permanent residents are usually immune.

Medical experts say the body usually adjusts within a few days to the complex changes in blood chemistry that come about because of the relative shortage of oxygen on high slopes. It produces more oxygen-carrying red blood corpuscles and more capillaries to carry them. The experts also recommend a gradual ascent, if possible. Some recommend medications, including diuretics, to ease the adjustments.

If you get symptoms of what is also called acute mountain sickness (including some that are often mistaken for flu), you should seek oxygen, move to a lower elevation, avoid exertion, and drink plenty of fluids. In 1992, researchers working with astronomers on 13,796-foot Mauna Kea in Hawaii found that floods of water helped ease splitting headaches in many healthy workers. Dehydration occurs because the body tries to thicken its blood to improve absorption of the scanty oxygen.

The Mauna Kea researchers also recommended a breathing technique in case of faintness, disorientation, or nausea: Take a deep breath and hold the nose and mouth tightly closed while pushing to expel the air from the lungs. The increased pressure of the air in the lungs is enough to drive more oxygen into the bloodstream.

FELINE FEVER

Q. What is cat scratch fever?

A. Cat scratch fever or cat scratch disease is a mild flu-like infection, usually causing swollen lymph nodes and a low-grade fever, that was first described in the 1950s as being associated with cat scratches, especially from kittens.

The infection usually goes away by itself in a few weeks and can be treated with antibiotics, but it can cause a severe inflammation called bacillary angiomatosis in patients with weakened immune systems.

A cat carrying the microbe does not show symptoms, and medical and veterinary authorities say it is not necessary to get rid of it. If someone in the household is at high risk, a test to detect the infection can be done and the cat can be treated. People who have not been exposed to cats can also be infected.

It was difficult to find the disease organism, and it was long assumed to be a virus. A small bacterium called *Afipia felis* was mistakenly identified as the cause in the 1980s, but later research found the disease was caused by a bacterium called *Rochalimaea henselae*, eventually reclassified as *Bartonella henselae*. It was named for Dr. Diane Hensel, a microbiologist who did some of the research.

The bacterium is closely related to *Bartonella quintana*, which caused trench fever in World War I and is spread from person to person by the human body louse. In cat scratch fever, however, it appears that fleas spread the infection from cat to cat, but not from person to person.

RESPIRATORY DISTRESS

Q. I know ARDS is a respiratory disorder, but what type?
A. ARDS, which stands for acute respiratory distress syndrome, or sometimes adult respiratory distress syndrome (to distinguish it from a lung problem in newborns), is not a disease itself, but a type of severe acute lung dysfunction that can result from disease or injury, according to the ARDS Support Center, a clearinghouse for information.

The condition stiffens the lungs, fills them with water, and causes shortness of breath from respiratory failure. Inflammation damages microscopic air sacs called alveoli, which collapse, and tiny blood vessels called capillaries, which leak fluid into the lung. The inflammation can cause permanent scarring.

When doctors first became aware of ARDS in World War II, it was invariably fatal, but modern mechanical respirators, delivering extra oxygen, now help many to survive it.

Treatment of the condition can cause its own damage, like oxygen burns, and may leave long-term problems.

Doctors have learned to look for ARDS and treat it in patients who have survived auto accidents or heart surgery or who have illnesses like pneumonia or severe infections like septic shock, but they do not know why some of these patients suffer ARDS and others do not.

MAD COWS AND YOU

Q. Can foot-and-mouth disease and mad cow disease be spread to humans by dairy products?

A. Foot-and-mouth disease is a danger only to animals, not to humans, and the chance of getting mad cow disease from dairy products is zero to almost zero. The risk is so slight that there is an exemption allowing the importation of milk from countries where mad cow disease has been found.

Transmissible spongiform encephalopathy, or TSE, is the umbrella term for illnesses—like bovine spongiform encephalopathy (the formal name of mad cow disease) and Creutzfeldt-Jakob disease—that are believed to be caused by prions. Neither viruses nor bacteria, prions are misfolded proteins. Other such diseases are scrapie in sheep and chronic wasting disease in deer and elk.

The prevailing theory is that a prion acts like a seed crystal, causing healthy proteins, usually in the brain, to misfold and bring on destruction of brain tissue, creating spongelike cavities. But the only tissues in diseased cattle likely to contain dangerous levels of prions are those in and around the nervous system and the very end of the small intestine.

AIDS AND MOSQUITOES

Q. What evidence do scientists have that mosquitoes don't carry HIV from person to person?
A. There are three kinds of evidence. First, there is epidemiological data from studies of AIDS outbreaks. For example, in sub-Saharan Africa, where mosquitoes are extremely plentiful, the very people who would get bitten most, young children who are outside playing, comprise the one group that is not HIV-infected. The AIDS epidemic is among the sexually active and newborns, except cases involving transfusion.

The mosquito is also incapable of biological transmission of the virus. HIV does not grow in any mosquito cells, and the life cycle component of biological transmission is not there, in contrast to malaria, for example, which depends on the mosquito. HIV cannot grow outside cells, and if the viruses don't infect any mosquito cells, they can't use the mosquito as a biological host.

What about mechanical transmission, in which a trace of HIV-infected blood could be transferred to the next person bitten? Epidemiologists consider what is known about the amount of blood necessary to transmit HIV through a needle stick, which is a rather large amount, about a tenth of a milliliter. Given the size of a mosquito's stinger and the amount that could reasonably be carried from one bite to another, thousands of mosquitoes all biting at once would be required to deliver the amount of blood necessary to pass on the virus.

AIDS IN AFRICA

Q. Why is AIDS so prevalent in Africa?

A. There are many theories about the high AIDS rates, especially in sub-Saharan Africa, and answers almost certainly lie in combined economic, sociological, political, and medical factors. For example, the rate of HIV infection in Botswana, the highest in the world at 35.8 percent of adults, has been linked to Botswana's location and excellent road system, making it a crossroads for sexually active truck drivers.

For another example, drugs to prevent transmission by mothers to infants are too expensive for most, while testing costs mean people with no symptoms spread HIV, unaware they are infected.

The highly different rates of AIDS from region to region within Africa have made it a laboratory for studying control policies. Factors that may theoretically explain the rate differences include different patterns of sexual activity; the frequency of other sexually transmitted diseases, especially those that break the skin; the presence of other infections such as malaria or tuberculosis that can increase the amount of HIV in the blood; differences in circumcision frequency; virological differences in the strains of AIDS; other behavior differences; and policy differences, like reducing the stigma of AIDS and promoting education on safe sex.

RODENTS AND RABIES

Q. If the rabies virus can be transmitted by any mammal, why do we not hear of its being spread by rats in the United States?

A. Scientists don't know for sure, but the most likely explanation is that rats probably would not survive an encounter with an infected carnivore, and so would not be around to transmit the disease to people. It is also possible that rats may lack a means of transmitting the virus within the species, because of mouth shape or some other factor, and so do not become significant reservoirs for the disease. There is not much fighting within the species that would lead to the bites that would spread the infection.

The most common wild reservoirs of rabies are raccoons, skunks, bats, foxes, and coyotes. Domestic mammals, including cats, cattle, and dogs, can also get rabies. But small rodents such as squirrels, mice, rats, hamsters, guinea pigs, gerbils, and chipmunks and lagomorphs such as rabbits are almost never found to be infected with rabies and have not been known to cause rabies among humans in the United States. From 1985 to 1994, woodchucks (or groundhogs) accounted for 86 percent of the 368 reported cases of rabies among rodents.

Missing the Bus

Q. My father told me to hold my breath when a bus passes. Would this do any good in terms of protecting my lungs from pollution?

A. Probably not, but more research is needed to know the degree of danger presented by the fumes emitted from diesel vehicles.

Cars, trucks, and buses, especially diesel buses, emit large amounts of tiny particles that remain airborne for long periods. Because they linger, holding the breath until the bus passes is ineffective in keeping them out of the nose.

Small particles of less than 2 microns (two one-thousandths of a millimeter, or roughly 0.00008 of an inch) predominate in vehicle exhaust, and because of their small size, they are not filtered out by the nose but are able to pass easily and deeply into the lungs. They are mostly carbon soot, but have a wide range of volatile organic compounds stuck to them. Among them are the polycyclic aromatic hydrocarbons, PAHs, which are known or suspected carcinogens. The particles also contain irritant compounds that can acutely affect the lungs.

Allergic to Winter

Q. My friend insists she is allergic to winter. Is that possible?

A. Conditions that are very like an allergy to winter are not only possible but common.

Your friend's problem could be an asthmatic reaction to exercising in the cold, or it could be an allergy to something she is exposed to in winter even more than in the traditional allergy season. It could even be that a humidifier she is using to fight winter dryness is spewing out allergens, the proteins that cause the body to react with the symptoms of an allergy.

Exercise-induced asthma symptoms are usually worse in cold weather and during activities that stir up a cold wind. Although the precise cause is not known, it is believed that they are set off by the drying and cooling effects of air moving rapidly in and out of the respiratory tract.

Allergies that are active year-round are called perennial allergic rhinitis. The symptoms can mimic those of the common cold. The American Academy of Allergy, Asthma and Immunology says that among the most common culprits are dust mites, animals, and mold spores.

Mold spores, the highly irritating feces of dust mites, and the dander of cats and dogs, trapped in a tightly sealed house, can be stirred up when the furnace goes on. And some humidifiers can breed molds themselves or add so much humidity that molds thrive elsewhere in the house.

CHAPTER 15

Ways Modern and Ancient

HOT STUFF

Q. Why do some kinds of cookware get very hot in the microwave?

A. There are two reasons why cookware may heat up excessively in a microwave oven. The first is the same effect that occurs in cooking: friction. Microwaves are rapidly fluctuating electromagnetic fields, which push on electric charges and twist naturally polarized particles like water molecules back and forth. In liquid water, this twisting leads to molecular friction and heating. If the cookware is wet, like a porous crockery cooker that is moistened before use, it will get very hot.

A second effect can also cause trouble as the microwaves push free electric charges around. In a good conductor of electricity through which the charges move easily, the microwaves are reflected. The metal walls of the oven, for example, barely heat at all. But in a poor conductor, the charges being pushed around in the material cause resistance heating, just like that in the heating element of a hair dryer.

To test pottery or dinnerware for use in a microwave, put the empty dish in the oven alongside a cup of water in a microwave-safe glass container. Microwave on high for one minute. If the dish stays cool, it is safe to use.

Don't use porcelain cups with gold rings around the lip. If you try to reheat your coffee in one, the ring burns up just like a lightbulb filament.

SEEING STEAM

Q. Why do I see more steam when I take the teakettle off the flame?

A. The "steam" you see is what steam engine enthusiasts call wet steam, because it contains unevaporated water as a mist within the actual water vapor, which is a colorless, odorless gas. Dry steam does not contain any unevaporated water.

Steam vapor forms at temperatures above the boiling point, normally 212 degrees Fahrenheit. Visible steam is either water that is not yet hot enough to form this vapor or, in the case of your kettle, water that has cooled slightly into water droplets.

When a whistling teakettle is taken off the heat, the

whistle gets weaker, because the pressure of the water vapor drops as the heat drops, although the visible water droplets momentarily increase.

FIGHTING FOG

Q. How do antifogging treatments for mirrors and eyeglasses work?

A. Antifogging agents are chemicals that force the tiny droplets of water that make up fog to merge into a transparent sheet. An agent is sprayed as liquid on the lens, and when it dries, it forms a clear film. Normally, water beads up, but with the film, the beads run together. The water is still there, but you can see through it.

Such agents are surfactants—chemicals that lower the surface tension of the liquid with which they are in contact, in this case water. Soap and detergents contain surfactants.

A low-cost emergency substitute for commercial antifogging agents is potato juice. In research on land mine removal at the University of Western Australia, potato juice was tested for use in poor countries to keep blast-protection visors from fogging up. It performed as well as some brand-name products.

The researchers cut a slice from a raw potato, rubbed it generously and evenly onto the inside surface of the visor, then wiped away solids and excess juice with a soft cloth.

OLD NEWS

Q. Why does paper, especially newsprint, turn yellow as it ages?

A. The paper is oxidizing, one of several destructive processes that affect paper. Newsprint is high in lignin, one of the main structural components of wood. When lignin is in contact with oxygen, a highly reactive chemical, the reaction changes the way the fibers reflect light, discoloring the paper. Oxidation also produces more acid, a major culprit in the breakdown of many modern papers.

Older paper was usually made from linen or cotton fibers, which required little treatment to offer a good writing surface. Wood is much cheaper, but manufacturers found they had to use a thin chemical layer called sizing on the paper surface to make it less absorbent and prevent blurring when ink is applied.

A commonly used sizing is a compound of alum, or aluminum sulfate, and when exposed to warmth and high humidity, alum molecules split up and form an acidic solution. Cellulose fibers, which are made of molecular chains of carbon atoms, are easily split by even weak acids. The strength of the fibers is destroyed, and the paper becomes fragile.

The acid problem affects nearly half the books published since 1850, conservators estimate, and it was not until the 1950s that publishers began to abandon alum sizing for alternatives to make some paper acid-free. Conservators are also working on treatments to deacidify paper.

THE BRAIN AS 3-D CAMERA

Q. How do those 3-D pictures work, the ones for which you focus your eyes to see hidden images?

A. They work somewhat the way an old-fashioned stereopticon viewer (holding two slightly different photos) works. Each eye focuses on a separate image, but the brain combines them into one image that gives the illusion of depth (the third dimension) in addition to width and height. It does this by matching up the similarities and adding in the small differences. The result looks like what you see when you look at a solid object from the two slightly different angles of your two eyes.

The first pairs of random dot stereograms, with images embedded in dots, that can be seen only by people with good depth perception, were produced in

1959 by Dr. Bela Julesz; twenty years later, Christopher Tyler, his student, found that patterns could be arranged in a single image to get the same effect.

The ability to see computer-generated 3-D images depends on having healthy vision with both eyes working smoothly together, and the images can be used as a test or exercise. Vision problems that can interfere with depth perception include amblyopia, or lazy eye, and strabismus, informally called walleyes or crossed eyes.

THE RIGHT TOUCH

Q. When using an ATM, sometimes you don't have to touch the screen, just place an object close to it. How does that work?

A. Several kinds of technology have been used for touch screens. If the screen responds without actually being touched, it probably uses a system that has tiny infrared light emitters and detectors along the edge of the screen. When a finger interrupts the grid of beams, a computer can tell its exact position.

Some screens sensitive to actual touch use low-voltage electrical fields; a touch completes a circuit, giving a readable location.

EXPLODING ELEVATORS

Q. Why is grain dust in elevators explosive?
A. Just about any organic material will explode if it is fine enough, dry enough, in suspension in air, and confined. All it takes is the fuel, oxygen, and a spark.

Sugar, coal dust, wood dust, walnut hulls, the ingredients of children's modeling dough, and some medications have also been involved in recent dust explosions. Organic particles vary in flammability, and wheat starch and cornstarch are more explosive than other kinds.

Often a primary explosion shakes the building, dislodging more dust, which ignites in turn. There is also a pressure wave ahead of the flame front that shakes loose still more dust. The stronger the elevator, the greater the danger—a stronger container lets pressure build up so that when it is finally released, the force is much stronger.

Proper venting to relieve pressure is one important safety measure. Others are cleaning grain of foreign material and broken kernels before storage, spraying edible mineral oil on conveying equipment to control dust, and installing pneumatic dust-collection systems using bag filters.

LIGHTNING TARGET

Q. Do buildings in Manhattan need lightning rods? I never see any.

A. Historically speaking, New York City is less prone to thunderstorms than many areas of the country, but the island of Manhattan is not immune to lightning. For example, the Empire State Building is struck by lightning on average about two dozen times a year.

The good news for Manhattanites is that modern high-rise buildings have built-in lightning protection systems. Because the highest object in the area runs the greatest risk of being struck, the tall, protected buildings help shield lower structures.

Lightning is an electric charge trying to complete a circuit, and it seeks the shortest route to earth to do so. A lightning protection system provides it with such a path to the ground, carrying the current around the structure.

The best time to plan the system is when the building is still on the drawing board. A complete lightning protection system, consisting of air terminals, bases, conductors, and groundings, can be concealed within the building's framework.

People who are outside in a thunderstorm, even in

Manhattan, should take shelter in a substantial structure (a bus shelter won't do) or failing that, a fully
enclosed metal vehicle. Inside, people should stay away
from water, windows, phone lines, and appliances until
30 minutes after the last thunderclap.

Swaying in the Breeze

Q. The last time I went to the Empire State Building, it
looked as if the building was swaying. Is this an illusion?
A. The building does move, but the motion is a very
slight bending, only about a quarter of an inch, in winds
of more than 75 miles an hour. The illusion of a larger
motion probably has to do with wind-whipped clouds;
an observer on the ground can see a tall building appear
to "fall" if the clouds above it are being blown in the
right direction.

Older skyscrapers like the Empire State Building and
the Chrysler Building would sway some inches or even
feet if they were not stiffened with a massive sheathing
of stone and masonry, engineers say.

Newer skyscrapers, with their barely covered skeletons of steel, may sway perceptibly. The 579-foot Trump
International Tower, the old Gulf and Western Building
on Columbus Circle, was stiffened to defeat a percepti-
ble twist in high winds of 2½ feet; a 44-by-15-foot brace
from the street to the roof was added. The reason is comfort, not safety, the developers say, because the amount
of sway that an office worker can ignore would be dis-
turbing to a full-time residential tenant.

Structural engineers, who are not concerned about
the movement's impact on the building's own integrity,

use a number of techniques to dampen the motion so that people inside a tower do not perceive it. Current strategies include making buildings heavier by using more concrete, cross-bracing the steel framework, or devising a mechanical system that uses rooftop weights to offset motion.

BURNING ISSUE

Q. Is spontaneous human combustion real?
A. There is no scientific evidence that any person ever spontaneously combusted, and no scientifically known means by which it could happen.

In a typical case where there has been a report of a body burning unusually, a simple or at least plausible explanation is available when the case is examined in detail.

A statistically typical case might involve an elderly or infirm woman who is alone and near a fire source at night and in winter. The fire typically starts on or near the person, and it often involves the clothing, chair, or bed. In all cases there are fuel sources, a plausible explanation for the ignition, and sufficient oxygen.

The idea that the body could spontaneously ignite was promoted by the nineteenth-century temperance movement. Leaders of that movement correctly noted that many fatal burning cases involved drinkers.

THE GREEKS HAD A NAME FOR IT

Q. Was there a secret Byzantine naval weapon called Greek fire?

A. Historians agree Greek fire existed, but debate its nature. Some credit Callinicus of Heliopolis with building fire-spouting ships that defended Constantinople from the Arabs in 673. Greek fire was described as a liquid that burned even on the sea surface, with smoke and whooshing sounds.

Candidates for ingredients include petroleum, resin, and quicklime, plus an oxidizing ingredient, possibly saltpeter, which would make Greek fire an important precursor of gunpowder.

One older theory was that rather than using saltpeter or some other oxidizer, the Byzantines instead distilled petroleum to make kerosene or gasoline. But more recent research suggests that undistilled petroleum was used, collected in the cooler months so that its volatile fractions were less likely to evaporate, and kept in heated containers on board ship.

LETTING IT ALL OUT

Q. Did bleeding the patient actually help any medical condition?

A. Not unless the victim—that is, patient—chanced to be suffering from a hypertension crisis or an abnormal buildup of iron in addition to whatever disease the doctor thought he was treating.

For example, draining 10 to 12 ounces of blood, for a start, and up to 80 ounces in all, was routinely prescribed during the American Revolution for yellow fever among Washington's troops. The practice, called phlebotomy, is unlikely to have done the soldiers any good, especially if they were already weakened by cold, malnutrition, purges, and enemas.

Bleeding or bloodletting was common for centuries, if not millennia. It was based on the ancient theory that bodily humors, called black bile, yellow bile (or choler), phlegm, and blood, had to be kept in balance. (The humors were also thought to determine temperaments, causing people to be choleric or sanguine, for example.) If a person was ill, the theory went, balance had to be restored by reducing whatever humor was thought to create the plethora, often by draining off blood.

Finally, in the nineteenth century, a French pathologist, P.C.A. Louis, decided to find out if bleeding really helped, by using what was then a revolutionary method: counting who got better and who got worse. His "numerical method" was applied to 78 cases of pneumonia, 33 cases of erysipelas (a flesh-eating strep infection of the skin), and 23 cases of inflammation of the throat. He found no advantage to bloodletting, and it was the beginning of the end for bleeding and leeching as well. However, using leeches to reduce a bloody swelling is still a practical part of modern medicine.

THE AWKWARD AMPHORA

Q. Why did the ancient world use amphorae? They appear awkwardly shaped for stacking.

A. The long pointed bottom of the typical amphora actually gave it an excellent shape for stacking against a ship's hull, ensuring that the oil or wine within would be safe during transport. In the evolution of amphorae, they often began rounded and egg-shaped and shifted to pointed, because the long bottom of the brittle pottery jar better withstood the pressure of being pushed sideways when stacked.

In many shipwrecks, amphorae are found still neatly stacked, though the packing between them has usually disappeared.

Many amphorae have what are called ear handles: small, round handles about as big as the hole made by the thumb and forefinger. The shape doesn't make sense for carrying; some archaeologists think the amphorae were probably tied down in rows through the handles. No ropes have been found, however.

ANCIENT CENSUS

Q. How do archaeologists estimate past populations?
A. There are some rules of thumb for estimates for a limited area, but estimates for whole countries or the world are just guesstimates. Archaeologists tend to find and count all the formerly inhabited sites in a study area; make an educated guess about which ones were occupied at a certain period, usually based on pottery of a certain age found on the surface; and then from the total occupied area make a rough estimate. Evidence from aerial photos and satellite images may also be used.

From studies of modern villages, archaeologists can

say about 100 or 200 people occupy a hectare, or two and a half acres, of a modern settlement, and apply this estimate to the past. But there are tremendous uncertainties in such estimates. For example, big sites covered with the pottery of one period may indicate big cities, and some, like old Damascus and old Jerusalem, show evidence of densities of 500 to 600 people per hectare.

DIGITAL COMPUTING

Q. The number system with a base of 10 is so common that I wonder why so many societies developed it independently. And where did some of the other systems come from, like the one based on 60?

A. Historians of science find the obvious explanation for the base-10 system at the fingertips of human beings, all ten of them. Not so coincidentally, the word *digit* comes from *digitus*, the Latin word for finger or toe.

Counting on the fingers (base 10) or the fingers and toes (base 20) is the apparent root of many ancient written number systems. The French language retains traces of a base-20 system, based on multiples of 20, like *quatre-vingt*, or four 20s, for 80. The Maya also developed a base-20 system 1,500 years ago.

The Babylonian-Sumerian base-60 system survives in the measurement of time, angles, and geographical position; some scientists suspect this was also derived from finger counting. But others think it might have arisen because of trade with some other people with a system of weights based on a different, larger unit, resulting in the need to find a common way to express fractional weights.

PINPOINT QUESTION

Q. How many angels can dance on the head of a pin?

A. Medieval theologian-philosophers tried to calculate that incalculable number based on the notion that angels were the smallest possible physical creatures, though with very large spiritual powers. Based on that same definition of size, a modern physicist actually made a calculation for an even smaller dance floor: the number of hypothetical angels that could dance on the point of a pin.

The calculation was offered in 1995 by Dr. Phil Schewe, spokesman for the American Institute of Physics. He presented his idea at a meeting of the Society for Literature and Science.

For the smallest possible angelic size, Dr. Schewe relied on an idea drawn from superstring physics that space itself is not infinitely divisible, but breaks down at a distance scale of 10^{-35} meters.

For the size of a pinpoint, he took the tip of the IBM scanning tunneling microscope, the one that arranged 35 xenon atoms in the shape of the letters IBM. The tip tapers down to a single atom.

From there, it is an easy calculation, Dr. Schewe concluded. Figuring that the point is an angstrom across, or 10^{-10} meters, you divide that by 10^{-35} and the answer is 10^{25} angels (that's a 1 followed by 25 zeroes) can fit on the point of a pin.

THE MUMMY'S CURSE

Q. Can you be cursed for going into an ancient tomb?

A. You can certainly be cursed at, by archaeologists. The history of ancient Egypt, for example, is full of holes left by grave robbers, and remaining tombs are at risk from tourism and development.

Egyptians believed tomb inscriptions could confer either blessings or curses on visitors, and early visitors probably believed so, too. Tomb builders wanted to encourage passersby to leave food for the dead or just to recite a standard ritual wish for bread, beer, cattle, and fowl, which, merely through the spoken word, would magically generate those commodities for the soul of the dead.

By 2000 B.C., standard inscriptions included both praise and blessings for those who recited the ritual and warnings cursing those who might damage the tomb or its images. The warnings invoked condemnation and even outright slaughter at the hands of the gods of the underworld. This was not an idle threat—there was a clear understanding that the dead could intervene in the lives of people on earth.

Notes on Sources

Chapter 1. *Reaching for the Stars*

Birth and Death: Nolan Walborn, an astronomer at the Space Telescope Science Institute.

In a Spin: Vera C. Rubin, an astrophysicist in the Department of Terrestrial Magnetism at the Carnegie Institution.

Death by Black Hole: Mitchell Begelman, professor of astrophysics and chairman of the Department of Astrophysical, Planetary, and Atmospheric Sciences at the University of Colorado at Boulder.

Averting Your Eyes: Alan J. Friedman, director of the New York Hall of Science in Queens.

Seeing Stars: Scott Kardel of the Lake Afton Public Observatory in Wichita, Kansas; Douglas Blanchard, chief of the Earth Science and Solar System Exploration Division at NASA-Johnson Space Center.

A South Star?: The Facts on File Dictionary of Astronomy; The International Encyclopedia of Astronomy (Orion Books).

Hello Out There!: The SETI Institute.

Sitcoms in Space: Seth Shostak, an astronomer at the SETI Institute.

Shine On, Harvest Moon: Alan J. Friedman; Joe Rao, lecturer at the American Museum of Natural History.

Mars Coordinates: Robert G. Strom, professor of planetary science at the University of Arizona.

Pale in Comparison: Joe Rao.

Cosmic Collision: Bryan G. Marsden, associate director for planetary sciences at the Harvard-Smithsonian Center for Astrophysics.

The Planetary Plane: Joe Rao.

Ring Around the Sun: NASA.

Space Traffic Control: Jonathan McDowell of the Harvard-Smithsonian Center for Astrophysics.

Steering the Shuttle: Kyle Herring, NASA Johnson Space Center.

Sci-Fidelity: John Lawrence, chief of operations and program support for the shuttle at NASA Johnson Space Center.

Getting Home from Mars: Mark Adler, Mars exploration program architect at NASA Jet Propulsion Laboratory.

Chapter 2. Down to Earth

From North to South: Phillip F. Schewe of the American Institute of Physics.

Rocks That Tell a Story: Understanding Earth, by Frank Press and Raymond Siever (W. H. Freeman).

Shocking Events: U.S. Geological Survey.

How Murky Water Gets That Way: Gulf of Maine Aquarium.

Putting the Pressure on Water: Alan J. Friedman, director of the New York Hall of Science in Queens.

Bends in the River: Understanding Earth, by Frank Press and Raymond Siever.

When the Equinox Comes Early: Joe Rao, lecturer at the American Museum of Natural History.

Chapter 3. The Weather, Rain or Shine

Laying Out the Odds: Sam Perugini, a meteorologist at Pennsylvania State University.

The Color of Clouds: Todd J. Miner, a meteorologist at Pennsylvania State University.

Cloud Capacity: Sam Perugini.

Trail of the Jet: Dr. Owen Brian Toon, professor of atmospheric and oceanic sciences at the University of Colorado.

Sowing the Skies: Weather Modification Association.

Measuring Rain: Todd J. Miner.

It's Raining Hamburger Buns: Todd J. Miner.

Bad Timing: Todd J. Miner.

Hot Air, Cold Peaks: James C. G. Walker, professor of geology at the University of Michigan.

Bending Sound: John Earshen, Angevine Acoustical Consultants of East Aurora, New York.

Invisible Ice: Fred Gadomski, a meteorologist at Pennsylvania State University.

Chapter 4. *Food, Glorious Food*

Holes in the Cheese: On Food and Cooking: The Science and Lore of the Kitchen, by Harold McGee (Scribner).

Forming a Skin: On Food and Cooking: The Science and Lore of the Kitchen, by Harold McGee.

The Telltale Fish: Joseph H. Hotchkiss, professor of food science at Cornell University.

Ginseng Pedigrees: Varro E. Tyler, emeritus professor of pharmacognosy at Purdue University.

The Physics of Noodles: Joseph H. Hotchkiss, professor of food science at Cornell University.

Chapter 5. *Flora! Flora! Flora!*

It's Easy Being Evergreen: Plant pathology department of Iowa State University extension service.

Unable to Let Go: A. Wayne Cahilly, manager of the arboretum and grounds at the New York York Botanical Garden in the Bronx.

Trees' Partners: Gerald Posner, an arborist with Arbor-Cultural Consultants in Brooklyn, New York.

Doomed Bamboo: American Bamboo Society.

Love That Salt: The Halophyte Biotechnology Center at the University of Delaware College of Marine Studies.

From Silk to Kernel: "How a Corn Plant Develops," a report by the Cooperative Extension Service of the Iowa State University of Science and Technology at Ames; Dale E. Farnham, assistant professor of agronomy at Iowa State.

The Dreaded Rhubarb: Rodney L. Dietert, professor at the Veterinary College of Cornell University and director of the Institute of Comparative and Environmental Toxicology.

Gaining a Toehold: Southern Wild Flowers and Trees, by Alice Lownsbery (Frederick Stokes Company).

Man-Eating Plants: Barry Meyers-Rice, conservation co-editor of *The Carnivorous Plant Newsletter.*

Chapter 6. All Bugs Great and Small

Bugs on the Windshield: Louis N. Sorkin, an entomologist at the American Museum of Natural History; James Jarratt, an entomologist at Mississippi State University; Michael May, an entomologist at Cook College of Rutgers University.

A Backyard Census: Kefyn M. Catley of the American Museum of Natural History.

The Swarms of the Annoying: The Natural History of the Mosquito, by Marston Bates (Peter Smith).

Aphid Husbandry: American Social Insects, by Charles D. and Mary H. Michener (Van Nostrand).

Lines of Communication: The Ants, by Bert Holldobler and Dr. Edward O. Wilson (Harvard University Press).

Butterflies over Broadway: The Monarch Program, Encinitas, California.

Fat for the Flight: David Marriott, founder of the Monarch Program.

High Flies: Elson J. Shields, professor of entomology at Cornell University.

Bites in the Sunlight: Associated Executives of Mosquito Control Work, New Jersey.

More of a Sting: International Toxin and Venom Data Base.

Long Live the Spider: American Spiders, by Willis J. Gertsch (Van

Nostrand); *The Black Widow Spider*, by Raymond W. Thorp and Eldon D. Woodson (Dover).

Source of the Flies: Rob DeSalle, the American Museum of Natural History.

Chapter 7. It's a Zoo Out There

How the Fittest Stay That Way: Pat Thomas, curator of mammals at the Bronx Zoo.

The Mighty Wolverine: Macmillan Illustrated Animal Encyclopedia; Encyclopedia of Mammals (Facts on File).

To Sleep, Perchance to Hibernate: Bears, by Wayne Lynch (Mountaineers Books).

Bear Pairs: The American Zoo and Aquarium Society.

Asleep on Their Feet: Katherine Houpt, a veterinarian who directs the Animal Behavior Clinic at Cornell University.

Calling a Snake a Snake: Darrel Frost of the Department of Herpetology at the American Museum of Natural History.

A Meal in One Gulp: William Holmstrom, collection manager in the Department of Herpetology at the Bronx Zoo.

Up a Creek with No Legs: Rattlesnakes, by Laurence M. Klauber.

Chameleon Colors: Macmillan Illustrated Animal Encyclopedia.

The Fertile Turtle: Grzimek's Animal Life Encyclopedia (Gale Group).

Frogs' Flypaper Tongues: Kraig Adler, professor of biology in the Department of Neurobiology and Behavior at Cornell University.

Flight of the Fish: Encyclopedia of Fishes: A Comprehensive Illustrated Guide by International Experts (Academic Press).

Telling the Dolphins from the Porpoises: Macmillan Illustrated Animal Encyclopedia.

Facts of Life for Whales: Gray Whales, by David G. Gordon and Alan Baldridge (Monterey Bay Aquarium Press).

Sex and the Single Fossil: John Krigbaum, an anthropologist at New York University.

The Species Census: Niles Eldridge, curator of the division of paleontology of the American Museum of Natural History; *The Diversity of Life,* by Edward O. Wilson (Belknap Press).

Chapter 8. Secrets of Cats and Dogs

A Cat's Mad Dash: Katherine Houpt, a veterinarian who directs the Animal Behavior Clinic at Cornell University.

Feline Antennae: James R. Richards, a veterinarian who heads the Cornell Feline Health Center at Cornell University.

Shocking Behavior: Alan J. Friedman, director of the New York Hall of Science in Queens.

A Kidney for the Cat: Clare R. Gregory, professor in the Department of Surgery and Radiological Sciences, University of California at Davis School of Veterinary Medicine.

Sensing a Storm: Lee Zasloff, associate director of the Center for Animals in Society at the University of California at Davis School of Veterinary Medicine; Dan Graf, a meteorologist at Pennsylvania State University.

Fido's Brain: Richard Joseph, a veterinarian and staff neurologist at the Animal Medical Center in Manhattan.

Garrulous Parrots: Timothy DeVoogd, associate professor of psychology at Cornell University.

Guinea Pig Identity Crisis: Michael Novacek, senior vice president and provost of the American Museum of Natural History and curator of vertebrate paleontology.

Chapter 9. Animal Aviators

Beyond Lungs: Manual of Ornithology: Avian Structure and Function, by Noble S. Proctor and Patrick J. Lynch (Yale University Press).

Sensing Something in the Air: Ornithology, by Frank B. Gill (W. H. Freeman); *The Cambridge Encyclopedia of Ornithology.*

Invasion of the Crows: Dr. Kevin J. McGowan, associate curator of birds and mammals at Cornell University.

Staying in the Pink: The Cambridge Encyclopedia of Ornithology; Ornithology, by Frank B. Gill.

Soaring into Old Age: The Audubon Society Encyclopedia of North American Birds (Knopf); *Manual of Ornithology: Avian Structure and Function.*

Turning on the Fly: Ron Rohrbaugh, an ornithologist at the Cornell Laboratory of Ornithology.

The Birds and the Bees and Birds: Ornithology, by Frank B. Gill.

Bird Bombs Away: Manual of Ornithology: Avian Structure and Function.

Where the Gulls Are: Ronald W. Rohrbaugh.

Hard-Heads: The Diversity of Life, by Edward O. Wilson.

Chapter 10. How Humans Get That Way

There Must Be a Reason: Margie Profet, an evolutionary biologist at the University of California at Berkeley.

The Advantages of Being Female: World Health Organization.

Boy Twins, Girl Twins: The Mothers of Twins Clubs; National Center for Health Statistics.

The Longest Digit: Randall L. Susman, professor of anatomy at the Medical School of the State University of New York at Stony Brook.

Limits to Growth: W. Ted Brown, a geneticist at the Institute for Basic Research on Staten Island.

Stroller Potatoes: Martin I. Lorin, pediatrician and author of *The Parents' Book of Physical Fitness for Children* (Atheneum).

Straightening the Spine: The Merck Manual of Diagnosis and Therapy; Stuart L. Weinstein of the Department of Orthopedic Surgery of the University of Iowa Hospitals and Clinics.

Chapter 11. Our Bodies, Our Aches and Pains

Manufacturing Blood: Robert L. Jones, president of the New York Blood Center.

Those Icy Fingers: Harry L. Bush, Jr., a vascular surgeon at New York Weill Cornell Medical Center.

Liver Spots: American Academy of Dermatology.

Those Aching Eyes: Daniel Wagner of the Sleep-Wake Disorder Center at New York Weill Cornell Medical Center.

Protecting the Ear: American Academy of Otolaryngology.

Not Just an Appendix: Carol Shoshkes Reiss, an immunologist at New York University.

Wrinkling Over Time: Larry Meyer, a dermatologist and geriatrician at the University of Utah Health Sciences Center.

Losing Color: National Vitiligo Foundation.

Damaging the DNA: Darrell Rigel, a professor of dermatology at New York University; American Cancer Society.

Putting the Pinch on a Nerve: The American Academy of Family Physicians Family Health & Medical Guide (Word Publishing).

Runaway Scars: The Merck Manual of Diagnosis and Therapy.

Too Much of a Good Thing: The Merck Manual of Diagnosis and Therapy.

Oldies but Goodies: United Network for Organ Sharing.

Final Changes: Anoka and Wright County Coroner's Office, Minnesota.

Chapter 12. Things You've Always Wanted to Know

An Icy Stare: Amilia Schrier, an ophthalmologist on the faculty of the Columbia Presbyterian Medical Center.

Sneezing After Hours: Gillian Shepherd, an allergist at New York Weill Cornell Medical Center.

Television Vision: American Academy of Ophthalmology.

Ticklish Subject: Sarah-Jayne Blakemore of the Wellcome Department of Cognitive Neurology at University College, London.

A Pain in the Side: Everett Murdock of California State University at Long Beach; *Running Injuries,* by Tim Noakes (Oxford University Press).

Catching Up on Sleep: Losing Sleep, by Lydia Dotto (Quill/William Morrow).

Nerves and Teeth: Daniel M. Meyer, head of the Division of Science of the American Dental Association.

No Stomach: Paul Basuk, a gastroenterologist at New York Weill Cornell Medical Center.

Chapter 13. Eat, Drink, and Be Healthy

All Pizza, All the Time: Marion Nestle, professor and chairwoman of the Department of Nutrition and Food Studies at New York University.

The Trouble with Mold: Donna L. Scott, a food scientist who is a senior extension associate at Cornell University.

Feeding the Nails: Hilary Baldwin, a dermatologist in Brooklyn, New York.

Priming the Heat Pump: Samir Zakhari, a pharmacologist who is director of the Division of Basic Research at the National Institute on Alcohol Abuse and Alcoholism.

Calcium Without Complaint: Food and Nutrition Information Center of the United States Department of Agriculture.

Tea for Therapy: The Honest Herbal, by Varro E. Tyler, emeritus professor of pharmacognosy at Purdue University (Haworth Press).

Colonizing the Gut: Kathryn Boor, assistant professor of food science at Cornell University.

Tempest in a Tuna Can: Rodney L. Dietert, an immunotoxicologist who is head of the Breast Cancer and Environmental Risk Factors Program at Cornell University.

Chapter 14. Battleground: The Body

Wash Your Troubles Away: American Medical Association.

Persistent Pathogens: John R. La Montagne, deputy director of the National Institute of Allergy and Infectious Diseases.

Long-Lasting Immunity: Regina Rabinovich of the National Institute of Allergy and Infectious Diseases.

Feline Fever: Article by Drs. Russell Regnery and Jordan Tappero in the journal *Emerging Infectious Diseases.*

Mad Cows and You: Peter Lurie, deputy director of the Public Citizen's Health Research Group and a member of the U.S. Food and Drug Administration's advisory committee on transmissible spongiform encephalopathy.

AIDS and Mosquitoes: Anthony Fauci, director of the National Institute of Allergy and Infectious Diseases.

Rodents and Rabies: Jean S. Smith of the Division of Viral and Rickettsial Diseases at the Centers for Disease Control and Prevention.

Missing the Bus: Patrick L. Kinney, assistant professor of public health at the Columbia University School of Public Health.

Chapter 15. Ways Modern and Ancient

Hot Stuff: Louis A. Bloomfield, professor of physics at the University of Virginia.

Fighting Fog: Ken Duffie, chief engineer for H. L. Bouton, Inc., Wareham, Massachusetts.

The Brain as 3-D Camera: Rachel Cooper, author of educational material for the Optometrists Network.

The Right Touch: Annette Burak, Microtouch Systems, Inc.

Exploding Elevators: Ralph Regan, safety director of the Federal Grain Inspection Service of the U.S. Department of Agriculture; Robert W. Schoeff, emeritus professor of grain science at Kansas State University.

Lightning Target: United Lightning Protection Association; National Lightning Safety Institute.

Burning Issue: Joe Nickell, a senior research fellow of the Committee for the Scientific Investigation of Claims of the Paranormal.

The Greeks Had a Name for It: Bert S. Hall, associate professor at the Institute for the History and Philosophy of Science and Technology at the University of Toronto; *A History of Greek Fire and Gunpowder,* by J. R. Partington (Johns Hopkins).

Letting It All Out: The Doctor's Dilemmas, Louis Lasagna (Harper).

The Awkward Amphora: Shelley Wachsmann, nautical and biblical archaeologist at the Institute of Nautical Archaeology at Texas A&M University.

Ancient Census: Tony Wilkinson, research associate at the Oriental Institute of the University of Chicago.

Digital Computing: From One to Zero: A Universal History of Nothingness, by Georges Ifrah (Viking); *The Nothing That Is: A Natural History of Zero,* by Robert Kaplan (Oxford).

The Mummy's Curse: Peter Dorman, former director of Egypt House, the Oriental Institute of the University of Chicago archeological installation in Luxor, Egypt.